W9-AFP-566

MANUAL OF
STRUCTURAL DETAILS FOR
BUILDING
CONSTRUCTION

ALONZO WASS

PRENTICE-HALL, INC., ENGLEWOOD CLIFFS, N.J.

© 1968 by Prentice-Hall, Inc.
Englewood Cliffs, N.J.

All rights reserved.
No part of this book may be reproduced in any form
or by any means
without permission in writing from the publisher.

Library of Congress Catalog Card Number 68-23547
Printed in the United States of America

PRENTICE-HALL INTERNATIONAL, INC., London
PRENTICE-HALL OF AUSTRALIA, PTY. LTD., Sydney
PRENTICE-HALL OF CANADA, LTD., Toronto
PRENTICE-HALL OF INDIA PRIVATE LTD., New Delhi
PRENTICE-HALL OF JAPAN, INC., Tokyo

Current printing (last digit)

10 9 8 7 6 5 4 3 2 1

PREFACE

An endeavor has been made to present within the covers of this book a critical and wide sampling of structural details from America, Australia, and Canada.

Details have been taken from houses, a pumphouse, sewage disposal installations, glue-laminated post and beam construction, heavy lumber construction, fireplaces, a city parking garage, a nursing home, an office building, steel framing, trusses, architectural metal work, steel decking, a home for Senior Citizens with fallout shelter, and a steel bridge. In addition, many very excellent details from manufacturers' brochures are included. Assignments follow every chapter.

Here I hasten to thank all those educators, architects, engineers, manufacturers, and technicians who freely gave me of their time and ideas for this book—and a special thanks to all those contributors who read the draft of what I had to say about their drawings. It has been a most heartwarming experience for me to have been in these countries, meeting men in their offices, schools, or on building sites where they have patiently laid aside their work and taken the time to help me make this contribution to technical education.

The text is designed for universities, technical institutes, or junior colleges. It may be used by technicians in the field who are furthering their professional experience with refresher courses in evening class studies or by those stout-hearted souls who are working alone in these areas. The book is designed to meet many technical educational standards.

Typical wall sections, presenting a good introductory concept of structural details, have been given a wide treatment and should be of immediate help to educators and technicians working with local tradesmen in underdeveloped areas.

Educators in Structural Technology face an annual problem: Acquiring and storing many different sets of drawings, and then having to decide whether or not students should be allowed to take these home. This question is compounded where parallel courses are offered both for day and evening classes. It is hoped that this book will partly resolve this question.

It is hoped also that students will be inspired to render vividly-drawn and clearly lettered details, unencumbered by artistic flourishes or extraneous material, remembering that drawings are often used on noisy building sites where those who read them should have a ready understanding of the fabricating devices for the intended structure. *Readers are sternly reminded that hard-to-read drawings are difficult to estimate or execute and that they usually cause contractors to increase their bids.* Drawings of structural details are most often used only once, and while we must recognize that there may be minor errors, these may be kept to a minimum by diligent work.

The object of any lecture, textbook, or drawing should be to allow the student to assimilate the intended knowledge in as little time as possible. It requires thought, patience, time, and knowledge to render structural details that convey a maximum of information with a minimum of lines and words. This is reminiscent of Pascal, who wrote in *Lettres Provinciales* on December 14, 1656:

"I have made this letter rather long only because I have not had time to make it shorter."

Thus, with perseverence and a mind open to new techniques, with wide reading within our chosen field, with research and frequent refresher courses, we may join our Oriental friends in saying,

"An intelligent person has a will; a dullard has a desire."

I extend very sincere thanks to my wife Joan Rose Wass for her patience with me, to Mrs. Bertha E. Cameron for the excellence of her secretarial work, to those architects, engineers, and manufacturers who read parts of the manuscript, and to my colleagues who made valuable suggestions.

Alonzo Wass

TABLE
OF
CONTENTS

v

12   A CITY PARKING GARAGE   245

13   A TECHNICAL SCHOOL SHOP BUILDING   263

14   A COUNTY OFFICE BUILDING   282

19   A STEEL BRIDGE   358

LIST
OF
ABBREVIATIONS

The following listed abbreviations *with open punctuation* have been used throughout this book. With open punctuation, periods are not used to denote contracted words unless such contractions would result in actual words.

EXAMPLE:

The contraction of the words 'Figure' and 'inch' without periods would produce the words 'Fig' and 'in' respectively. In such cases a period has been used.

Consider the following sentence written in full: There are 328 cubic yards of reinforced concrete in the continuous footings for the wall.

The same sentence with contractions and periods: There are 328 cu. yds. of rein, conc. in the cont. ftgs. for the wall.

The same sentence as written in this book: There are 328 cu yds of rein conc in the cont ftgs for the wall.

It is generally believed that open punctuation (in a textbook) is easier to read.

A.I.A.	American Institute of Architects	ft	feet
A.I.S.C.	American Institute of Steel Construction	ftg	footing(s)
alum	Aluminum	G.A.	gauge or gage
anch	anchor	G.E.	galvanized iron
approx	approximately	glu-lam	glue laminated
Arch	architectural	horiz	horizontal
A.S.T.M.	American Society for Testing Materials	H.P.	high point
		H.R.	heat register
A.W.S.	American Welding Society	i.d.	inside diameter
		in.	inches
bldg	building	kip	force of 1000 lb
btm	bottom	L	angle
B.M.	bench mark	lam	laminated
bd	board(s)	lin	lineal
c to c,	center to center	LLO	long leg outstanding
circ	circular	Lt Wt	light weight
clg	ceiling	max	maximum
conc	concrete	min	minimum
cont	continuous	M.S.	mild steel
C.S.A.	Canadian Standards Association	N	North
		Nos or #	numbers
cu in.	cubic inches	o.c.	on center(s)
cu yd	cubic yards	oz	ounces
D.D.	double diamond or double-strength glass 24 oz per sq ft)	pcs	pieces
		PL or ℄	plate
		p.s.i.	pounds per sq in.
		rd	round
		rect	rectangular
		ref	reference
dbl	double	rein	reinforce(ment)
diag	diagonal	S	South
diam	diameter	S.C.P.I.	Structural Clay Products Institute
D.F.	Douglas fir		
D.L.	dead load	S.L.O.	short leg outstanding
D.P.	dampproofing	S.L.V.	short leg vertical
D.P.C.	dampproof course	sp	space
dt'l	detail	specs	specifications
dwg	drawing(s)	Stiff.	stiffeners
dim.	dimension(s)(ing)	struct	structural
E	East	T & B	top and bottom
E.F.	each face	T & G	tongue and groove
el	elevation	temp	temperature
Engr	engineer	TR	truss
E & W	East and West	vert	vertical
E.W.	each way	V.T.	Vierendeel truss
fdn	foundation	W	West
F.F.L.	finished floor level	wd	wood
fin.	finished	W.P.	waterproofing
flr	floor	w.w.m.	welded wire mesh

ARCHITECTURAL DRAWING PRACTICES 1

In this chapter we are going to examine architectural drawing practices currently used in North America. Like music, which may be read in most parts of the world, architectural drawing practices should be universal. Dwgs and specs (drawings and specifications) may be made in almost any country for a structure that is to be erected in another country, and while architecture is an art, the dwgs should be kept free from ambiguities and artistic flourishes.

It should be constantly kept in mind that most dwgs are used on noisy bldg sites and often in very extreme and trying climatic conditions. They should be clearly presented so that readers will have a vivid impression of the true intent and meaning of the originators.

It is most strongly urged that all dwg sheets be well section marked so that users may turn back and forth thru them by fingertip references. *Remember that good dwgs elicit good bids.* Before submitting their bids, contractors often have a limited time to use the dwgs and specs. Unless they can easily estimate their costs from clearcut dwgs and well defined specs, they will tend to present high bids—if they bid at all.

The following extracts are reprinted by courtesy of the Department of Defence Production, Ottawa, Canada.

CANADIAN GOVERNMENT SPECIFICATIONS BOARD
Standard on
ARCHITECTURAL DRAWING PRACTICES

FOREWORD

ARCHITECTURAL WORKING DRAWINGS HAVE THE IMPORTANT FUNCTIONS OF (A) RECORDING CLEARLY THE CLIENTS' REQUIREMENTS SO THAT COST ESTIMATING AND BIDDING ARE FACILITATED, (B) FORMING A PART OF THE CONTRACT BETWEEN THE CLIENT AND BUILDER AND (C) PROVIDING INSTRUCTION TO THE BUILDER FOR THE PURPOSE OF CONSTRUCTION. TO FULFIL THESE FUNCTIONS MOST EFFICIENTLY THE DRAWINGS MUST BE COMPLETE, ACCURATE AND CONCISE. THE USE OF UNIFORM PRACTICES IN PRODUCING THE DRAWINGS IS A VALUABLE AID TOWARD ACHIEVING THIS GOAL

THIS STANDARD IS PRESENTED AS A GUIDE TOWARD SUCH UNIFORMITY AND TOWARD CLARITY AND SIMPLICITY RATHER THAN ARTISTRY IN ARCHITECTURAL DRAWING. IT IS INTENDED PRIMARILY FOR USE WITHIN CANADIAN GOVERNMENT AGENCIES, BUT IS AVAILABLE FOR USE GENERALLY AND, INDEED, ITS GENERAL AND WIDESPREAD USE IS ENCOURAGED.

THE STANDARD IS NOT EXHAUSTIVE IN ITS TREATMENT OF ARCHITECTURAL DRAWING PRACTICES, PARTICULARLY AS REGARDS SYMBOLS FOR ELECTRICAL, PLUMBING AND HEATING APPLICATIONS, BUT DEALS WITH WHAT ARE CONSIDERED TO BE THE MOST BASIC AND COMMONLY ENCOUNTERED ELEMENTS OF ARCHITECTURAL DRAWING.

TITLE AND REVISION BLOCKS

THE TITLE BLOCK SHOULD BE POSITIONED IN THE LOWER RIGHT-HAND CORNER OF THE DRAWING SHEET AND SHOULD NORMALLY PROVIDE THE FOLLOWING INFORMATION:

- NAME AND LOCATION OF THE PROJECT
- NAME OF THE AGENCY RESPONSIBLE FOR THE DRAWING
- TITLE OF THE DRAWING
- NUMBER OF THE DRAWING
- DRAWING SCALES
- INITIALS OF THE DESIGNER, CHECKER, DRAFTSMAN AND SUPERVISOR, TOGETHER WITH APPROPRIATE DATES

THE REVISION BLOCK SHOULD BE ADJACENT TO THE TITLE BLOCK, EITHER DIRECTLY ABOVE IT OR ON ITS LEFT, AND SHOULD READ FROM THE BOTTOM UPWARD.

LETTERING

IT IS NOT CONSIDERED PRACTICAL NOR DESIRABLE TO SUGGEST A SPECIFIC STANDARD FORM OF LETTERING FOR ARCHITECTURAL DRAWINGS. THE LOGICAL GOAL IS TO PROVIDE DISTINCT, UNIFORM LETTERS AND FIGURES THAT WILL ENSURE THE PRODUCTION OF CLEAR, LEGIBLE PRINTS.

IT IS RECOMMENDED HOWEVER THAT VERTICAL UPPER CASE LETTERING BE USED AND THAT PREFERENCE BE GIVEN TO A MINIMUM NUMBER OF BASIC LETTER SIZES. IT IS CONSIDERED THAT THREE BASIC SIZES ARE SUFFICIENT FOR MOST ARCHITECTURAL DRAWING APPLICATIONS, THE LARGER SIZE BEING RESERVED FOR MAJOR HEADINGS, AN INTERMEDIATE SIZE FOR SUBHEADINGS AND THE SMALLER SIZE FOR NOTES. IT IS RECOMMENDED THAT THE LETTER SIZE FOR NOTES AND FOR DIMENSIONS SHOULD BE NOT LESS THAN $\frac{3}{32}$ INCH.

MICROFILMING

DRAWINGS THAT ARE TO BE MICROFILMED WILL REQUIRE SPECIAL CARE IN PREPARATION AS OUTLINED IN CANADIAN GOVERNMENT SPECIFICATIONS BOARD SPECIFICATION 72-GP-I : 35 MM MICROFILMING OF ENGINEERING AND ARCHITECTURAL DRAWINGS.

DOOR AND ROOM FINISH SCHEDULES

IT IS RECOGNIZED THAT NO STRICT RULES CAN OR SHOULD BE PROPOSED AS TO THE EXACT FORM AND ARRANGEMENT OF DOOR AND ROOM FINISH SCHEDULES. THE EXAMPLES SHOWN ON THE FOLLOWING PAGES ILLUSTRATE DOOR AND ROOM FINISH SCHEDULES THAT ARE IN COMMON USE IN SOME AREAS OF ARCHITECTURAL DRAWING, AND THEY ILLUSTRATE THE KIND OF INFORMATION THAT SHOULD BE PROVIDED BY SUCH SCHEDULES.

SUGGESTED
REFERENCE
SYMBOLS

LETTER DESIGNATES SECTION

NUMERAL INDICATES SHEET NUMBER

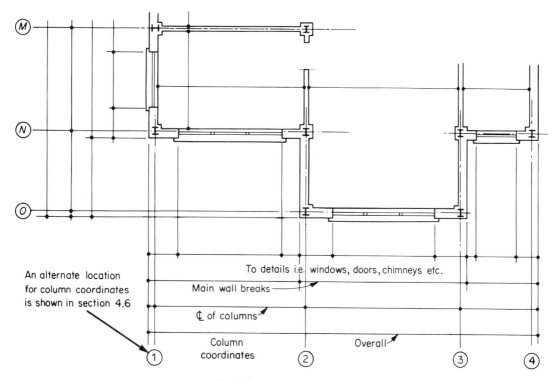

An alternate location
for column coordinates
is shown in section 4.6

To details i.e. windows, doors, chimneys etc.

Main wall breaks

℄ of columns

Column
coordinates

Overall

Steel frame construction dimensioning – Plan

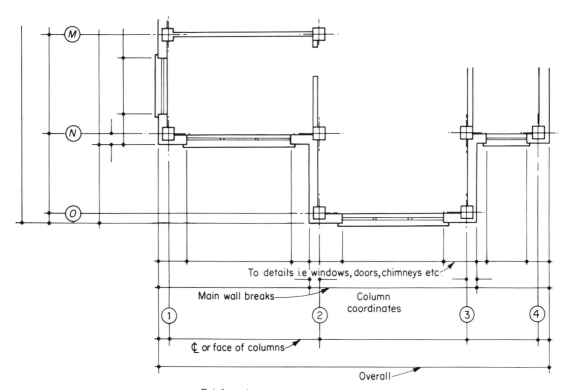

To details i.e windows, doors, chimneys etc.

Main wall breaks

Column
coordinates

℄ or face of columns

Overall

Reinforced concrete construction dimensioning – Plan

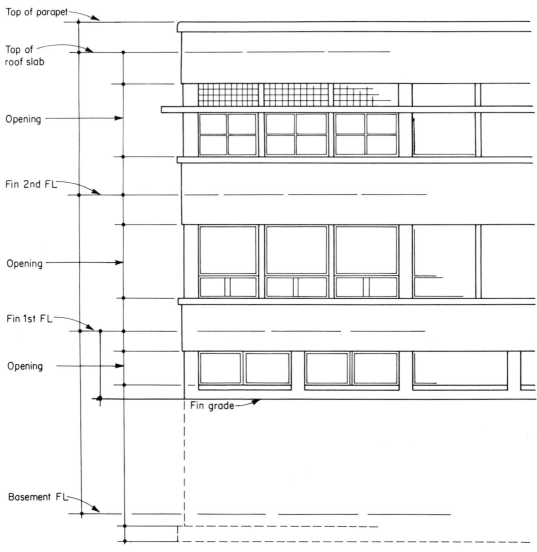

Top of parapet

Top of
roof slab

Opening

Fin 2nd FL

Opening

Fin 1st FL

Opening

Fin grade

Basement FL

Steel frame or reinforced concrete
construction dimensioning — Elevation

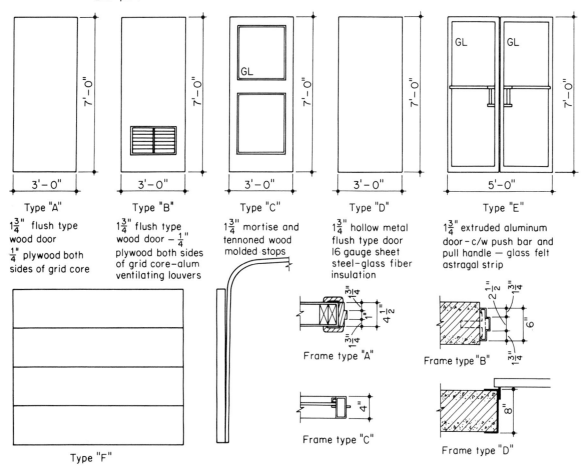

Door and hardware schedule

Example 1

Type "A"
1¾" flush type wood door
¼" plywood both sides of grid core

Type "B"
1¾" flush type wood door — ¼" plywood both sides of grid core–alum ventilating louvers

Type "C"
1¾" mortise and tennoned wood molded stops

Type "D"
1¾" hollow metal flush type door 16 gauge sheet steel–glass fiber insulation

Type "E"
1¾" extruded aluminum door–c/w push bar and pull handle — glass felt astragal strip

Type "F"
Sectional overhead aluminum door c/w tracks, counterbalance, lock latch, etc.

Frame type "A"

Frame type "B"

Frame type "C"

Frame type "D"

Doorway number ➤	1	2	3	4	5	6	7	8	9	10	11	12	13	14	15	16	17	Doorway numbers as required ➤														
Door type	D	E	B	A	C	F	D	A	E	B	B	B	F	A	A	A	A																
Frame type	B	C	A	A	A	D	B	A	C	A	A	B	D	A	A	A	A																
1½" pair 4"x 4" steel butts			✓	✓	✓			✓		✓	✓	✓		✓	✓	✓	✓																
1½" pair 4"x 4" brass butts-ball bearing	✓						✓																										
Offset alum hinges		✓							✓																								
Latch set			✓					✓		✓	✓	✓				✓																	
Dead lock		✓				✓		✓				✓																					
Combination dead lock and latch	✓			✓	✓		✓						✓	✓	✓																		
Bracket type door closer				✓	✓									✓	✓																		
Floor type door closer		✓							✓																								
Combination door stop and holder	✓		✓		✓		✓	✓		✓	✓	✓		✓	✓	✓																	
Top and bottom bolts																																	
Overhead door hardware complete						✓							✓																				
Aluminum threshold	✓		✓	✓					✓	✓	✓		✓	✓		✓																	
Push and pull hardware		✓							✓																								

Items as required →

Door and hardware schedule
Example 2

Door schedule

Floor	Number of doors	Revisions	Location of door — Outside room	Location of door — Inside room	Door — Swing	Door — Type	Door — Width	Door — Height	Door — Thickness	Door — Material	Door — Finish	Frame — Type	Frame — Thickness	Frame — Material	Hardware	Remarks
First floor	2		Exterior	Vestibule 1–01	PD	D–1	3'–0"	7'–0"	$1\frac{1}{2}$"	AL		F–1		AL		See DWG #14
	2	*A	Vestibule 1–01	Foyer 1–02	PD	D–2	3'–0"	7'–0"	$1\frac{3}{4}$"	Wood	Laq	F–2	14 GA	Met		
			Foyer 1–02	Gen office 1–04	RH	D–4	2'–8"	6'–8"	$1\frac{3}{4}$"	Wood	Laq	F–3	14 GA	Met		
			Foyer 1–02	Corridor 1–03	RHR	D–3	3'–6"	6'–8"	$1\frac{1}{2}$"	Met		F–5	14 GA	Met		
			Corridor 1–03	Public lav 1–07	LH	D–6	2'–6"	6'–8"	$1\frac{3}{4}$"	Wood	Laq	F–3	14 GA	Met		
			Coffee shop1–10	Kitchen 1–12	DA	D–5	3'–0"	6'–8"	$1\frac{1}{2}$"	AL		F–7		AL		

Swings PD – Pair of doors
DA – Double-acting
RH – Right hand
LH – Left hand
RHR – Right hand reverse
LHR – Left hand reverse

* Revision table added only when necessary

	Date	Revisions
A	15·2·65	Swing changed to LH from RH

Room finish schedule
Example 1

| Room | | Floor | | | Base | | Walls Dado | | Walls Field | | Ceiling Field | | Notes |
Name	No.	Vinyl tile	Terrazzo	Lino tile	Rubber	Terrazzo	Matl	HT	Paint	Block	Acoustic	Painted	
Dining rm	1	●			●				●		●		
Kitchen vest.	2		●		●				●			●	
Kitchen	3		●		●				●			●	
Snack bar	4	●			●				●		●		
Office	5			●	●				●		●		
Baggage rm	6	●			●					●		●	
Concessions	7		●		●				●		●		
Concessions	8		●		●				●		●		
Concessions	9		●		●				●		●		
Waiting rm	10		●		●				●		●		
Airport attend.	11			●	●				●			●	

Extend downward as required by no. of rooms

The schedule is usually extended in width to include more detailed subdivisions under floors, walls, etc.
Room number should be indicated on plan thus [1]

Room finish schedule
Example 2

Leave extra spaces in each column for additions

No.	Name	Floor: Concrete	Floor: Terrazzo	Floor: Quarry tile	Floor: Vinyl tile 0.080"	Floor: Broadloom by owner	Base: Terrazzo	Base: Quarry tile	Base: Vinyl	Dado: Vinyl fabric 4'-6"	Dado: Ceramic tile 7'-0"	Wall: Unfinished	Wall: Plaster	Wall: Walnut	Ceiling: Plaster	Ceiling: Gypsum board	Ceiling: Acoustic tile	Accessories: Counter cupboards	Accessories: Lockers	Remarks
1.	Vestibule			●				●		●			●		●					Inset door mat
2.	Display area		●				●						●				●			See dwg. #7 for terrazzo
3.	Information office				●				●				●				●	●		
4.	Conference room	●				●			●					●		●	●			
5.	Cloak room				●			●					●			●			●	
6.	Projects office				●				●				●				●			
7.	Women's lav.		●								●		●		●					

Room finish schedule
Example 3

Schedule of finishes

Item number	Rooms and areas	Floor Border Material (a)	Floor Border Finish (b)	Floor Field Material (c)	Floor Field Finish (d)	Base Material (e)	Base Finish (f)	Dado Material (g)	Dado Finish (h)	Walls Field Material (i)	Walls Field Finish (j)	Cornice Material (k)	Cornice Finish (l)	Ceiling Border Material (m)	Ceiling Border Finish (n)	Ceiling Field Material (o)	Ceiling Field Finish (p)	Door Material (q)	Door Finish (r)	Window Material (s)	Window Finish (t)
1.	Entrance vestibule, lobby, waiting rooms and corridors	To	Pd	To	Pd	To	Pd	P1	VP1	P1	PT1	—	—	P1	PT1	At	PT1	St	PT2	Al	
2.	Below grade, offices, laboratory, exam room, canteen, locker room, pharmacy, pack stores, c.r. rest rooms	To	Pd	Va	Wx	To	Pd	P1	VP1	P1	PT1	—	—	—	—	At	PT1	St	PT2	Al	
3.	Above grade, wards	To	Pd	Hv	Wx	To	Pd	P1	VP2	P1	PT1	—	—	P1	PT1	P1	PT1	St	PT2	Al	
4.	Utility rooms, janitor rooms	To	Pd	To	Pd	To	Pd	P1	VP1	P1	PT1	—	—	—	—	At	PT1	St	PT2	Al	
5.	Toilets and bath rooms	Ct	—	Ct	—	Ct	—	Gt	—	Kp	PT1	—	—	—	—	At	PT1	St	PT2	Al	
6.	Auditorium	Wd	Vd	Wd	Vd	Wd	Vd	P1	VP1	P1	PT1	—	—	—	—	At	PT1	St	PT2	Al	
7.	Dining room	To	Pd	Hv	Wx	To	Pd	P1	VP1	P1	PT1	—	—	—	—	At	PT1	St	PT2	Al	
8.	Arts and crafts	To	Pd	Hv	Wx	To	Pd	P1	VP1	P1	PT1	—	—	—	—	At	PT1	St	PT2	Al	
9.	Stairways	To	Pd	To	Pd	To	Pd	—	—	Tg	—	—	—	—	—	—	—	St	PT2	Al	
10.	Serveries	Qt	—	Qt	—	Qt	—	—	—	Gt	—	—	—	—	—	At	PT1	St	PT2	Al	
11.	Overhead passage	To	Pd	Hv	Wx	To	Pd	P1	VP1	P1	PT1	—	—	—	—	At	PT1	St	PT2	Al	

Key

Symbol	Materials and finishes
At	Acoustic tile
Cp	Cement plaster
Ct	Ceramic floor tile
Gt	Glazed wall tile
Hv	Homogeneous vinyl
Kp	Keenes cement plaster
Pl	Gypsum plaster
PT1	Paint–gloss
PT2	Paint–enamel
Pd	Polished
Qt	Quarry tile
St	Steel
Tg	Glazed structural terra cotta
To	Terrazzo
Vd	Varnished
Va	Vinyl asbestos
VP1	Vinyl plastic 0.020" clear vinyl
VP2	Vinyl plastic 0.012"
Wd	Wood hardboard
Wx	Wax

Electrical symbols

Ceil	Wall	
○	─○	Outlet ○ Ceiling outlet with pull chain
		PC
Ⓕ	─Ⓕ	Fan outlet
Ⓧ	─Ⓧ	Exit light outlet
Ⓒ	─Ⓒ	Clock outlet. Specify voltage

═⊖   Duplex convenience outlet

═⊖₁,₃   1 = single, 3 = triplex, etc.

═⊖ᵣ   Range outlet

═⊖ₛ   Switch and convenience outlet

⊙   Motor outlet

⬤   Special purpose outlet

⬚A⬚   Fluorescent fixture. Letter designates type

◐▭   Fluorescent fixture with outlet box

S   Single pole switch

S₂   Double pole switch
S₃   Three way switch
S₄   Four way switch

Sₚ   Switch and pilot lamp

▶◁   Outside telephone

◁   Interconnecting telephone

▬   Lighting panel

▨   Power panel

Overhead
Underfloor   } Home run to panel board. Indicate no. of circuits by no. of arrows

Cable designation   Dia / No. of wires
$\frac{3}{4}$ – 5–12 ← Gauge of wire

Plumbing symbols

───────   Soil and waste

─ ─ ─ ─ ─   Soil waste or leader below grade

─/─/─/─   Soil and waste underground

- - - - - - -   Vent

─ · ─ · ─ ·   Cold water

─ ─ · · ─ ─   Hot water

─ · ─────   All other special lines. Insert initials as required and shown on legend

FL/DR
or ⬚   Floor or roof drain
RF/DR

RWC○   Rainwater conductor

Soil ○   Soil stack

Wall type   Floor type   Urinals

▯▭   Water closet, tank type

∘◯   Water closet, flush valve type

▭   Recessed bath

▭   Free standing bath

▭   Sink

▯SS   Service or slop sink

▤   Drain board

⋈ ⋈   Shower

├─HB   Hose bib

Compa
├─   Compressed air outlet

⊙─ Riser   ─▷◁─ Valve

└   Elbow   ┼├ Tee

Heating symbols

Symbol	Description		Symbol	Description
	High-pressure steam			Supply outlet (wall)
	Medium-pressure steam			Exhaust inlet
	Low-pressure steam			Deflecting damper
	High-pressure return			Volume damper
	Medium-pressure return			Forced convection cooling unit
	Low-pressure return			Motor-compressor, sealed crankcase, rotary
	Air relief line			Pressure switch
	Boiler blow off			Pressure switch with high pressure cut-out
	Hot water heating supply			Spray pond
	Hot water heating return			Thermal bulb
	Gate valve		12 x 20	Duct { 1st dim. applies to side shown / 2nd dim. to side not shown
	Riser Elbow			
	Tee			Duct section (supply)
	Rad or convector			Duct section (exhaust or return)
	Finned tube			Ceiling register or grille
	Baseboard convector			Duct and direction of flow

Welding symbols

The following introductory information on welding was supplied by my Technical Education colleague Mr. R. R. Shearer, Welding Section Head, Metals Department, Southern Alberta Institute of Technology, Calgary, Alberta, Canada, and is published with the permission of the Principal.

For a full treatment on welding, contact the American Society of Mechanical Engineers, 29 West 39th Street, New York, N.Y. 10018, U.S.A.

If welding is to take its proper place as a fabricating process, some means of conveying information from the designer to the welding operator must be provided. The practice of writing, "To be welded throughout," on a drawing tells the operator very little since he must guess what filler metal, process, size of weld and method of application to use. In effect, it amounts to the same thing as placing "To be nailed" on the blueprint of a house, with no mention made of the nail type, size, or quantity of nails required. Such a practice can be dangerous and costly. Some shops, in an honest effort to be safe, will apply too much weld metal, while others may tend to use too little with resulting weld failure.

Welding symbols provide the means of placing complete welding information on drawings. In practice, many companies will probably need only a few of the symbols and, if they desire, can select only such parts of the scheme as fits their needs. If they are used universally, all will be speaking the same language even though some use but a few of the symbols contained herein.

Symbols are used in conjunction with an arrow, a reference line, and a tail, which we show below as separate units in Fig. 1-1, but which are normally all hooked together as in Fig. 1-2.

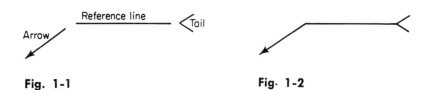

Fig. 1-1   **Fig. 1-2**

Significance of "arrow side" and "other side"

The use of the words "far side" and "near side" in the past has led to confusion because when joints are shown in section, all welds are equally distant from the reader and the words "near" and "far" are meaningless. In the present system the joint is the basis of reference. Any joint, the welding of which is indicated by a symbol, will always have an "arrow side" and an "other side." Accordingly, the words *"arrow side," "other side,"* and *"both sides"* are used herein to locate the weld with respect to the joint. See Fig. 1-3.

When the weld symbol appears on the *"arrow side"* of the reference line, the weld must be made on that side of the joint to which the arrow points. In Fig. 1-4 the proposed weld and preparation are shown in dotted lines.

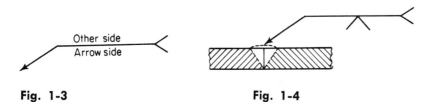

Fig. 1-3   **Fig. 1-4**

If the weld symbol appears on the *"other side"* of the reference line, the weld is made on that side of the joint opposite to where the arrow points. See Fig. 1-5.

However, if two like symbols appear on either side of the reference line, then both sides of the joint will be prepared and welded, as indicated in Fig. 1-6.

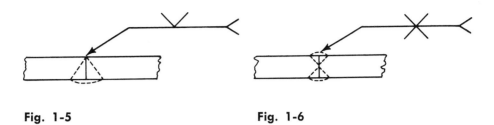

Fig. 1-5   **Fig. 1-6**

Note: To keep the above sketches simple, we have used only the Vee preparation. Other symbols will follow later.

The tail of the welding symbol

The tail of the welding symbol is used for designating welding specifications, procedures, or other supplementary information to be used in making the weld. *To know the size and type of the weld is not enough!* The process to be used, identification of filler metal, whether piening or back chipping is required, and other pertinent information must be known. Where this information becomes too bulky to place in the tail of the symbol, the user will generally establish a code of letters and/or numbers, the meaning of which is established in the specifications or in a separate shop code.

Note: Where notations are not required, the tail of the symbol may be omitted.

Weld symbols

Weld symbols differ from welding symbols in that they represent only one part of a welding symbol, namely the weld to be made. Thus they are the symbol or symbols which are attached to the reference line. In conventional oxy-acetylene and electric welding the weld symbols are as shown in Fig. 1-7.

Type of weld							
Bead	Fillet	Plug or slot	Groove				
			Square	V	Bevel	U	J
⌒	◺	▽	||	V	V	Y	U

Fig. 1-7

Multiple bead

Where the multiple bead weld symbol is used, the minimum height of the deposit is shown to the left of the symbol. Where other than the whole surface is to be built up, the extent, location, and orientation shall be shown on the drawing.

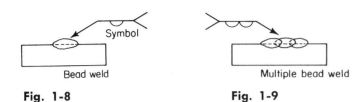

Fig. 1-8   **Fig. 1-9**

Note: Since no joint is being made, there is no "arrow or other side" significance. *The arrow must point to the surface to be built-up.*

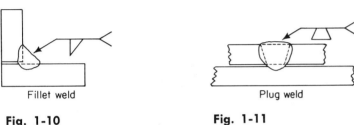

Fig. 1-10   **Fig. 1-11**

The plug weld symbol is used for either plug or slot welds, but if used for slot welds, the dimensions of the slot must be given.

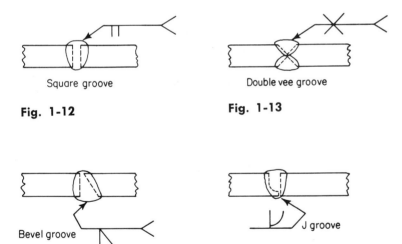

Fig. 1-12   **Fig. 1-13**

Fig. 1-14   **Fig· 1-15**

Note: Where only one edge of a joint is to prepared, a broken arrow is used, which must indicate clearly which plate is to be prepared. Regardless of the position of the reference line, the side toward the reader is the "arrow side," and the perpendicular leg of the weld symbol must be the reader's left. See Figs. 1-10, 1-12, 1-14, 1-15.

EXERCISE:

In the space provided to the right, draw in the preparation and end view outline of the weld indicated by the symbols and sketches in the left hand column. Use dotted line for preparation and solid line for weld outline.

Note: For interpretation, the end view at right will be what you would see when looking from right to left in each question.

	Sample question	Solution
⓪	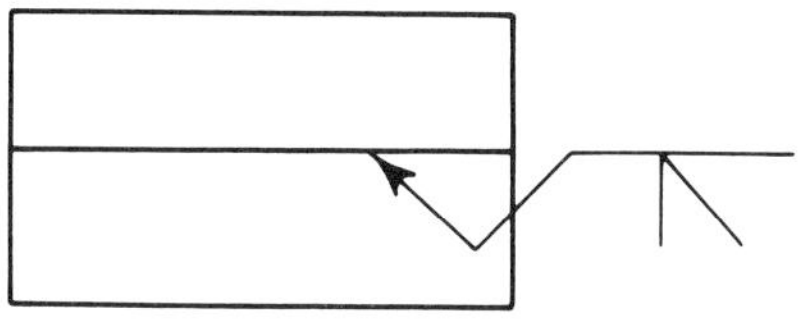	
①	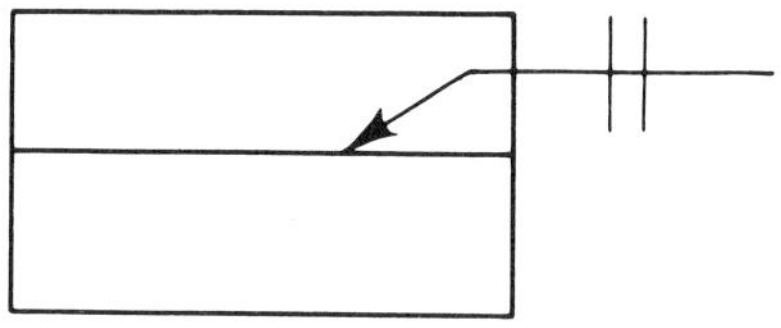	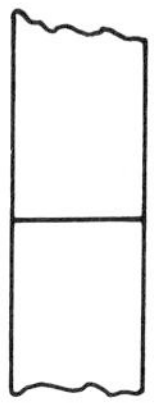
②	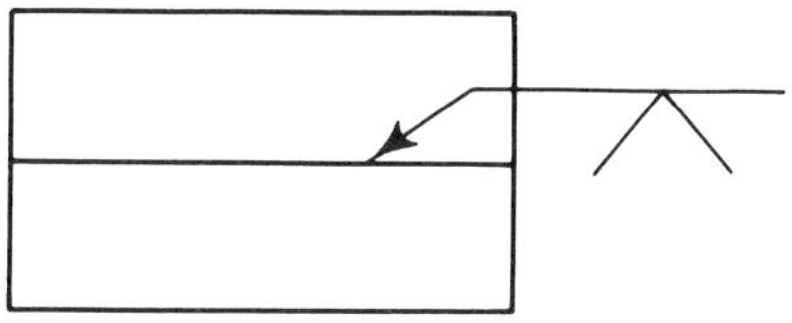	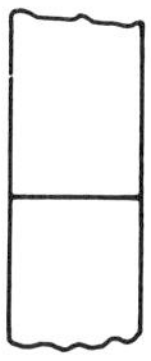
③	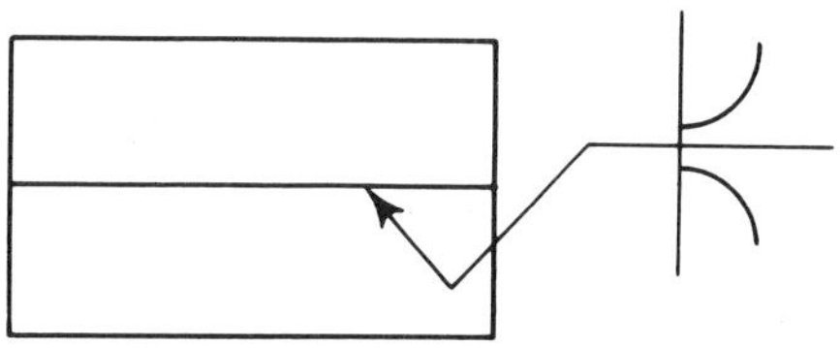	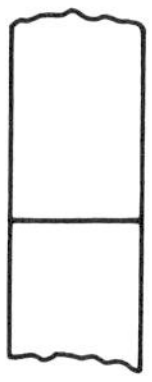
④	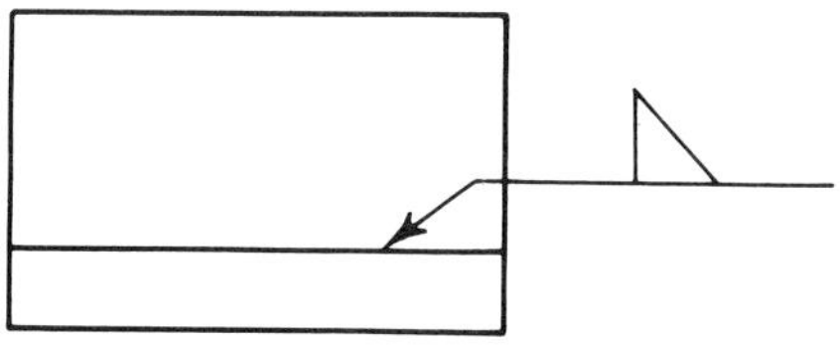	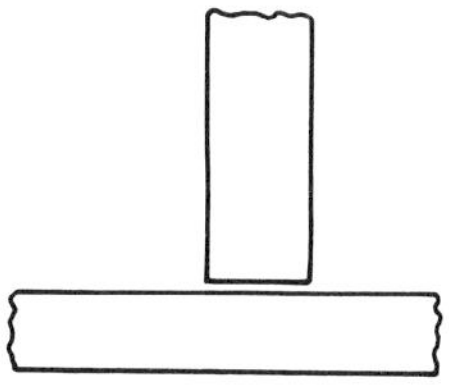

EXERCISE (Continued)

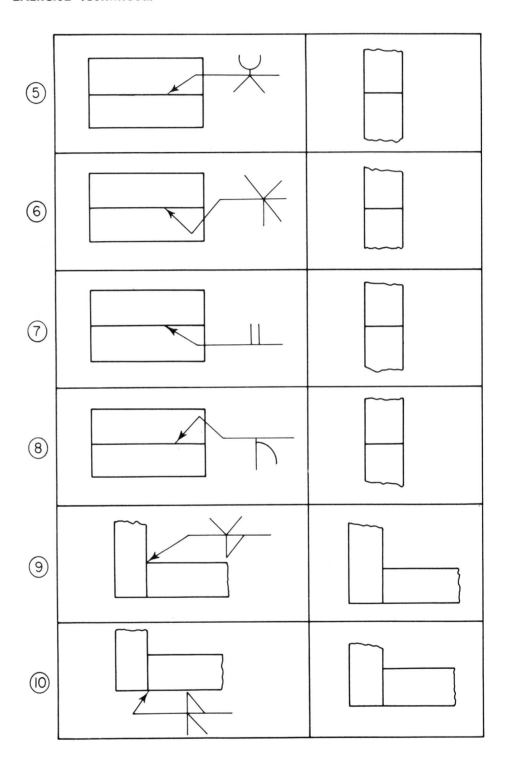

UNIFORM SYSTEM 2
FOR CONSTRUCTION
SPECIFICATIONS,
DATA FILING, AND
COST ACCOUNTING

In this chapter we are going to learn about the Uniform System for Construction Specifications, Data Filing, and Cost Accounting, with special interest in Data Filing.

Manufacturers are constantly researching bldg materials, improving existing types, and producing new materials and new bldg techniques. Their literature, technical data, and structural dwgs are a rich source of information. *It is very important that all students in architecture, engineering, and the construction technologies be aware of the procuring, filing, and ready retrieving of this bldg material data.*

For many years the American Institute of Architects (AIA) and the Royal Architectural Institute of Canada (RAIC) and the building industry generally, very efficiently used "The American Institute of Architects' Filing System." To meet the computer age, that system has now been superseded by the "Uniform System for Construction Specifications, Data Filing, and Cost Accounting." This document has been developed by the cooperative effort of some twelve construction industrial organizations in the U.S.A. and Canada, using the 16-division format developed by the Construction Specifications Institute as an organizational framework. *Extracts from this material have been reproduced from Document K103 copyrighted by the American Institute of Architects, with the permission of the copyright owner.*

Document K103 is in four parts, viz:

Part 1—Specifications   Part 3—Cost accounting guide
Part 2—Filing system   Part 4—Index of key words

Parts 1, 2, and 3 are in a 16-division format as follows:

Divisions

1. General requirements
2. Site work
3. Concrete
4. Masonry
5. Metals
6. Carpentry
7. Moisture protection
8. Doors, windows, and glass
9. Finishes
10. Specialties
11. Equipment
12. Furnishings
13. Special construction
14. Conveying systems
15. Mechanical
16. Electrical

The following extracted pages from Document K103 are reprinted here by permission: (a) The front cover and introductory pages of the whole document; (b) the cover and two or three pages of Parts 1, 2, 3, and 4; (c) a *partial* Catalog and Order Form of Publications and Documents.

ASSIGNMENT:

1. *If you are working alone* on this text, research manufacturers' literature for several items on each of the sixteen divisions. *Read it and file.*

2. (a) *If you are instructing a class,* allocate one or two divisions to each member for research of manufacturers' literature.
   (b) Each student is to write to at least ten different manufacturers for their material.
   (c) Each student is to obtain enough copies to supply every member of the class, plus one for the school.
   (d) Each student is to study intensely any one structural detail shown on a manufacturer's data sheet which he has obtained and is to give a ten- to fifteen-minute talk on the subject to the whole class.

3. *If you are in a new school,* get at least three standard filing cabinets for your classroom. Have each student write to at least thirty manufacturers and build up a classroom Uniform System for Construction Specifications, Data Filing, and Cost Accounting. *Be aware of the importance of discarding superseded material.*

4. Write to the American Institute of Architects for a Catalog and place orders for any documents you need.

UNIFORM SYSTEM

for CONSTRUCTION SPECIFICATIONS, DATA FILING & COST ACCOUNTING

Title One - Buildings

© 1966
AMERICAN INSTITUTE OF ARCHITECTS
ASSOCIATED GENERAL CONTRACTORS OF AMERICA, INC.
THE CONSTRUCTION SPECIFICATIONS INSTITUTE, INC.
COUNCIL OF MECHANICAL SPECIALTY CONTRACTING INDUSTRIES, INC.

ALL RIGHTS RESERVED.

This document is based on concepts and material from the following publications with the permission of the copyright owners:

The CSI Format For Building Specifications
© The Construction Specifications Institute, Inc., 1963 & 1964.

Suggested Guide for Field Cost Accounting for Building Contractors
© Associated General Contractors of America, Inc., 1961.

Standard Filing System and Alphabetical Index
© American Institute of Architects, 1963.

Architectural Sheet Metal Manual
© The Sheet Metal & Air Conditioning Contractors National Association, Inc., 1965.

Duct Manual and Sheet Metal Construction for Ventilating and Air Conditioning Systems
—*High Velocity Systems* © SMACCNA, 1965.
—*Low Velocity Systems* © SMACCNA, 1963.

Manual of Labor Units—NECA Technical & Training Service
© National Electrical Contractors Association, Inc., 1962.

AIA Document K103
ASLA Document 3D
AGC Document 19
CSI Document 001a
NSPE Document 1924

UNIFORM SYSTEM DEVELOPMENT

The Uniform System has been developed in response to pressing needs for better and more rapid classification of technical data. Current technology has created these needs by introducing new materials and techniques at a rate that threatens to outstrip our ability to assimilate essential new information and to correlate it with the old.

Previous data filing systems, through obsolescence, complexity, and inflexibility, have been unable to adapt to an expanding body of knowledge. In recent years, the research/storage/retrieval/application relationships existing between technology and specifications have led many to suggest the creation of a data filing system based on specifications.

The American Institute of Architects recognized that its Standard Filing System, in general use throughout the building industry since 1920, was obsolete, and in January 1962 invited the Construction Specifications Institute to join with it in sponsoring a construction industry meeting to develop a more broadly based system. The first Conference on Uniform Indexing Systems was held under joint sponsorship in October 1962 to discuss development of a filing system for building product data based on specifications, a concept later enlarged to embrace a specification outline and a contractors' cost accounting guide as well.

The organizations that have helped develop and now endorse the Uniform System are

American Institute of Architects
American Society of Landscape Architects
Associated General Contractors of America, Inc.
Construction Specifications Institute
Council of Mechanical Specialty Contracting Industries, Inc.

National Society of Professional Engineers
Producers' Council, Inc.

The first widely publicized document advocating a nation-wide approach to uniformity of specification writing was published by the Construction Specifications Institute in March 1963 as *The CSI Format for Building Specifications.* It proposed the organization of technical specifications into 16 basic groupings designated "Divisions", each of which was to be based on an interrelationship of place, trade, function, or material. There has been a widespread acceptance of the principle advocated by this document within Federal and State agencies throughout the USA and Canada and among private practitioners in the architectural and engineering profession.

The Associated General Contractors of America have long been working on a national standard for cost accounting of construction. In 1961, they published the *Suggested Guide for Field Cost Accounting,* which has been recognized as the first major step toward the establishment of a national standard. With the development of accounting by computer and the trend among contractors more and more to use the computer for keeping records, this national standard takes on added significance. The AGC, recognizing the natural correlation between specifications and project cost accounting, has participated in the development of this Uniform System, and the Cost Accounting Guide, Part 3, is included on their recommendation. The next edition of the *Suggested Guide for Field Cost Accounting* will be based on this outline.

In devising this Uniform System, the endorsing organizations have realized that a data filing system must be flexible enough to accept changes in technology readily, yet sufficiently systematic to establish logical guidance for both user and producer in their classification and identification of technical literature. By providing an approach to data classification designed to remain highly consistent for many years to come, the Uniform System will help producers and publishers get a maximum return on their investment of time, effort, and money in product literature. The endorsing organizations, however, recognize a need for broader flexibility in applying the Specification Outline part of the System. While the Filing System applies in theory to all construction work collectively, the Specification Outline applies in practice to only one project at a time. Conformity to the System is recommended in the interest of ultimate consistency, but no mandate is implied for any individual to limit his application of the Specification Outline to its literal detail. Divergent trade practices alone make an inflexible adherence to the Outline impossible. The professional must remain free to serve his client as he sees best.

It is expected that continuing investigations will be made by all endorsing organizations to improve the document. In addition to trade practice differences, which will require regional studies, there remain the fields of civil, mechanical and electrical engineering, in which the system is relatively untried.

The Uniform System is therefore a statement of both principle and mechanics to encourage closer communication and understanding among three of the dominant forces in the construction industry: manufacturer, designer/specifier, builder. Unless significant steps are taken to bridge inconsistencies, particularly in our regional differences, the industry will remain chaotic.

THE SPECIFICATION OUTLINE

The Specification Outline, Part One of the Uniform System, contains the same 16 Divisions that make up the technical part of *The CSI Format*. Each Division is restated in terms of specific Section titles, but the basic content of each remains unchanged except for a few shifts of individual subjects. Those shifts are generally made to bring Sections of closely related nature into the same Division.

The technical Divisions in the 1966 issue of *The CSI Format* are identical with the Divisions in Part One of the Uniform System. From this common starting point, CSI has indicated its intention to direct the continuing development and expansion of the *Format* to embrace more subject matter than that currently included in the Uniform System under Title One, Buildings.

The Specification Outline is based on two premises:

(1) Related units of work called "Sections" are grouped under broad generic headings known as "Divisions" and

(2) Divisions are constant in sequence, few in number, and short in name. It must be emphasized that "Divisions" do not reflect units of work but rather relationships of units of work. The units are the "Sections".

The Uniform System accepts the principle that only the Divisions are immutable and fixed. It suggests, however, that in the interest of consistency, certain common denominator Sections deserve to be used in very nearly the same context. These are the units of work

that are found in the typical job situation. These are called BROAD-SCOPE Sections and are printed entirely in capital letters. The System recommends the inclusion of these titles, with the wording and in the sequence proposed, whenever the project requires their use. The Narrowscope Section titles (initial caps only) are less typical Sections.

The Broadscope Section may include anything implied by the Narrowscope Sections in the group immediately following. The Narrowscope Section, however, may be sufficiently important in a particular project to supplant completely the Broadscope Section, for example, "Demolition" in lieu of "CLEARING OF SITE". In any case, each Section title, whether Broadscope or Narrowscope, is capable of standing alone as an independent Section title. The selection is determined by the need of the project.

The Division-Section concept of specification arrangement encourages the preparation of smaller and more specific Sections by providing a framework for the related grouping of Sections. While this may lead to a somewhat greater number of Sections than has been common in past specifications, it should provide greater consistency without sacrifice of flexibility.

This document reflects the basic principle that the Section (whether Broadscope or Narrowscope) constitutes a unit of work. The need for clear communication of the scope and intent of this principle, particularly to bidders, lies behind

the basic philosophy of the Section titles as listed. It is further recognized that, since new concepts of units of work are constantly developing, Section titles may in time be modified and redesignated.

The "unit of work" concept of the Section title is to the advantage of both contractor and specification writer, since it allows arrangement within the Division of a large number of Sections in a sequence that minimizes the separation of related items within the specifications. The greater number of Sections allows the contractor to exercise optimum control in awarding subcontracts, because several small Sections may be combined and the need to split larger sections is minimized.

It is expected that experience gained through increasing use of the Uniform System will indicate needed changes in both the techniques of application and refinement of the specification listings. The endorsing organizations will be alert to the need to revise this document, but do not intend to do so indiscriminately. Changes will come only after deliberate consideration based upon experience. Therefore, it is hoped that specification writers will accept this outline as the basis for a rational, nation-wide specification system. While every professional must follow his own judgment in terms of his obligations to clients, the broad aim of optimum consistency in writing specifications will be obtained only through the maximum use of such organized method as shown here.

THE FILING SYSTEM

The Uniform System provides for product literature and related material to be filed numerically under one of the sixteen Divisions. Each is composed of certain generic subdivisions corresponding generally with Section titles appearing in Part One, the Specification Outline.

The concept provides several advantages. First, the user will be able to relate the Filing System

readily to the Specification Outline since both are based on the fundamental Division Concept. Second, with a basic structure consisting of only sixteen Divisions, Division numbers and names are soon memorized through the repetitions of normal use. Third, the Division title and number remain constant, giving stability to the System. Fourth, most of the generic and subgeneric classifications within the Divisions are already familiar

to the construction industry. Fifth, manufacturers are assured of consistent classification of their product, since the proper classification for preprinting on their product literature will be assigned by a central agency staffed for that purpose. The manufacturer is also assured that those who wish to locate a particular product among the filed material will be using the same system used when catalogs were premarked.

THE FILING SYSTEM, continued

The Filing System is based on the premise that there be only one correct place for each subject to be filed. This premise often is inappropriate in the writing of specifications, for some products must be specified in several Divisions. Herein lies a basic difference between the requirements of the Specification Outline and the Filing System. Clearly, a choice of filing classification must be made in such situations, for the user would find intolerable a system that required the filing of identical catalogs in several places merely because a product might someday be specified under one of those several headings. In the Uniform System, the decision has been made by designation of a single classification for each product based on most prevalent use of the product. Cross-reference to other locations where the product may be specified is provided both in the text of Part Two and in Part Four, the Index of Key Words.

The necessity of providing a constant frame of reference for the preclassification and filing of product literature precludes the retention by the Filing System of the broad flexibility provided by the Specification Outline. However, provision must be made for ready inclusion of new materials and techniques as they develop, and for this reason an alphabetical sequence has been used for Filing System subheadings to provide the needed adaptability without necessitating the revision of an established sequence or provision of unassigned numbers as would be the case if a fixed numerical system were used.

The Filing System is composed of Divisions identical in number, title, and sequence to those found in the Specification Outline. Each Division is made up of headings closely related to the Section titles used in Part One. The heading entitled "General Information" at the beginning of each Division except the first, provides a place for filing literature related to more than one heading in a single Division.

PRECLASSIFICATION OF PRODUCT LITERATURE

Product literature is most quickly and accurately filed when it has been imprinted with the appropriate filing classification. Producer, designer, specifier, and buyer alike are assured that literature so identified will not be overlooked because it has been improperly classified. To maintain order within the user's files of product literature, it is necessary that the Filing System be consistently and uniformly applied and that certain regularities in format be observed.

The correct classification will be assigned to any piece of product literature, subject to the following considerations, upon its submission in triplicate to UNIFORM SYSTEM, 1735 New York Ave., N.W., Washington, D.C. 20006. A classification fee is charged to defray administrative costs including maintenance of complete and current files on all product literature premarked with Uniform System designations.

1) Overall size, including projecting cover if any, should be not less than 8¼"x10¾" nor more than 8½"x11".

2) Use of projecting tabs of any sort is discouraged.

3) Consumer advertising and similar material containing little or no technical product information are beyond the intent of the Filing System, and submission of such material for classification is discouraged.

4) It is recommended that literature be prepunched for standard three-hole ring binders and that the format be so designed that no printed data is removed or obscured by such punching.

5) Products, systems, and techniques encompassed by a single piece of literature must fall within a single Division and preferably within a single Section.

6) Uniform System designations for preprinting on product literature are assigned solely by the Conference on Uniform Indexing Systems.

7) Literature bearing preprinted Uniform System designations assigned by the Conference on Uniform Indexing Systems will be exclusively identified by a distinctive logotype alongside the filing designations. The logotype is intended only for use with officially assigned classifications and may be used for other purposes only by written permission.

8) Assignment of a filing classification implies no approval by the Conference on Uniform Indexing Systems or its member organizations of the company on whose literature the classification is to be imprinted nor of the products therein presented.

IDENTIFICATION SYMBOLS

In the identification symbol for the Filing System, the most prominent feature is the large numeral which represents one of the sixteen Divisions. Significantly, the title of the Division is never shown. Since the titles of the Divisions will be very shortly committed to memory by the user, the Division number will bring to mind the actual Division name. Elimination of the Division name simplifies the identification symbol, making it easier to grasp at a glance. The Division numeral is followed by a horizontal line separating the upper case heading above from the lower case subheading below. Each of the headings and subheadings to be used in the preclassification of product literature is shown under the appropriate Division in Part Two of the Uniform System. Thus, a manufacturer's catalog encompassing various types of resilient flooring products will be classified under Division 9, Finishes, and the proper

IDENTIFICATION SYMBOLS, continued

identification symbol to be imprinted thereon is

9 RESILIENT FLOORING

However, if the piece of literature is concerned with only one specific type of resilient flooring, such as vinyl asbestos, the basic identification symbol should include the appropriate subheading. This secondary identification appears below the horizontal line in lower case letters and the proper symbol becomes

9 RESILIENT FLOORING
vinyl asbestos

It is appropriate that the manufacturer display the name of his company prominently and uniquely on the cover of his catalog material. However, the user should be able to find the manufacturer's name consistently located on each piece of literature to facilitate identification of a particular filed catalog. To accomplish this, the company name should be included immediately to the left of the filing symbol as an integral part of the catalog identification, regardless of whether the name appears elsewhere on the cover.

One of the most frequent complaints from users of other systems is the absence of a date on many catalogs. It is often impossible to determine which of two undated catalogs from the same manufacturer supersedes the other. Each manufacturer should, therefore, indicate both year and month of publication.

Consistent use of the same type face, point size, arrangement of information, and location on the page all contribute to rapid recognition and assimilation by the user. For this reason these factors will be closely controlled, and the symbol will be located in the upper lefthand corner and the lower righthand of the front cover parallel to the cover's long dimension as indicated on this page.

The heading "GENERAL INFORMATION" appears at the beginning of each filing Division. Product literature encompassed by the Division and related to more than one of its Sections should be filed under this first heading. This heading provides for the filing of literature on such subjects as general workmanship and code requirements, as well as product lines related to more than one Section within the Division. Product literature will be classified under this heading where appropriate, and such classification will be indicated by imprintation of the correct Division number followed by the heading title and its accompanying underscore only. No subheading will be used in this case.

Catalogs are marked in this manner for convenient filing under GENERAL INFORMATION, but the user is free to assign a different category as his requirements may dictate, altering the imprinted designation to his selected classification. Conversely, where the user's needs so indicate, certain literature premarked with other headings may be filed under GENERAL INFORMATION, with preprinted headings covered or marked through.

USING THE FILING SYSTEM

When a building product catalog or other literature arrives preclassified and premarked, the Uniform System designation permits a file clerk without technical knowledge to file it correctly and rapidly. The only policy decision which must be made is whether the literature is to be kept or not. An architect or engineer may review a stack of catalogs, pull out those that do not pertain to his practice, and hand the rest to the file clerk with instructions to file the new material. Classification beyond the Section heading level may, sometimes, be unnecessary. Where further subdivision is required it may be done by alphabetical arrangement of subheadings, alphabetical arrangement by manufacturer's name, separation of products locally represented from the others, or any other system convenient to the user's needs. The important consideration is that filing classification and designation be constant but not so restrictive that the user cannot make the minute adjustments he may desire.

It should be noted that the logotype with large numeral indicating one of the sixteen Divisions, a heading title and horizontal line to the right, and publishing source and date to the left are parts of the identification symbol that are always present. The name of manufacturer or publisher is shown in the same type-face used for heading and subheading, with initial letters in upper case, or in other distinctive form normally used. The upper part of the right hand fraction is always capitalized and designates the generic group or section. The lower part of the fraction is always in lower case and is used when further subdivision of the generic group or section is desired.

HAND MARKING MATERIAL

Material that originates with the user and material received without premarking can be hand marked with a felt pen or other marking instrument having a bold stroke.

If the background of the cover material is quite dark or if the surface with not accept ink, gummed labels can be applied.

The piece may be a technical article torn from a current trade magazine, a bibliography published by a trade association, a catalog published before adoption of the Uniform System and carrying an obsolete AIA File Number, or part of a catalog torn apart for proper filing under the Uniform System. Catalogs not divided in accordance with the Uniform System may be taken apart, their pages grouped for filing in the appropriate Division or Section, and each group of pages stapled and hand marked with the proper filing symbol.

COST ACCOUNTING GUIDE

The Cost Accounting Guide is an orderly arrangement of the items of work required by the contractor during the course of a construction project. It is presented here in a format readily applicable to computer processing techniques.

Section titles appearing in the Cost Accounting Guide are, with few exceptions, identical in name and order to those used in the Specification Outline. A fixed number has been assigned to each Division and Section. The first pair of digits, reading from left to right, indicate the Division number, the second pair, the Section number. These four digits are always used and are separated from those for the designation of subordinate material by a decimal point. Subordinate material should be indexed by pairs of digits to the right of the decimal point.

No attempt has been made to include any classification of material below the Section level. Use of such subordinate material will be the rule rather than the exception in actual practice, but its inclusion in a fixed numbering system would make the Cost Accounting Guide too inflexible. It is left to the individual to establish titles and numbers for the subordinate items required by the project and by his organization.

THE INDEX OF KEY WORDS

An exhaustive collection of key words referring to the entire Uniform System has been compiled and arranged alphabetically in the Index. Titles and classifications varying from one part of the document to another are so noted.

Each key word is referred to the appropriate Division by number and to the correct Section or heading by title. Section or heading titles are always capitalized and, where omitted from Parts One, Two, or Three, include a note as to their location.

COMPARATIVE TABLE OF CONTENTS

Broadside Section titles for Parts One and Three are shown below in the sequence in which they appear in the text. Corresponding Broadscope Headings from the Filing System are shown in a sequence altered from that used in the text to place them in closer juxtaposition to corresponding Section titles in Parts One and Three. The Filing System text arranges these same titles in alphabetical sequence.

Part One, Specification Outline	Part Two, Filing System	Part Three, Cost Accounting Guide
		Page 3.3
		CONDITIONS OF THE CONTRACT

GENERAL REQUIREMENTS		DIVISION 1
Page 1.3	Page 2.2	Page 3.3
	CODES & STANDARDS	
	PLANNING GUIDES	
	SPECIAL SERVICES	
		0100. ALTERNATES OF PROJECT SCOPE
SUMMARY OF THE WORK		
SCHEDULES & REPORTS		0110. SCHEDULES & REPORTS
SAMPLES & SHOP DRAWINGS		0120. SAMPLES & SHOP DRAWINGS
TEMPORARY FACILITIES	TEMPORARY FACILITIES	0130. TEMPORARY FACILITIES
CLEANING UP		0140. CLEANING UP
PROJECT CLOSEOUT		0150. PROJECT CLOSEOUT
ALLOWANCES		0160. ALLOWANCES
ALTERNATES		

SITE WORK		DIVISION 2
Page 1.5	Page 2.2	Page 3.3
	GENERAL INFORMATION	
		0200. ALTERNATES
CLEARING OF SITE	CLEARING OF SITE	0210. CLEARING OF SITE
EARTHWORK	EARTHWORK	0220. EARTHWORK
PILING	PILING	0230. PILING
CAISSONS	CAISSONS	0235. CAISSONS
SHORING & BRACING	SHORING & BRACING	0240. SHORING & BRACING
SITE DRAINAGE	SITE DRAINAGE	0250. SITE DRAINAGE
SITE UTILITIES		0255. SITE UTILITIES
ROADS & WALKS	ROADS & WALKS	0260. ROADS & WALKS
SITE IMPROVEMENTS	SITE IMPROVEMENTS	0270. SITE IMPROVEMENTS
LAWNS & PLANTING	LAWNS & PLANTING	0280. LAWNS & PLANTING
RAILROAD WORK	RAILROAD WORK	0290. RAILROAD WORK
MARINE WORK	MARINE WORK	0295. MARINE WORK

CONCRETE		DIVISION 3
Page 1.10	Page 2.3	Page 3.3
	GENERAL INFORMATION	
		0300. ALTERNATES
CONCRETE FORMWORK	CONCRETE FORMWORK	0310. CONCRETE FORMWORK
CONCRETE REINFORCEMENT	CONCRETE REINFORCEMENT	0320. CONCRETE REINFORCEMENT
CAST-IN-PLACE CONCRETE	CAST-IN-PLACE CONCRETE	0330. CAST-IN-PLACE CONCRETE
PRECAST CONCRETE	PRECAST CONCRETE	0340. PRECAST CONCRETE
CEMENTITIOUS DECKS	CEMENTITIOUS DECKS	0350. CEMENTITIOUS DECKS

MASONRY		DIVISION 4
Page 1.11	Page 2.4	Page 3.3
	GENERAL INFORMATION	
		0400. ALTERNATES
MORTAR	MORTAR	0410. MORTAR
UNIT MASONRY	UNIT MASONRY	0420. UNIT MASONRY
STONE	STONE	0430. STONE
MASONRY RESTORATION	MASONRY RESTORATION	0440. MASONRY RESTORATION

Part One - SPECIFICATION OUTLINE

UNIFORM SYSTEM

for CONSTRUCTION SPECIFICATIONS, DATA FILING & COST ACCOUNTING

Title One - Buildings

NOTES

Many Section titles are shown in the plural in the Uniform System Specification Outline. These titles should be changed to the singular where project requirements indicate.

Specification Sections may be numbered by the specification writer in any way he prefers. He may choose to use the Uniform System Division number followed by a capital letter identifying each of the several Sections in that Division, "8A" for example. When a fixed numbering system is preferred, use of the four-digit system shown in the Cost Accounting Guide, Uniform System Part 3, is recommended.

The Specification Outline includes both BROADSCOPE and Narrowscope Sections in great variety and number, and the individual project specifications will rarely, if ever, follow Section titles and sequence in every detail. Typical specifications will use only a portion of the titles listed, and some will require the modification of Uniform System Section titles or the introduction of new titles. However, it is recommended that Section titles be selected whenever possible from the comprehensive set shown in Part 1.

Division 1 encompasses certain aspects of project requirements often included in the General Conditions. When the recommendations of Division 1 are followed, the Conditions of the Contract should include appropriate Supplementary Conditions to avoid duplication of material contained in such General Conditions as those published by the American Institute of Architects, the Consulting Engineers Council of the United States, and others.

SPECIFICATION OUTLINE   **GENERAL REQUIREMENTS**

SUMMARY OF THE WORK

Encompasses summaries of work under this contract, work under other contracts related to the project, work & equipment to be provided by the owner, and work to be postponed to a date later than the designated completion date. It should be clearly stated here whether work is to be completed under a single contract or under several contracts.

SCHEDULES & REPORTS

Encompasses the certification of lines & levels, reference to applicable building standards of such organizations as American Society for Testing & Materials, American Standards Association, American Institute of Steel Construction, American Concrete Institute, and General Services Administration; required inspections; a schedule of required tests; a list of approved testing agencies or criteria for their selection & approval; subsurface soil reports; progress reports & photographs; work progress & critical path schedules; project master color schedule; a glossary of standard abbreviations & symbols; and similar items related to the project as a whole. See 2 EARTHWORK for testing related to soil compaction; 2 PILING for piling tests; 3 CAST-IN-PLACE CONCRETE & 3 PRECAST CONCRETE for testing & inspection of concrete.

SAMPLES & SHOP DRAWINGS

Encompasses procedures for submission of shop drawings & samples. Required shop drawings & samples are normally best specified here in scheduled or tabular form, but it is recommended that a reference to this portion of the Specifications be included in each of the various Sections covering work for which samples or shop drawings are required.

TEMPORARY FACILITIES

Encompasses access roads, barricades & lanterns, construction elevators & hoists, construction stairs, construction offices, storage of tools & equipment, first aid facilities, temporary fences & guardrails, moisture control, parking, runways, scaffolding, staging platforms, signs, site access restrictions, temporary telephone service, outdoor toilet facilities, watchman, and similar provisions necessary to the safe and expeditious progress of the work. This portion of the Specifications normally encompasses the *temporary* provision of electrical power, lighting, space heating, water, or indoor toilet facilities. It is recommended that a reference to this Section be included in each of the other Sections covering similar work of a permanent nature.

CLEANING UP

Encompasses the sweeping, brushing, and other general cleaning of completed work and the removal of debris, surplus material, tools not in active use, and scaffolding & other equipment no longer needed. See various Sections in other Divisions for removal of unwanted material, for initial cleandown of newly installed work, and for cleaning of existing work.

PROJECT CLOSEOUT

Encompasses procedures for delivering guarantees & bonds, for preparing the punchlist, and for final inspection of the project; as-built drawings & specifications required and procedure for their submission; scope & content of the maintenance manual and procedure for its submission; and similar items related to the project as a whole. It is recommended that a reference to this portion of the Specifications be included in each of the various Sections covering work for which as-built drawings & specifications, guarantees, bonds, or maintenance manual data are required.

ALLOWANCES

Tabulates and defines all cash allowances for specified portions of the work. It is recommended that dollar amounts appear only in a master list located here and that reference to this portion of the Specifications be included in each of the various Sections covering work similar to that for which cash allowance is to be made. Cash allowances may also be itemized on the Bid Form.

ALTERNATES

Lists all Alternates, describing in complete detail those Alternates that affect the scope of the project and summarizing those Alternates that deal with materials & methods of construction. Further reference to Alternates of project scope normally is limited to the Bid Form, but Alternates of materials & methods must be specified in complete detail in each of the various Sections affected and in brief in the Bid Form. It is essential that the Bid Form list all Alternates, assign a number or other reference designation to each, describe each briefly, and provide space beside each for the bidders' insertion of consequent additions to or deductions from the base bid.

SPECIFICATION OUTLINE

SITE WORK 2

CLEARING OF SITE

Broadscope Section encompasses work described below under Demolition, Structures Moving, Clearing & Grubbing.

Demolition

Narrowscope Section encompasses demolition of and materials salvage from designated buildings, sheds, towers, tanks, covered walkways, and other existing above-grade structures. Capping of existing utility lines is normally best specified here, but may in some instances be specified instead in appropriate Section or Sections of Divisions 15 and 16. See 2 EARTHWORK for demolition and removal of such on-grade or below-grade improvements as concrete slabs, foundation walls, footings, underground tanks, underground utility lines, paving, culverts, curbs, and gutters.

Structures Moving

Narrowscope Section encompasses the intact relocation, on the project site or elsewhere, of designated existing structures or portions thereof. Earthwork, foundations, utility lines, and other new work related to the relocated structures are normally best specified in other appropriate Sections.

Clearing & Grubbing

Narrowscope Section encompasses the felling of trees and shrubs and removal or other disposition of resulting trash and timber, stumps, and other vegetation. See 2 EARTHWORK for removal of rocks, boulders, and other on-grade or below-grade obstructions.

EARTHWORK

Broadscope Section encompasses work described below under Site Grading, Excavating & Backfilling, Dewatering, Subdrainage, Soil Poisoning, Soil Compaction Control, Soil Stabilization.

Site Grading

Narrowscope Section encompasses the movement of significant quantities of earth to alter the fundamental contours of the site. This Section normally includes large earth fills, particularly those requiring use of borrow pits off the site; relocation & compaction of earth in the general overlot grading; disposition of excess excavated material; and removal of natural rock formations by ripping, blasting, or other means. See Excavating & Backfilling below for the localized movement of earth for accommodating the various portions of the building and its equipment, for tunneling work, and for removal of various isolated obstructions on or below grade.

Excavating & Backfilling

Narrowscope Section encompasses the localized movement of earth for accommodating the various portions of the building and its equipment. This Section normally includes the digging of footing trenches, foundation pits, & basements and required working space around them; removal of rocks, boulders, & other obstructions encountered; shaping of footing & other pits & trenches; fine grading under slabs; tunneling under walks, roads, & other existing work; and required backfilling.

Dewatering

Narrowscope Section encompasses removal of subsurface water from the soil during the construction period by means of pitting & pumping, wellpointing, trenching below the water table, or other means. This Section normally includes control of subsurface water by use of cofferdams constructed of closely driven piles supporting impervious clay fill or wood lagging, of interlocking steel sheet piling, or of prefabricated assemblies of special design. See Subdrainage below for subsurface drainage provisions of a permanent nature. See 2 SITE DRAINAGE for storm drainage system external to the building. See 7 SHEET METAL WORK for gutters & downspouts.

Subdrainage

Narrowscope Section encompasses drainage fields below basement floor slabs and other concrete slabs on grade, footing tile drains, and drainage fields required to drain an underground spring or other subsurface water source. See Dewatering above for removal of subsurface water during the construction period. See 2 SITE DRAINAGE for storm drainage system external to the building. See 7 SHEET METAL WORK for gutters & downspouts.

Soil Poisoning

Narrowscope Section encompasses the introduction of poison into the soil around and under structures for control of termites, other vermin, and undesirable plant growth.

Soil Compaction Control

Narrowscope Section encompasses field sampling & laboratory testing for control of soil compaction. See 1 SCHEDULE & REPORTS for preliminary subsurface soil investigation.

Soil Stabilization

Narrowscope Section encompasses the pressure-injection or other introduction of portland cement or other substances into fissured or porous rock or soil in order to stabilize it, to increase its bearing capacity, to reduce its tendency to flow, or to make it more water-resistant. This Section normally includes rock bolting and vibratory methods of soil stabilization.

PILING

Broadscope Section encompasses treated wood piling, precast concrete piling, 'H'-section steel piling, drilled-&-poured concrete piling, concrete-filled steel pipe piling, and mandrel-driven thin-shell steel piling with concrete fill. This Section normally includes load-sustaining requirements and tests.

CAISSONS

Broadscope Section encompasses both drilled and excavated caissons. Furnishing and placement of attendant formwork, reinforcing, and concrete are normally best specified here, but may in some instances be specified instead in 3 CONCRETE FORMWORK, 3 CONCRETE REINFORCEMENT, & 3 CAST-IN-PLACE CONCRETE, respectively. When formwork, reinforcing, & concrete are specified here, it is recommended that a reference to this Section be included in these Sections of Division 3 as may be appropriate.

SHORING & BRACING

Broadscope Section encompasses work described below under Sheeting, Underpinning.

Sheeting

Narrowscope Section encompasses wood sheeting, interlocking steel sheeting, whalers & shores, cribbing, and piling with intermediate lagging serving as, or incorporated in, permanent retaining walls. Sheeting installed as temporary retaining walls is normally best specified in 1 TEMPORARY FACILITIES.

Underpinning

Narrowscope Section encompasses temporary or permanent support of portions of buildings being remodeled or of buildings adjacent to new construction by means of shoring, needling, or underpinning.

SITE DRAINAGE

Broadscope Section encompasses the storm drainage system external to project building or buildings and is distinguished from the subdrainage system by its collection of rain and other surface water rather than subsurface water. This Section normally includes drop inlets, side inlets, catchbasins, manholes, manhole covers & frames, headwalls, culverts, drainage ditches & related rip-rap, concrete raceways & flumes, downspout connections, and piping of terra cotta, concrete, steel, or other material suitable for the system. External downspouts, gutters, & leaders are normally specified in 7 SHEET METAL WORK, roof drains and internal rainwater piping in 15 ROOF DRAINAGE SYSTEM. When a Section on SITE UTILITIES is included as part of this Division, this Section may be combined with it as SITE UTILITIES & DRAINAGE.

Part Two—FILING SYSTEM

UNIFORM SYSTEM

for CONSTRUCTION SPECIFICATIONS,
DATA FILING
& COST ACCOUNTING

Title One - Buildings

GENERAL REQUIREMENTS

 SITE WORK

CODES & STANDARDS

building codes
electrical codes
fallout shelters
housing codes
plumbing codes
safety codes
standards & tests
testing laboratories

PLANNING GUIDES

building restoration
color guides
modular coordination
solar heat & light
urban planning

SPECIAL SERVICES

financing
models & renderings
photography
soil mechanics
surveying

TEMPORARY FACILITIES

barricades & lanterns
construction elevators
construction hoists; see 14 HOISTS & CRANES
hand trucks; see 14 MATERIALS HANDLING
  SYSTEM
ladders
mixing equipment; see 3 CAST-IN-PLACE
  CONCRETE
motor trucks
portable tools; see 11 EDUCATIONAL EQUIPMENT
ropes & chains
scaffolding
staging platforms
welding equipment; see 5 FASTENERS & SUPPORTS

GENERAL INFORMATION

CAISSONS

CLEARING OF SITE

building moving
building demolition
logging equipment

EARTHWORK

compaction equipment
earth drills
earthmoving machines
explosives
soil laboratories
soil poisons & herbicides
soil stabilization

LAWNS & PLANTING

erosion control material
fertilizer
ground covers
lawns & grasses
mulches
planting & seeding equipment
soil aeration
soil preparation equipment
soil treatments
sprays & sprayers
trees & shrubs

MARINE WORK

docks & slips
dredging equipment
fender piles
marine accessories
marine hardware
seawalls & jetties

PILING

RAILROAD WORK

ballasts
rails
ties
turnouts & crossings

SITE WORK, continued

 CONCRETE

FILING SYSTEM

ROADS & WALKS

airports & heliports
barriers & bumpers
base courses
bituminous paving
bridle trails
concrete paving; see 3 CAST-IN-PLACE CONCRETE
curb guards
*drive-up ticket dispensers; see 11 PARKING
    EQUIPMENT*
guard rails
ice & dust control
paving machines
roadway fittings
signs & signals
soil cements; see 2 EARTHWORK
striping material
traffic gates; see 11 PARKING EQUIPMENT

SHORING & BRACING

sheeting
underpinning

SITE DRAINAGE

catch basins
cofferdams
culverts
drains & inlets
manholes
pipe & fittings
pumps; see 15 PUMPS & COMPRESSORS
well-points

SITE IMPROVEMENTS

athletic facilities
fences & gates
fountains
garden structures
irrigation equipment
playground equipment
yard equipment

site utilities; see various headings, Divisions 15 & 16

GENERAL INFORMATION

CAST-IN-PLACE CONCRETE

admixtures
aggregates
anchors & inserts
cements
conveying equipment
curing materials
floats & trowels
mixing equipment
special concretes
special finishes
vibrators
waterstops

CEMENTITIOUS DECKS

bulb-tees & planks
cement-fiber decking
poured gypsum decks

CONCRETE FORMWORK

expendable forms
form accessories
form coatings
form liners
permanent forms
preassembled stair forms
reusable forms
supports & shoring

CONCRETE REINFORCEMENT

accessories
bars
cable
prestressing anchorages
prestressing equipment
wire fabric

PRECAST CONCRETE

decorative panels
lift-slab equipment
prestressed units
structural units
tanks & bins
tilt-up equipment

MASONRY

 METALS

GENERAL INFORMATION

MASONRY RESTORATION
cleaning materials
pointing materials
resurfacing materials; see 9 SPECIAL COATINGS

MORTAR

STONE
granite
limestone
marble
quartzite
sandstone
serpentine
simulated stone
slate
soapstone
travertine

UNIT MASONRY
clay tile units
coated units
common brick
concrete units
face brick
facing tile units
glass units
gypsum units
pavers
refractory units
screen units
terra cotta units
ties & reinforcement

GENERAL INFORMATION

FASTENERS & SUPPORTS
bolts
connectors
nails
rivets
screws
supporting devices
welding studs
welding equipment

LIGHTGAGE FRAMING
studs & joists
tubing

METAL DECKING
cellular
corrugated
ribbed & fluted

METALS & ALLOYS
aluminum
bronze
cast iron
copper & brass
electroplating
lead
magnesium & titanium
metal treatments
nickel
porcelain enamelling
stainless steel
steel
terne
wrought iron
zinc

METALS, continued

 CARPENTRY

MISCELLANEOUS METAL

ash dumps; see 10 FIREPLACE EQUIPMENT
balconies
catwalks
fire escapes
fire shutters
fireplace dampers; see 10 FIREPLACE EQUIPMENT
floor plates & grids
folding gates
foundation vents
gratings
hangers
ladders
linteis
pipe railings
preassembled stair forms; see 3 CONCRETE FORMWORK
stage gridiorns; see 11 STAGE EQUIPMENT
stairs
weathervanes
wheel guards

OPEN-WEB JOISTS

anchors & bridging
longspan joists
shortspan joists

ORNAMENTAL METAL

custom metalwork
facias & copings
ornamental grilles
ornamental railings
ornamental spandrels

SPECIAL FORMED METAL

STRUCTURAL METAL

arches & frames
domes
pipe columns
plates
rolled shapes
trusses

GENERAL INFORMATION

CUSTOM WOODWORK

FINISH CARPENTRY

custom millwork
finish lumber
hardboard
paneling
particleboard
plastic laminates
plywood
stairs & railings
unfinished cabinets
wood door frames
wood louvers
wood moldings & trim
wood shingles; see 7 SHINGLES & ROOFING TILES
wood siding
wood veneers

GLUE-LAMINATED WOOD

arches & frames
beams & columns
decking
glues

ROUGH CARPENTRY

asbestos-cement sheets
asbestos-cement shingles; see 7 SHINGLES & ROOFING TILES
beams & timbers
decking
framing lumber
pool construction
sheathing
subflooring
synthetic lumber
wood framing systems
wood trusses

WOOD TREATMENT

7   MOISTURE PROTECTION

GENERAL INFORMATION

BUILDING INSULATION

board insulation
foamed-in-place
gypsum roof decks; see 3 CEMENTITIOUS DECKS
high-temperature; see 15 MECHANICAL SYSTEMS
    INSULATION
low temperature; see 13 INSULATED ROOMS,
    15 MECHANICAL SYSTEMS INSULATION
paper, felt, & foil
pellet insulation
perimeter insulation
pipe & duct; see 15 MECHANICAL SYSTEMS
    INSULATION
rolls & batts
vapor barriers; see 7 DAMPPROOFING

CALKING & SEALANTS

elastomers, preformed
elastomers, single-component bulk
elastomers, two-component bulk
gaskets
glazing compounds
oil-base, bulk
packing, fibrous
packing, resilient
tape sealants

DAMPPROOFING

bituminous dampproofing
cementitious dampproofing
liquid dampproofing
preformed vapor barrier

MEMBRANE ROOFING

base sheets
bituminous binders
cants & edge strips
felts & fabrics
roll roofing
roof aggregates
roofing cements
roofing systems
synthetic binders & toppings
synthetic sheets

PREFORMED ROOFING & SIDING

asbestos-cement units
custom roofing panels
plastic units
roofing units
siding units

ROOF ACCESSORIES

framed skylights
plastic skydomes
roof hatches
roof vents

SHEET METAL WORK

ductwork; see 15 AIR-TEMPERING SYSTEM
downspouts
facias & copings; see 5 ORNAMENTAL METAL
gutters
scuppers
sheet metal roofing
vermin shields

SHINGLES & ROOFING TILES

asbestos-cement
asphalt
backing material
concrete
fired clay
metal
porcelain enamel
slate
wood

WALL FLASHING

expansion joints
felts & fabrics
metal & metal-coated
preformed units
synthetic sheets

WATERPROOFING

hydrolithic waterproofing
integral waterproofing; see 3 CAST-IN-PLACE
    CONCRETE
liquid waterproofing
membrane waterproofing
metallic oxide waterproofing
preformed elastic sheets

Part Three—COST ACCOUNTING GUIDE

UNIFORM SYSTEM

for CONSTRUCTION SPECIFICATIONS, DATA FILING & COST ACCOUNTING

Title One - Buildings

0 CONDITIONS OF THE CONTRACT

0000. - 0099. unassigned

1 GENERAL REQUIREMENTS

0100. ALTERNATES OF PROJECT SCOPE
0101. - 0109. unassigned
0110. SCHEDULES & REPORTS
0111. - 0119. unassigned
0120. SAMPLES & SHOP DRAWINGS
0121. - 0129. unassigned
0130. TEMPORARY FACILITIES
0131. - 0139. unassigned
0140. CLEANING UP
0141. - 0149. unassigned
0150. PROJECT CLOSEOUT
0151. - 0159. unassigned
0160. ALLOWANCES
0161. - 0199. unassigned

2 SITE WORK

0200. ALTERNATES
0201. - 0209. unassigned
0210. CLEARING OF SITE
0211. Demolition
0212. Structures Moving
0213. Clearing & Grubbing
0214. - 0219. unassigned
0220. EARTHWORK
0221. Site Grading
0222. Excavating & Backfilling
0223. Dewatering
0224. Subdrainage
0225. Soil Poisoning
0226. Soil Compaction Control
0227. Soil Stabilization
0228. - 0229. unassigned
0230. PILING
0231. - 0234. unassigned
0235. CAISSONS
0236. - 0239. unassigned
0240. SHORING & BRACING
0241. Sheeting
0242. Underpinning
0243. - 0249. unassigned
0250. SITE DRAINAGE
0251. - 0254. unassigned
0255. SITE UTILITIES
0256. - 0259. unassigned
0260. ROADS & WALKS
0261. Paving
0262. Curbs & Gutters
0263. Walks
0264. Road & Parking Appurtenances
0265. - 0269. unassigned
0270. SITE IMPROVEMENTS
0271. Fences
0272. Playing Fields
0273. Fountains
0274. Irrigation System
0275. Yard Improvements
0276. - 0279. unassigned
0280. LAWNS & PLANTING
0281. Soil Preparation
0282. Lawns
0283. Ground Covers & Other Plants
0284. Trees & Shrubs
0285. - 0289. unassigned
0290. RAILROAD WORK
0291. - 0294. unassigned
0295. MARINE WORK
0296. Boat Facilities
0297. Protective Marine Structures
0298. Dredging
0299. unassigned

3 CONCRETE

0300. ALTERNATES
0301. - 0309. unassigned
0310. CONCRETE FORMWORK
0311. - 0319. unassigned
0320. CONCRETE REINFORCEMENT
0321. - 0329. unassigned
0330. CAST-IN-PLACE CONCRETE
0331. Heavyweight Aggregate Concrete
0332. Lightweight Aggregate Concrete
0333. Post-Tensioned Concrete
0334. Nailable Concrete
0335. Specially Finished Concrete
0336. Specially Placed Concrete
0337. - 0339. unassigned
0340. PRECAST CONCRETE
0341. Precast Concrete Panels
0342. Precast Structural Concrete
0343. Precast Prestressed Concrete
0344. - 0349. unassigned
0350. CEMENTITIOUS DECKS
0351. Poured Gypsum Deck
0352. Insulating Concrete Roof Decks
0353. Cementitious Unit Decking
0354. - 0399. unassigned

4 MASONRY

0400. ALTERNATES
0401. - 0409. unassigned
0410. MORTAR
0411. - 0419. unassigned
0420. UNIT MASONRY
0421. Brick Masonry
0422. Concrete Unit Masonry
0423. Clay Backing Tile
0424. Clay Facing Tile
0425. Ceramic Veneer
0426. Pavers
0427. Glass Unit Masonry
0428. Gypsum Unit Masonry
0429. Reinforced Masonry
0430. - 0439. unassigned
0440. STONE
0441. Rough Stone
0442. Cut Stone
0443. Simulated Stone
0444. Flagstone
0445. - 0449. unassigned
0450. MASONRY RESTORATION
0451. - 0499. unassigned

5 METALS

0500. ALTERNATES
0501. - 0509. unassigned
0510. STRUCTURAL METAL
0511. - 0519. unassigned
0520. OPEN-WEB JOISTS
0521. - 0529. unassigned
0530. METAL DECKING
0531. - 0539. unassigned
0540. LIGHTGAGE FRAMING
0541. - 0549. unassigned
0550. MISCELLANEOUS METAL
0551. Metal Stairs
0552. Floor Gratings
0553. Construction Castings
0554. - 0569. unassigned
0570. ORNAMENTAL METAL
0571. - 0579. unassigned
0580. SPECIAL FORMED METAL
0581. - 0599. unassigned

6 CARPENTRY

0600. ALTERNATES
0601. - 0609. unassigned
0610. ROUGH CARPENTRY
0611. Framing & Sheathing
0612. Heavy Timber Work
0613. - 0619. unassigned
0620. FINISH CARPENTRY
0621. Wood Trim
0622. Millwork
0623. Wood Siding
0624. - 0629. unassigned
0630. GLUE-LAMINATED WOOD
0631. - 0639. unassigned
0640. CUSTOM WOODWORK
0641. Custom Cabinetwork
0642. Custom Panelwork
0643. - 0699. unassigned

7 MOISTURE PROTECTION

0700. ALTERNATES
0701. - 0709. unassigned
0710. WATERPROOFING
0711. Membrane Waterproofing
0712. Hydrolithic Waterproofing
0713. Liquid Waterproofing
0714. Metallic Oxide Waterproofing
0715. DAMPPROOFING
0716. Bituminous Dampproofing
0717. Silicone Dampproofing
0718. Cementitious Dampproofing
0719. Preformed Vapor Barrier
0720. BUILDING INSULATION
0721. - 0729. unassigned
0730. SHINGLES & ROOFING
TILES
0731. Asphalt Shingles
0732. Asbestos-Cement Shingles
0733. Wood Shingles
0734. Slate Shingles
0735. Clay Roofing Tiles
0736. Concrete Roofing Tiles
0737. Porcelain Enamel Shingles
0738. Metal Shingles
0739. unassigned
0740. PREFORMED ROOFING &
SIDING
0741. Preformed Metal Roofing
0742. Preformed Metal Siding
0743. Asbestos-Cement Panels
0744. Preformed Plastic Panels
0745. Custom Panel Roofing
0746. - 0749. unassigned
0750. MEMBRANE ROOFING
0751. Builtup Bituminous Roofing
0752. Prepared Roll Roofing
0753. Elastic Sheet Roofing
0754. Elastic Liquid Roofing
0755. - 0759. unassigned
0760. SHEET METAL WORK
0761. Sheet Metal Roofing
0762. Metal Roof Flashing & Trim
0763. Gutters & Downspouts
0764. Grilles & Louvers
0765. Decorative Sheet Metal
Work
0766. - 0769. unassigned
0770. WALL FLASHING
0771. - 0779. unassigned
0780. ROOF ACCESSORIES
0781. Plastic Skylights
0782. Metal-Framed Skylights
0783. Roof Hatches
0784. Gravity Ventilators
0785. - 0789. unassigned
0790. CALKING & SEALANTS
0791. - 0799. unassigned

8 DOORS, WINDOWS, & GLASS

0800. ALTERNATES
0801. - 0809. unassigned
0810. METAL DOORS & FRAMES
0811. Hollow Metal Doors &
Frames
0812. Aluminum Doors & Frames
0813. Stainless Steel Doors &
Frames
0814. Bronze Doors & Frames
0815. Metal Storm & Screen Doors
0816. - 0819. unassigned
0820. WOOD DOORS
0821. - 0829. unassigned
0830. SPECIAL DOORS
0831. Sliding Metal Firedoors
0832. Metal-Covered Doors
0833. Coiling Doors & Grilles
0834. Plastic-Faced Doors
0835. Folding Doors
0836. Overhead Doors
0837. Sliding Glass Doors
0838. Tempered Glass Doors
0839. Revolving Doors
0840. Flexible Doors
0841. Hangar Doors
0842. - 0849. unassigned
0850. METAL WINDOWS
0851. Steel Windows
0852. Aluminum Windows
0853. Stainless Steel Windows
0854. Bronze Windows
0855. - 0859. unassigned
0860. WOOD WINDOWS
0861. - 0869. unassigned
0870. FINISH HARDWARE
0871. - 0874. unassigned
0875. OPERATORS
0876. - 0879. unassigned
0880. WEATHERSTRIPPING
0881. - 0884. unassigned
0885. GLASS & GLAZING
0886. - 0889. unassigned
0890. CURTAINWALL SYSTEM
0891. - 0894. unassigned
0895. STOREFRONT SYSTEM
0896. - 0899. unassigned

Part Four — INDEX OF KEY WORDS

UNIFORM SYSTEM

for CONSTRUCTION SPECIFICATIONS, DATA FILING & COST ACCOUNTING

Title One - Buildings

USING THE INDEX

The Index of Key Words includes terms from Parts One, Two, and Three, as well as familiar synonyms. Many terms are followed by modifying terms in alphabetized and indented series.

Section titles appear in the left column in boldface type, all capitals identifying BROADSCOPE titles and initial capitals, Narrowscope titles. Where an indented term appears in boldface type, it also indicates, with the indexed term preceding it, a BROADSCOPE or Narrowscope title.

Numerals in parentheses indicate Uniform System Part or Parts where the accompanying Section title appears, (1) for the Specification Outline, (2) for the Filing System, and (3) for the Cost Accounting Guide. If the title is used in all three Parts, the parenthetical numeral is omitted.

INDEX OF KEY WORDS

INDEX OF KEY WORDS

UNIFORM SYSTEM FOR CONSTRUCTION SPECIFICATIONS, DATA FILING & COST ACCOUNTING

INDEX OF KEY WORDS

INDEX OF KEY WORDS

THE AMERICAN INSTITUTE OF ARCHITECTS

CATALOG AND ORDER FORM
OF PUBLICATIONS AND DOCUMENTS

Available from

The American Institute of Architects
1735 New York Avenue   Wash., D. C. 20006

REVISED JANUARY 1968

DISCOUNT STRUCTURE

A — Contract Documents

Over 100 (any combination of A, B or C Series) 30%
Over 1500 (any combination of A, B or C Series) 40%

B — Accounting & Project Forms

Over 500 sheets (any combination of F & G Series) 30%
Over 4000 sheets (any combination of F & G Series) 40%

C — Miscellaneous

Handbook of Architectural Practice (5 or more) 30%
Specification Worksheets (5 or more) 30%
Uniform System for Construction Specification, Data Filing & Cost Accounting (5 or more) 30%
Handbook Chapters — any combination of 100 or more 30%
The Economics of Architectural Practice (5 or more) 30%

SHIPPING PROCEDURES

A — Packages weighing under 20 lbs. will be shipped prepaid — 4th class — Special handling.

B — Packages over 20 lbs. will be sent by common carrier (express truck) at the expense of the Purchaser. Because our facilities are limited we will reserve the right to select the carrier.

MISCELLANEOUS INFORMATION

A — All orders under $5.00 must be accompanied by cash, check, or money order. Add 20% to order for Special Mailing request for airmail, first class or special delivery.

B — Orders received from foreign countries (including Canada) must be accompanied by a check or money order plus estimated postage. (Add 20%)

C — On charge orders all special requests for airmail, first class, or special delivery will be billed to the purchaser.

D — To expedite your order, please use this form when ordering. A price catalogue will be sent to you with each order or upon request.

E — Do not combine document orders with orders from other dep'ts.

NAME_____ STREET_____ DATE_____

CITY & STATE_____ ZIP CODE_____

No.	Title	Current Edition	Catalog Number	Quantity	Price	Total
A Series — Owner-Contractor Document						
A101	Owner Contractor Agreement — Stipulated Sum	Sep 67	A-101	....	$ .25	....
A105	Jacket for Construction Contracts	Sep 66	A-105	....	.10	....
A107	Short Form for Small Construction Contracts — Stipulated Sum .	Sep 66	A-107	....	.30	....
A111	Owner Contract Agreement Form — Cost Plus Fee	Sep 67	A-111	....	.20	....
A201	General Conditions of the Contract for Construction	Sep 67	A-201	....	.60	....
A305	Contractors Qualification Statement	Sep 64	A-305	....	.20	....
A310	Bid Bond	Sep 63	A-310	....	.20	....
A311	Performance Bond and Labor and Material Payment Bond	Sep 63	A-311	....	.20	....
A331	Guaranty for Bituminous Roofing	Jan 66	A-331	....	.20	....
A401	Contractor-Subcontractor Agreement	Sep 67	A-401	....	.20	....
A501	Recommended Guide for Bidding Procedure and Contract Awards	Sep 63	A-501	....	.50	....
Complete Set Includes A101, A105, A201, A310, A311			Comp. Set	....	1.20	.....
B Series — Owner-Architect Documents						
B131	Owner-Architect Agreement — Percentage of Construction Cost	Sep 67	B-131	....	.20	....
B231	Owner-Architect Agreement — Multiple of Direct Personnel Expense	Sep 67	B-231	....	.20	....
B331	Owner-Architect Agreement — Fee Plus Expense	Sep 67	B-331	....	.20	....
B352	Duties, Responsibilities and Limitations of Authority of Full Time Project Representative	Sep 66	B-352	....	.10	....
B431	Questionnaire for Selection of Architects for School Building Projects	Sep 63	B-431	....	.10	....
B451	Code for Architectural Competitions	Sep 63	B-451	....	.10	....
C Series — Architect-Consultant Documents						
C-131	Architect-Engineer Agreement — Percentage of Construction Cost	Sep 67	C-131	....	.20	....
C-231	Architect-Engineer — Multiple of Direct Personnel Expense	Sep 67	C-231	....	.20	....
C-331	Architect-Engineer Agreement Fee Plus Expense	Sep 67	C-331	....	.20	....
C502	Professional Collaboration in Environmental Design	Jun 66	C-502	....	.10	....
D Series — Architect-Industry Documents						
D101	Architectural Area and Volume of Buildings	Sep 67	D-101	....	.10	....
D301	Filing System for Architectural Plates & Articles	Apr 61	D-301	....	1.20	....
D401	Directory of Federal Agencies Contracting for Buildings Design	1967	D-401	....	1.00	....
E Series — Architect-Producer Documents						
E101	Technical Literature for the Architect	Jun 66	E- 101	....	.10	....
E301	Replaced by K103 — See Listing Under K Series					
F Series — Architect's Accounting Documents						
F100	Instructions for Standardized Accounting for Architects. This contains a sample of each accounting form with explanation ...	1954	F-100	....	6.00	....
Offer No. 1	Contains all of F100, plus year's supply of accounting forms, Fabricord binders, cash and payroll Journal and Ledger		Offer No. 1	....	50.00	....
Offer No. 2	Contains all of F100, plus year's supply of accounting forms ...		Offer No. 2	....	35.00	....
Offer No. 3	Contains all of F100, plus offer No. 2, less G701, 2, 2A, 3, 4		Offer No. 3	....	25.00	....
		Sheets				
F101	Cash Journal	25 1949	F-101	....	1.25	....
F102	Cash Journal	25 1949	F-102	....	1.10	....
F103	Cash Journal	25 1949	F-103	....	1.10	....
F104	Cash Journal	25 1953	F-104	....	1.10	....
F105	Cash Journal	25 1949	F-105	....	1.10	....
F106	Cash Journal	25 1949	F-106	....	1.10	....
F107	Journal Form	25 1949	F-107	....	1.25	....
F201	Payroll Journal	25 1953	F-201	....	1.25	....
F202	Payroll Journal	25 1949	F-202	....	1.10	....
			TOTALS	=====		$_____

Order Form

ORDERS UNDER $5.00 MUST BE ACCOMPANIED BY CHECK

REVISED JAN. 68

3 PUMP HOUSES, SEWAGE, AND DRAINAGE

In this chapter we are going to study a detail cross section of a small pump-house for fresh water, a country house sewage disposal system, and some city catch basins and drainage units. In most rural areas, plumbing, heating, and electrical units are installed by registered master tradesmen and their work is government inspected. All these assemblies, unless expertly checked, could be public hazards.

The following material is from the Canada Cement Company and is published by permission.

PUMP HOUSES AND PUMP PITS

A pump house or off-the-basement pump pit provide excellent protection for the pumping equipment of a modern water system and add to its serviceability. Pump houses are usually more sanitary then pump pits. A concrete masonry pump house as shown in Fig. 3.1 provides durable weathertight protection for pumping equipment. The roof can be taken off to permit removal of the well pipe. Electric lamps or oil or gas burners can be used to help maintain the temperature above freezing in extremely cold weather.

Some types of deep well installations can be made free from frost danger by placing the pressure tank in the basement and connecting it to the well below the frostline. Piping from basement pumping installations to shallow wells can be made frostproof as shown in Fig. 3.2.

This is a comprehensive detail, so make a careful study of it from the underpinning to the removable roof.

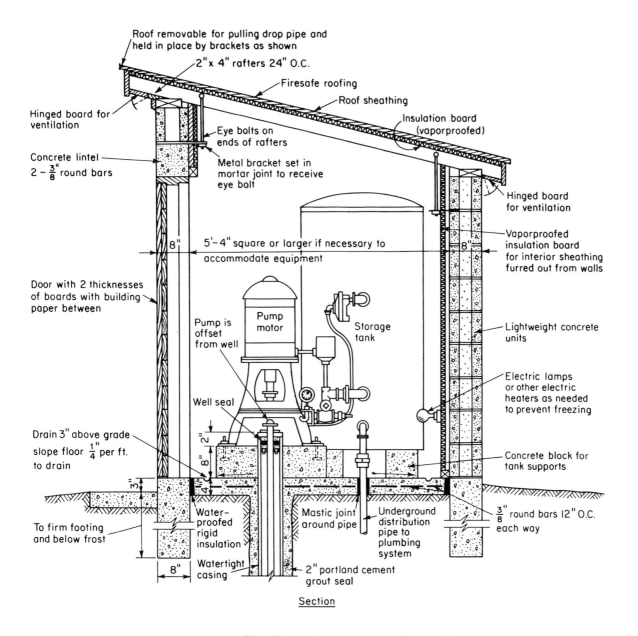

Fig. 3-1. Suggested construction of insulated concrete masonry pump house to protect automatic pumps.

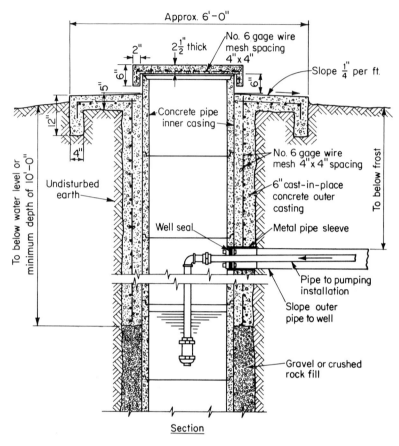

Fig. 3-2. Typical method of protecting dug or bored wells with offset pump. Large, heavy manhole cover prevents children from uncovering well.

SAFE SEWAGE DISPOSAL

A septic tank sewage disposal system makes it possible for farm and suburban families to enjoy the comforts and conveniences of modern plumbing. A system that has been properly designed, built, and operated provides safe, convenient, and inoffensive disposal of household wastes. Typical sewage disposal systems are illustrated in Fig. 3.3 and consist of a house drain, house sewer, septic tank, outlet sewer, and distribution field.

HOUSE SEWER DRAIN LINE

The septic tank is connected to the house drain with a line of pipe called the house sewer. It is usually built of 6 in. bell and spigot sewer pipe. All joints should be thoroughly filled with a mortar composed of 1 part portland cement, 3 parts mortar sand, and enough water to make a plastic mix. When properly made, such joints will normally keep out roots. Sometimes, as a further precaution against root penetration, a mortar band 1 in. thick and 3 in. wide is made around the joint (Fig. 3.4).

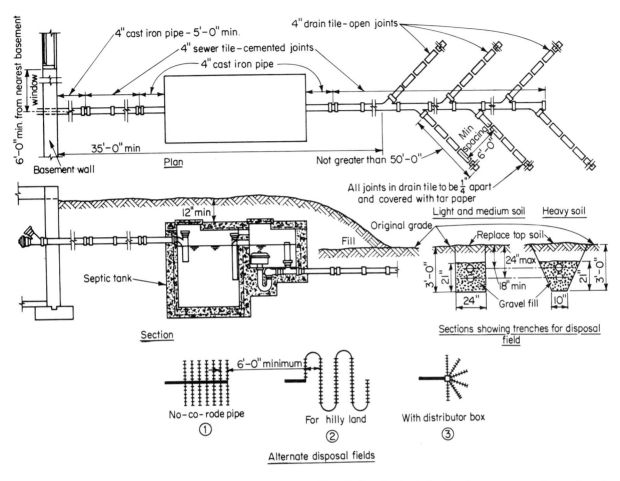

Fig. 3-3. Typical family-size sewage disposal system.

Fig. 3-4. Mortar band around joints in house sewers provides protection against root penetration.

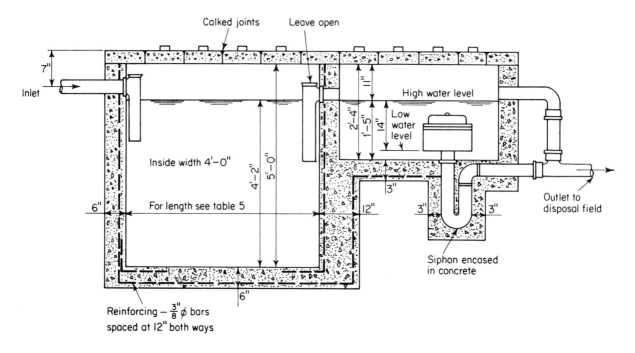

Fig. 3-5. Double chamber septic tank with siphon.

DOUBLE CHAMBER SEPTIC TANK

Septic tanks with a separate chamber which discharges intermittently are required for large households of more than 12 people and are required in parts of Canada where severe freezing weather endangers operation of the normal single-chamber tank. This type of system consists of a main chamber from which the outlet pipe leads to a smaller connected tank which is fitted with a siphon. This tank automatically discharges when it becomes full, and thus distributes an even load to all disposal tile at a higher temperature than effluent reaching the field of a single-chamber tank. See Fig. 3.5.

INLET AND OUTLET TILE TO SEPTIC TANK

Fig. 3.6 shows a method of building an inlet or outlet pipe to the septic tank. These joints must be positively watertight.

CONCRETE COVER SLAB

The concrete cover slab (Fig. 3.7) is made 3½″ thick and 12″ wide and long enough to reach across the tank. Each slab is reinforced with ⅜″ round bars spaced 3″ apart and placed about 1″ above the btm.

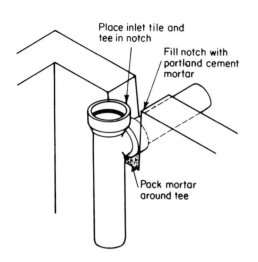

Fig. 3-6. Detail showing how inlet and outlet tile are mortared into notch at end of septic tank.

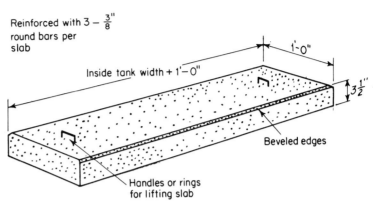

Fig. 3-7. Concrete cover slab.

DISTRIBUTION BOX

The distribution box is a small tank which distributes the liquids from the septic tank to disposal lines. This box helps to equalize the flow into the disposal lines and permits the inspection of the sewage liquids. See Fig. 3.8.

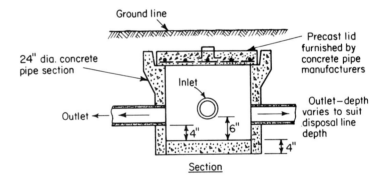

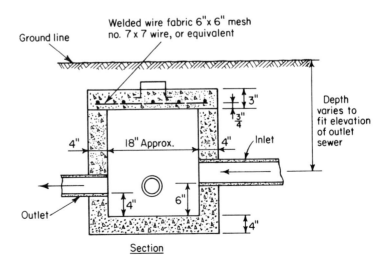

Fig. 3-8. Section through distribution box with three outlets (top), with four or more outlets (bottom).

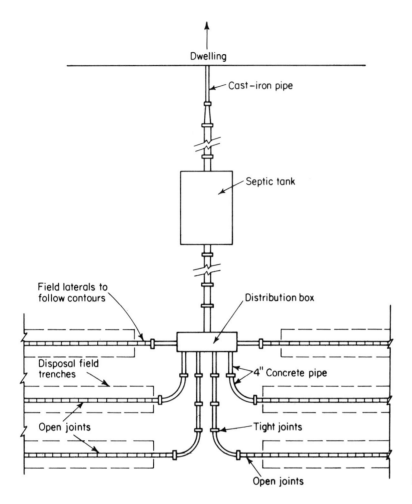

Fig. 3-9. Layout for disposal field on hillside.

LAYOUT FOR DISPOSAL FIELD

The disposal field consists of two or more lines of drain tile laid with open joints in specially prepared trenches. The sewage liquid flows from the distribution box into the tile lines, where it seeps out through the open joints into the gravel fill. Here it is worked on by bacteria, which complete the disposal process. See Fig. 3.9.

DISPOSAL TILE LINE

Fig. 3.10 shows a cross section and a longitudinal section of disposal tile lines. The whole of the sewage disposal system should be laid down with absolute thoroughness.

The foregoing dwgs are presented for serious study. If we were limited to making only one contribution to newly emerging countries, I would unhesitatingly say, "This is it."

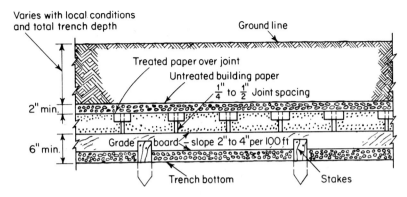

Longitudinal section of disposal tile lines

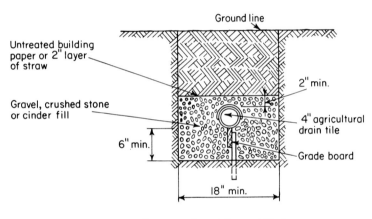

Cross–section of disposal tile lines

Fig. 3-10. Sections of disposal tile lines.

ASSIGNMENT:

Go to your nearest local Health Board or Government agency, obtain all the material available on drinking water and sewage disposal, and file it in your library.

CITY STORM DRAINAGE CONTROL

The following seven details of storm drainage control, vividly drawn, are published through the courtesy of the City of Spokane, State of Washington, Department of Public Works, Engineering Division. All our cities have a great variety of below-ground installations for fresh water, storm water sewage disposal, and many other city services and conveniences. There is a wide field of opportunities for first-class detailers in every phase of industry.

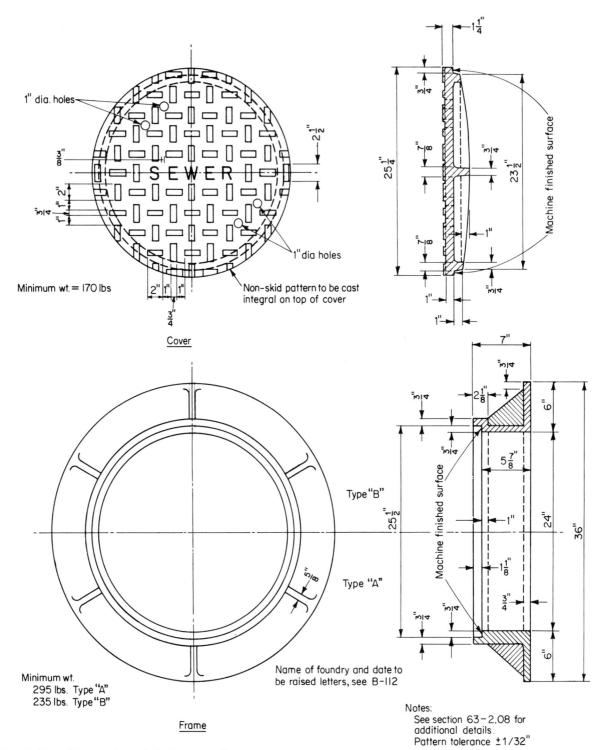

Fig. 3-11. Standard manhole frame and cover.

Fig. 3.11 shows a standard manhole frame and cover that is easy to read and may be readily understood by tradesmen who will cast it in the foundry.

Fig. 3.12 shows a standard gutter inlet frame and cover. Note the clarity of the lettering. Pattern makers and foundry metal workers could not mistake this detail dwg.

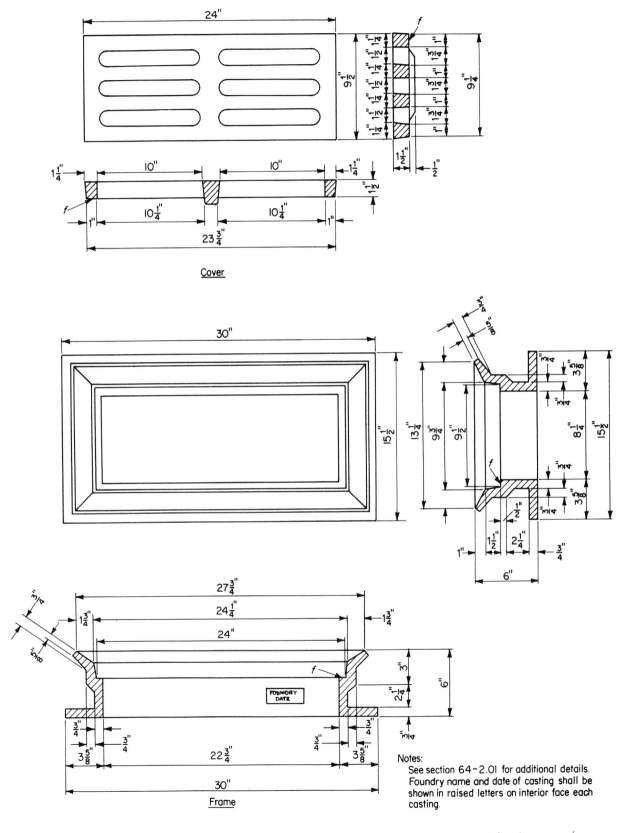

Cover

Frame

Notes:
See section 64-2.01 for additional details.
Foundry name and date of casting shall be
shown in raised letters on interior face each
casting.

Fig. 3-12. Standard gutter inlet frame and cover.

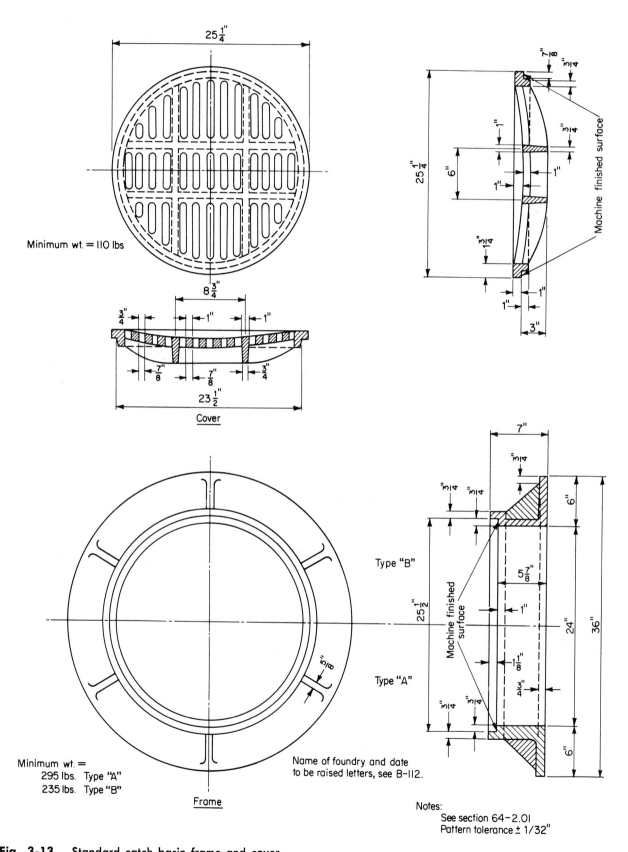

Fig. 3-13. Standard catch basin frame and cover.

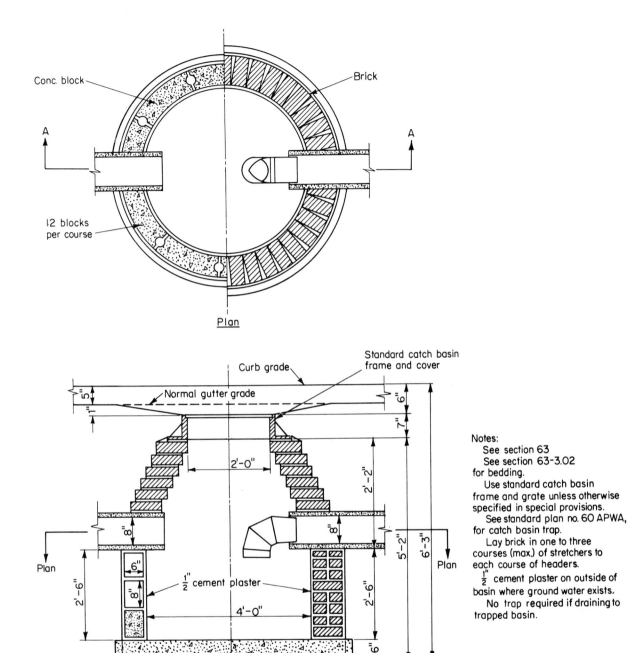

Fig. 3-14. Standard catch basin No. 0, masonry.

Notes:
  See section 63
  See section 63-3.02
for bedding.
  Use standard catch basin
frame and grate unless otherwise
specified in special provisions.
  See standard plan no. 60 APWA,
for catch basin trap.
  Lay brick in one to three
courses (max.) of stretchers to
each course of headers.
  $\frac{1}{2}$" cement plaster on outside of
basin where ground water exists.
  No trap required if draining to
trapped basin.

Fig. 3.13 shows a standard catch basin frame and cover. Carefully note the difference between Type "A" and Type "B" and the machine-finished surface for the cover.

Fig. 3.14 shows a standard masonry catch basin, which may be built with concrete block or brick. Notice that the concrete blocks are cast circular in plan, but the bricks are standard. What is the difference between *stretcher* and *header* courses of brickwork?

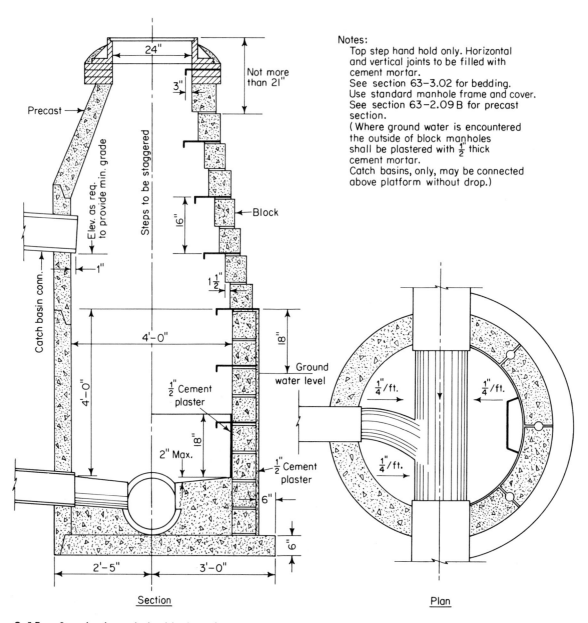

Notes:
Top step hand hold only. Horizontal and vertical joints to be filled with cement mortar.
See section 63–3.02 for bedding.
Use standard manhole frame and cover.
See section 63–2.09 B for precast section.
(Where ground water is encountered the outside of block manholes shall be plastered with $\frac{1}{2}$ thick cement mortar.
Catch basins, only, may be connected above platform without drop.)

Fig. 3-15. Standard manhole, block and precast.

Fig. 3.15 shows a standard manhole in concrete block or precast. These manholes may be of indefinite depth according to existing or future grade elevations. Note the treatment of the precast joints and the traditional ftg (footing) joint of the concrete blocks. *Ask your City Engineering Department for a profile of a sewer system for an undulating area.* Consider the kind of fastening detail you would draw for the steps to a precast manhole.

Fig. 3.16 shows a corrugated pipe anchor. This is an interesting detail in an age where more and more commercial material is being transported over long distances in pipelines. Consider a section subject to a frost depth of 14'-0."

Fig. 3.17 shows a seepage basin for private parking. The disposal field must be well installed to prevent future subsidence in the parking area. A study of local conditions would determine the minimum lengths of drain tile required.

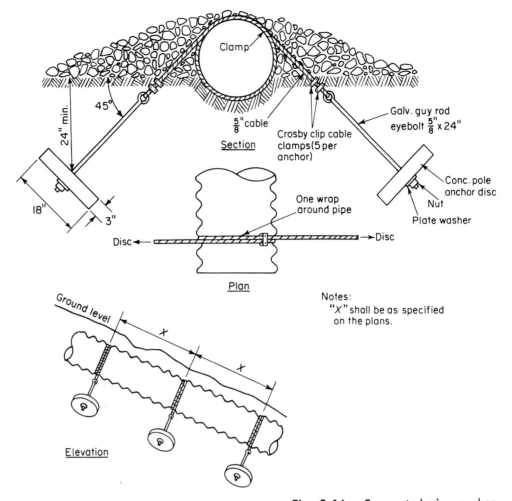

Section

Plan

Notes:
  "X" shall be as specified on the plans.

Ground level

Elevation

Fig. 3-16. Corrugated pipe anchor.

Fig. 3-17. Seepage basin for private parking.

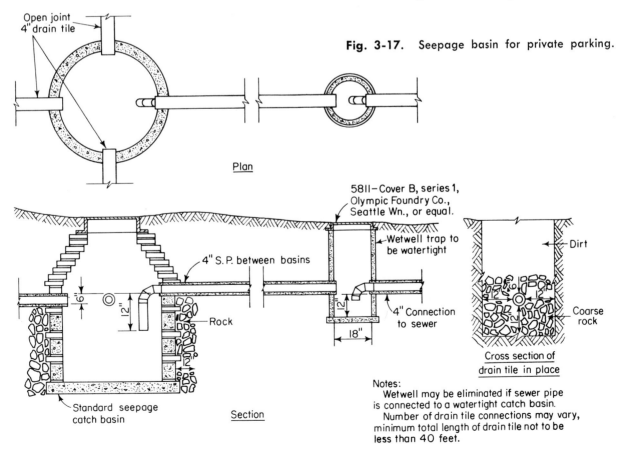

Open joint 4" drain tile

Plan

5811—Cover B, series 1, Olympic Foundry Co., Seattle Wn., or equal.

Wetwell trap to be watertight

4" S.P. between basins

4" Connection to sewer

Standard seepage catch basin

Section

Rock

Dirt

Coarse rock

Cross section of drain tile in place

Notes:
  Wetwell may be eliminated if sewer pipe is connected to a watertight catch basin.
  Number of drain tile connections may vary, minimum total length of drain tile not to be less than 40 feet.

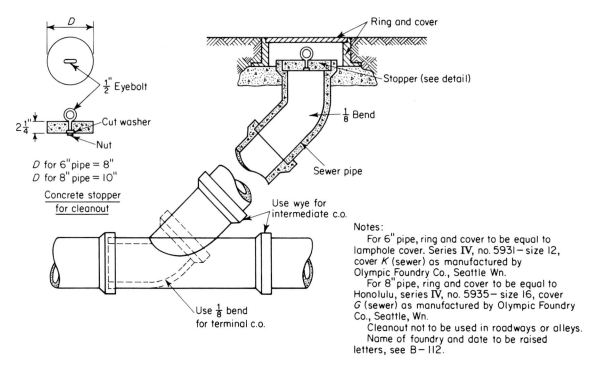

D for 6" pipe = 8"
D for 8" pipe = 10"

Concrete stopper
for cleanout

Notes:
    For 6" pipe, ring and cover to be equal to
lamphole cover. Series IV, no. 5931 – size 12,
cover K (sewer) as manufactured by
Olympic Foundry Co., Seattle Wn.
    For 8" pipe, ring and cover to be equal to
Honolulu, series IV, no. 5935 – size 16, cover
G (sewer) as manufactured by Olympic Foundry
Co., Seattle, Wn.
    Cleanout not to be used in roadways or alleys.
    Name of foundry and date to be raised
letters, see B – 112.

Fig. 3-18.   Standard cleanout.

Fig. 3.18 shows a standard cleanout. In all sewer and drainage systems, strategic placing of cleanouts is imperative.

These are excellent examples of a few of the many below-ground city piping systems in use today. Recommended reading: the American Concrete Pipe Association's *Concrete Pipe for Irrigation and Drainage.*

HOUSE DETAILS 4

In this chapter we are going to carefully examine a number of sectional detail dwgs of housing units from several countries. These dwgs will form the basis of our study of other commercial bldg (building) dwgs. *It is very important to understand thoroughly and know the names of the components of all these sections.*

We must remember that the greatest hope of many people in many lands is not only to own their own homes, but to be able to build them with their own hands. Our drawings must be explicit, drawn and notated as simply as the technical details will permit, so that all users (particularly the people in emerging countries) may easily assimilate the information through their own technicians.

Since architecture is a universal art, we should think of global requirements in all work. Housing units are built to house people comfortably in temperatures exceeding 40° below zero or 116° above. These conditions have to be taken into account in detailing insulation, heating, air conditioning, plumbing, acoustics, and so on. It is not only necessary for the person making the details to draw the sections; he must also have an intimate knowledge of the material that he is detailing. The only way to keep abreast of modern developments is to study manufacturers' brochures and "mockups" and to get out onto building sites during weekends to make a close study of all components.

TRADITIONAL HOUSE WALL SECTION (NORTH AMERICAN)

At Fig. 4.1 is shown a typical North American traditional house wall section. To refresh our memories, all the parts of this dwg are named. All the components of any typical wall section should be memorized.

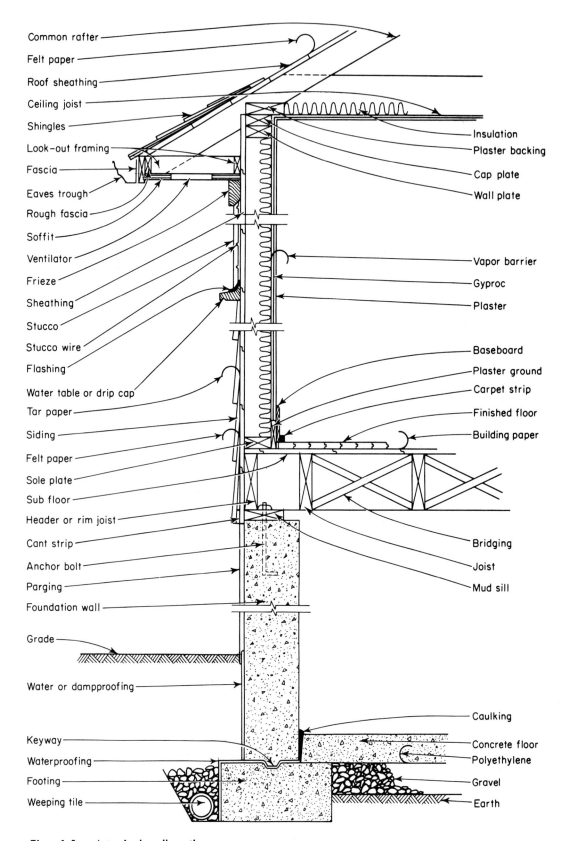

Common rafter
Felt paper
Roof sheathing
Ceiling joist
Shingles
Look-out framing
Fascia
Eaves trough
Rough fascia
Soffit
Ventilator
Frieze
Sheathing
Stucco
Stucco wire
Flashing
Water table or drip cap
Tar paper
Siding
Felt paper
Sole plate
Sub floor
Header or rim joist
Cant strip
Anchor bolt
Parging
Foundation wall
Grade
Water or dampproofing
Keyway
Waterproofing
Footing
Weeping tile

Insulation
Plaster backing
Cap plate
Wall plate

Vapor barrier
Gyproc
Plaster

Baseboard
Plaster ground
Carpet strip
Finished floor
Building paper

Bridging
Joist
Mud sill

Caulking
Concrete floor
Polyethylene
Gravel
Earth

Fig. 4-1. A typical wall section.

Examine the walls of the house in which you live, make a freehand sketch of a typical wall section, and name the parts.

CONCRETE FOOTINGS FOR MODULAR CONCRETE CAVITY WALLS

The following four typical wall sections are published by permission of the South Australian Housing Trust through their Technical Officer Mr. Douglas N. Linnett.

Concrete footings for modular concrete cavity walls (Australia)

Examine the conc ftg details in Fig. 4.2. They are designed to receive modular concrete masonry cavity walls with wooden joists on the left and a masonry floor on the right. Notice that the right-hand footing is specially designed for a wet area or porch. The ftgs are reinforced against soil and minor earthquake conditions. The cavity wall spacing and dampproofing are shown very clearly on the wall sections which follow.

The walls on either side of the cavity are called wythes (sometimes spelled withes). The wythes are bonded together with galvanized metal ties. Notice the modular size of the inside wythes; they cover twice the depth of the outside ones.

Go back to your dwgs from time to time to ensure that no foolish mistake has unwittingly crept in. It's easy. Draw so that technicians anywhere in the world can readily give explanations to local tradesmen.

Fig. 4-2. Concrete footing details.

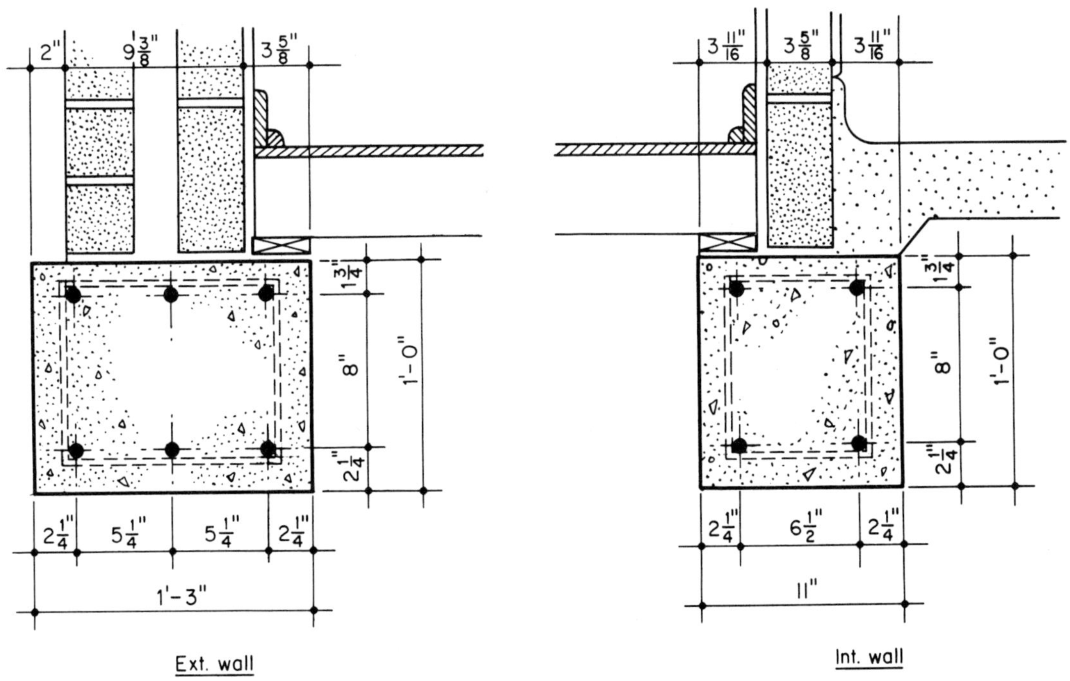

Ext. wall

Int. wall

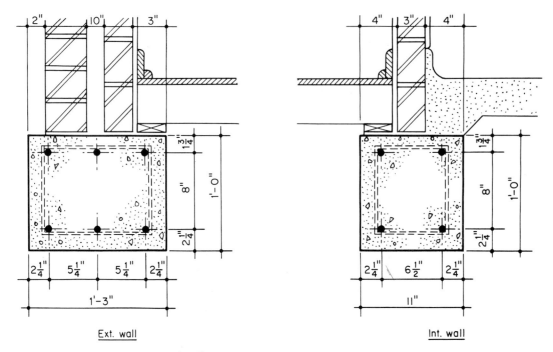

Ext. wall

Int. wall

Fig. 4-3. Concrete footing details.

Fig. 4-4. Concrete footing details.

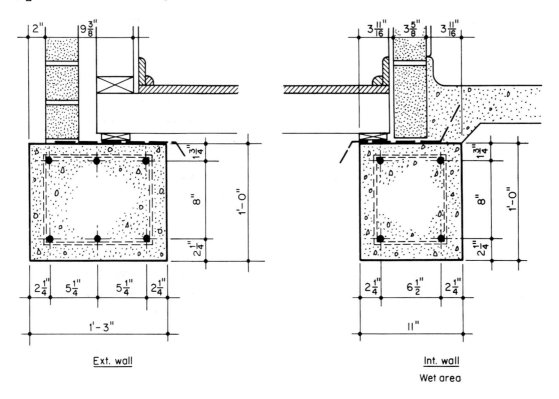

Ext. wall

Int. wall
Wet area

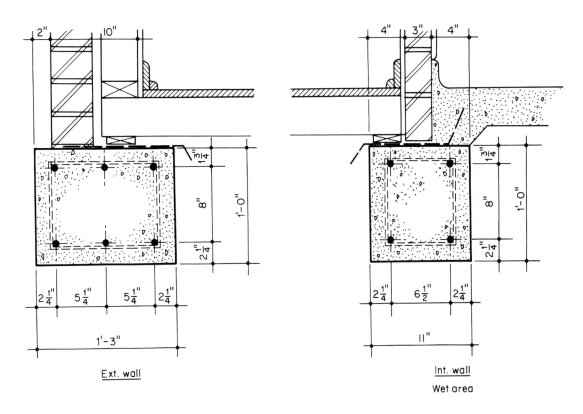

Ext. wall

Int. wall

Wet area

Fig. 4-5. Concrete footing details.

Concrete footings for brickwork cavity walls (Australia)

Notice that these conc ftgs are of the same design used in the first and the last two dwgs of this Australian series, but the walls that they support are of different widths. See Fig. 4.3. This is very important to keep in mind since the widths of walls will affect the overall length of the outside walls and the inside dimensions of the rooms. Why is this so?

Concrete footings for modular masonry veneer and wood interior framing (Australia)

The modular conc masonry veneer has a 1¾" cavity wall. See Fig. 4.4.

A point of interest here is that in Australia and some other countries, lumber is used as it comes from the saw. An example would be:

One piece of 4" × 2"—12'-0" long. This is the actual size.

In North America, lumber is sold dressed (planed on a machine) and a similar piece of lumber would be described as:

One piece of 2 × 4—12'-0" long, but the finished planed size is 1⅝" × 3⅝"—12'-0" long.

In North America a piece of 2 × 4 is a name and not a size of lumber and is written 2 × 4. If a finished size of 2" × 4" is required, it would be noted both on the detail and in the specs.

Concrete footings with modular brick veneer and wood framing (Australia)

Observe the difference in the total width of the wall in Fig. 4.5 from the previous dwg. The object of modular construction is economy of material and time. All wall lengths, wall openings, doors, windows, and so on are centered so that there will be a positive minimum of cutting required.

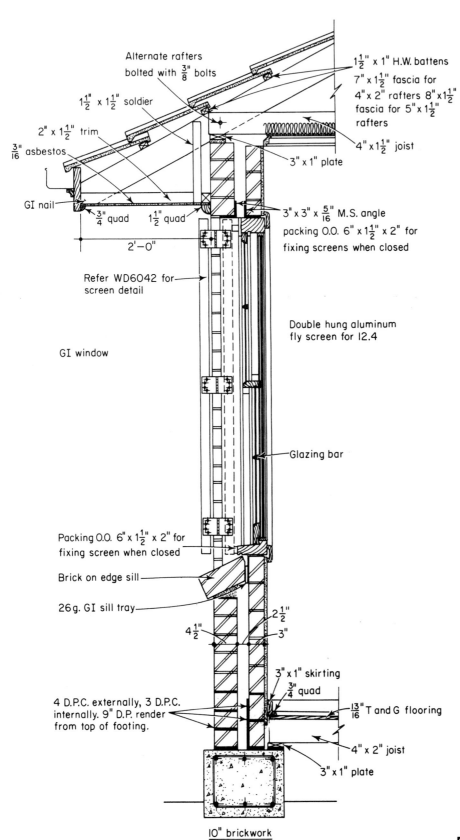

Alternate rafters bolted with $\frac{3}{8}$" bolts

$1\frac{1}{2}$" x $1\frac{1}{2}$" soldier

2" x $1\frac{1}{2}$" trim

$\frac{3}{16}$" asbestos

GI nail

$\frac{3}{4}$" quad $1\frac{1}{2}$" quad

2'–0"

Refer WD6042 for screen detail

GI window

$1\frac{1}{2}$" x 1" H.W. battens

7" x $1\frac{1}{2}$" fascia for 4" x 2" rafters 8" x $1\frac{1}{2}$" fascia for 5" x $1\frac{1}{2}$" rafters

4" x $1\frac{1}{2}$" joist

3" x 1" plate

3" x 3" x $\frac{5}{16}$" M.S. angle packing O.O. 6" x $1\frac{1}{2}$" x 2" for fixing screens when closed

Double hung aluminum fly screen for 12.4

Glazing bar

Packing O.O. 6" x $1\frac{1}{2}$" x 2" for fixing screen when closed

Brick on edge sill

26g. GI sill tray

$2\frac{1}{2}$"

$4\frac{1}{2}$"   3"

3" x 1" skirting

$\frac{3}{4}$" quad

$\frac{13}{16}$" T and G flooring

4 D.P.C. externally, 3 D.P.C. internally. 9" D.P. render from top of footing.

4" x 2" joist

3" x 1" plate

10" brickwork

Fig. 4-6. Typical wall section.

TYPICAL WALL SECTION FOR 0'-10" BRICKWORK (AUSTRALIA)

Examine the wall section at Fig. 4.6. The brick cavity wall is 0'-10". The outside wythe is 4½", the cavity 2½", and the inside wythe is 3", making a total thickness of 10". When dimensioning dwgs, always check by adding them together; unless the total agrees with the overall thickness, something is either incorrectly dimensioned or the addition is incorrect. On long wall lengths with lots of openings a mistake can be a very serious and costly error.

Notice the dampproof course of four bricks on the outside of the wall and three courses on the inside. The dampproofing (d.p.) is also carried down to a depth of 9" on the outside of the concrete ftg. Although no weeping tile is shown on the dwg, it would be specified for certain areas as necessary. The word "skirting" means "baseboard" in North America. Observe the 26-gauge galvanized iron sill tray for the window. Some of the details for the eaves are:

Soffit of ³⁄₁₆" asbestos. Alternate rafters are to be bolted to the ceiling joists with ⅜" bolts. Insulation in the ceiling. The fascia bd (board) is 7" × 1½" or 8" × 1½" according to the size of the rafter specified. The 3" × 1" wall plate is placed on the outside wythe, and a control point for settlement is formed at the intersection of the inside wall and the ceiling, which is carried by 4" × 1½" joists.

An angle iron is shown supporting the brickwork over the window. This type of member comes under miscellaneous metals and is a very big item on large buildings. *It is most important that all miscellaneous metals be shown on all dwgs.* Building construction estimators have more trouble with miscellaneous metals than with any other feature of estimating.

TYPICAL WALL SECTION FOR 9⅜" MODULAR CONCRETE (AUSTRALIA)

This wall section shows a 4" concrete floor to the kitchen or bathroom. See Fig. 4.7. The masonry sill to the window is quite different from the previous dwg. Notice 3" × 1" architrave at the flyscreen: in North America, architrave is trim. Supporting the outside masonry units over the window is a 2" × ⅜" mild steel bar. Miscellaneous metal.

TYPICAL WALL SECTION FOR 0'-10" BRICK VENEER (AUSTRALIA)

This is a kitchen wall section with the top of the sink and the ₵ (center line) of the taps shown. See Fig. 4.8. The ³⁄₁₆" asbestos soffit is nailed direct to the underside feet of the rafters, affording an economy of labor and

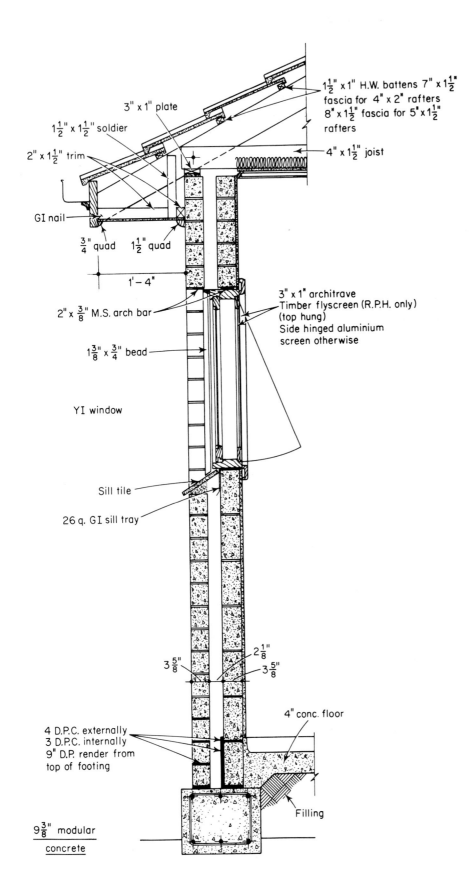

$1\frac{1}{2}$" x 1" H.W. battens 7" x $1\frac{1}{2}$"
fascia for 4" x 2" rafters
8" x $1\frac{1}{2}$" fascia for 5" x $1\frac{1}{2}$"
rafters

3" x 1" plate

$1\frac{1}{2}$" x $1\frac{1}{2}$" soldier

2" x $1\frac{1}{2}$" trim

4" x $1\frac{1}{2}$" joist

GI nail

$\frac{3}{4}$" quad $1\frac{1}{2}$" quad

1'– 4"

2" x $\frac{3}{8}$" M.S. arch bar

3" x 1" architrave
Timber flyscreen (R.P.H. only)
(top hung)
Side hinged aluminium
screen otherwise

$1\frac{3}{8}$" x $\frac{3}{4}$" bead

YI window

Sill tile

26 q. GI sill tray

$3\frac{5}{8}$" $2\frac{1}{8}$"
          $3\frac{5}{8}$"

4" conc. floor

4 D.P.C. externally
3 D.P.C. internally
9" D.P. render from
top of footing

Filling

$9\frac{3}{8}$" modular
concrete

Fig. 4-7. Typical wall section.

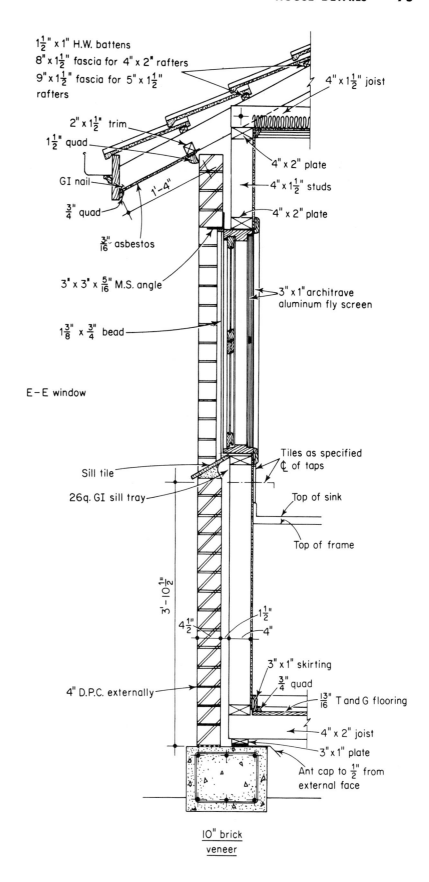

$1\frac{1}{2}$" x 1" H.W. battens
8" x $1\frac{1}{2}$" fascia for 4" x 2" rafters
9" x $1\frac{1}{2}$" fascia for 5" x $1\frac{1}{2}$" rafters

4" x $1\frac{1}{2}$" joist

2" x $1\frac{1}{2}$" trim
$1\frac{1}{2}$" quad

4" x 2" plate
4" x $1\frac{1}{2}$" studs

GI nail

4" x 2" plate

1'-4"

$\frac{3}{4}$" quad

$\frac{3}{16}$" asbestos

3" x 3" x $\frac{5}{16}$" M.S. angle

3" x 1" architrave
aluminum fly screen

$1\frac{3}{8}$" x $\frac{3}{4}$" bead

E−E window

Sill tile

Tiles as specified
₵ of taps

26q. GI sill tray

Top of sink

Top of frame

$3'-10\frac{1}{2}$"

$1\frac{1}{2}$"

$4\frac{1}{2}$"

4"

3" x 1" skirting
$\frac{3}{4}$" quad
$1\frac{3}{16}$" T and G flooring

4" D.P.C. externally

4" x 2" joist

3" x 1" plate

Ant cap to $\frac{1}{2}$" from external face

10" brick
veneer

Fig. 4-8. Typical wall section.

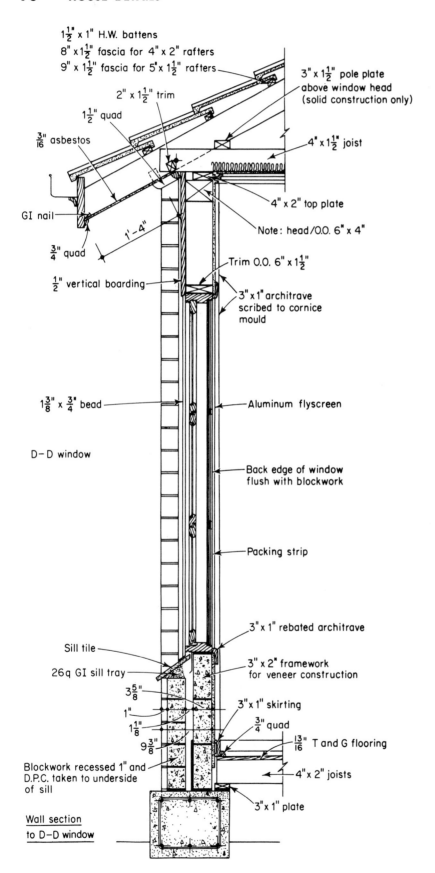

$1\frac{1}{2}$" x 1" H.W. battens
8" x $1\frac{1}{2}$" fascia for 4" x 2" rafters
9" x $1\frac{1}{2}$" fascia for 5"x $1\frac{1}{2}$" rafters

2" x $1\frac{1}{2}$" trim

$1\frac{1}{2}$" quad

$\frac{3}{16}$" asbestos

3" x $1\frac{1}{2}$" pole plate
above window head
(solid construction only)

4" x $1\frac{1}{2}$" joist

GI nail

4" x 2" top plate

Note: head/O.O. 6" x 4"

$\frac{3}{4}$" quad

1'-4"

Trim O.O. 6" x $1\frac{1}{2}$"

$\frac{1}{2}$" vertical boarding

3" x 1" architrave
scribed to cornice
mould

$1\frac{3}{8}$" x $\frac{3}{4}$" bead

Aluminum flyscreen

D-D window

Back edge of window
flush with blockwork

Packing strip

3" x 1" rebated architrave

Sill tile

3" x 2" framework
for veneer construction

26q GI sill tray

$3\frac{5}{8}$"

1"

3" x 1" skirting

$\frac{3}{4}$" quad

$1\frac{1}{8}$"

$\frac{13}{16}$" T and G flooring

$9\frac{3}{8}$"

Blockwork recessed 1" and
D.P.C. taken to underside
of sill

4" x 2" joists

3" x 1" plate

Wall section
to D-D window

Fig. 4-9. Typical wall section.

materials. The rafters are shown supported by the top plate of the inside wood framing. Any settlement in the brickwork would be covered by the 1½" quad (quarter round) nailed to the underside of the rafter feet where they meet the outside wall. Shrinkage of lumber lengthways of the grain is discounted. The only possible shrinkage is in the plates, but there may be a little settlement in the building.

TYPICAL WALL SECTION THROUGH A D.D. WINDOW (AUSTRALIA)

D.D. is a term used in the glazing industry meaning 24-oz. glass or double diamond. See Fig. 4.9. The D.D. window with bars is detailed with the flywire screen on the inside of the window. The roof is supported over the window (read up) with a 6" × 1½" wood frame secured to a 6" × 4" solid wood beam, over which is a 4" × 2" top plate. The ceiling joists are secured to the rafter feet and to the wall plates. Every second rafter foot is bolted to the ceiling joists. This is secure construction. *Every wall section in all parts of the world must be designed to meet local conditions.* The dwg shows the masonry roof tile secured to 1½" × 1" hardwood battens.

TYPICAL WALL SECTION (CANADA)

The wall section shown at Fig. 4.10 is published through the courtesy of the Central Mortgage and Housing Corporation. It was designed to meet a demand for inexpensive housing. The world is in dire need of millions of easily built, durable, but inexpensive homes. This is an interesting section, and we will study it very carefully. Read from the bottom up:

1. *Concrete footings* 2' × 0'-8" not reinforced unless necessitated by local conditions. These could be precast.

2. *Concrete piers* 10" × 10" to go down below frost line. These could be precast. In all, there are 12 piers, four along each long wall and four at or near the center of the house. The house is 24'-4" × 36'-1".

3. *Laminated wood beams* strap anchored to the piers. Note that there are no below-floor-level perimeter walls to this house. Removable 1 × 12 boards are provided to surround the below-floor area during cold weather.

4. *Floor assembly* is framed with 2 × 8 Douglas fir or equal.

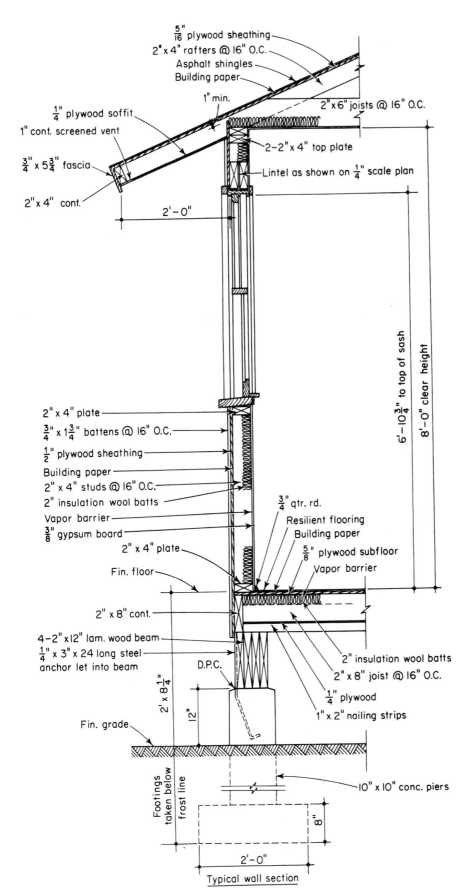

$\frac{5}{16}$" plywood sheathing
2"x 4" rafters @ 16" O.C.
Asphalt shingles
Building paper
1" min.
2"x 6" joists @ 16" O.C.

$\frac{1}{4}$" plywood soffit
1" cont. screened vent
$\frac{3}{4}$" x 5$\frac{3}{4}$" fascia
2"x 4" cont.

2-2"x 4" top plate
Lintel as shown on $\frac{1}{4}$" scale plan

2'-0"

2"x 4" plate
$\frac{3}{4}$" x 1$\frac{3}{4}$" battens @ 16" O.C.
$\frac{1}{2}$" plywood sheathing
Building paper
2"x 4" studs @ 16" O.C.
2" insulation wool batts
Vapor barrier
$\frac{3}{8}$" gypsum board
2"x 4" plate
Fin. floor

6'-10$\frac{3}{4}$" to top of sash
8'-0" clear height

$\frac{3}{4}$" qtr. rd.
Resilient flooring
Building paper
$\frac{5}{8}$" plywood subfloor
Vapor barrier

2"x 8" cont.
4-2"x12" lam. wood beam
$\frac{1}{4}$" x 3" x 24 long steel
anchor let into beam

D.P.C.

2" insulation wool batts
2"x 8" joist @ 16" O.C.
$\frac{1}{4}$" plywood
1"x 2" nailing strips

2' x 8$\frac{1}{4}$"
12"

Fin. grade

Footings taken below frost line

10" x 10" conc. piers

8"

2'-0"

Typical wall section

Fig. 4-10. Typical wall section.

5. *Floor insulation*

(a) A piece of 1×2 is nailed to the bottom side of the joists to receive pieces of ¼" plywood which fit between parallel rows of joists. This forms a wind check.

(b) There is a dead air space between the top of the plywood and the top of the joists. Secured to the top of the joists is a 2" batt of insulation.

6. *Vapor Barrier.* A sheet of polyethylene is laid across the floor framing, over which is laid a ⅝" plywood subfloor.

7. *Resilient floor.* On the subfloor is placed a building paper, over which is placed lino, cork, or tiles. This is a very well insulated floor, and the dwg is quite deliberate and definite.

ASSIGNMENT:

1. Draw to the scale of ¾" to 1'-0" an end section of this floor assembly showing:

(a) Four contiguous joists.

(b) The 1×2 nailed to the bottom sides of the joists.

(c) The ½" plywood laid between the joists and nailed to the 1×2 strips.

(d) Insulation secured to the upper edges of the joists.

(e) Vapor barrier.

(f) The ⅝ plywood subfloor.

(g) Building paper.

(h) Resilient floor.

2. Research and draw a floor assembly suitable for a home to be built on permafrost.

WOOD FRAME STRUCTURAL DETAILS FOR HOUSING UNIT

The following fifteen groups of details are presented as a study in design, construction, and clarity of structural details for house framing. They are published thru the courtesy and by permission of the Canada Wood Development Council. Study them closely, visit building sites, make models, and identify the types of structural housing details in your locality.

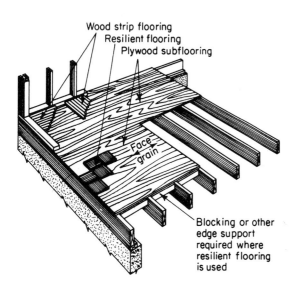

Wood strip flooring
Resilient flooring
Plywood subflooring

Face grain

Blocking or other edge support required where resilient flooring is used

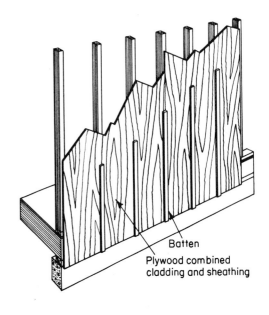

Batten
Plywood combined cladding and sheathing

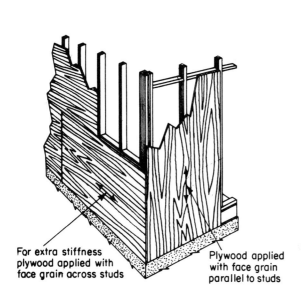

For extra stiffness plywood applied with face grain across studs

Plywood applied with face grain parallel to studs

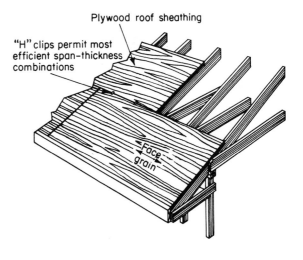

Plywood roof sheathing

"H" clips permit most efficient span-thickness combinations

Face grain

Fig. 4-11.   Floor, wall, and roof applications of plywood sheathing.

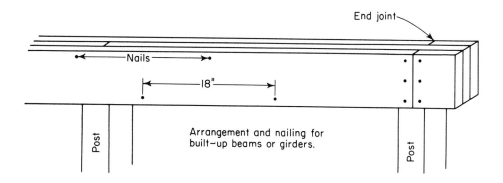

Arrangement and nailing for built-up beams or girders.

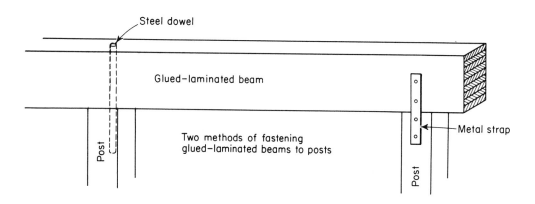

Two methods of fastening glued-laminated beams to posts

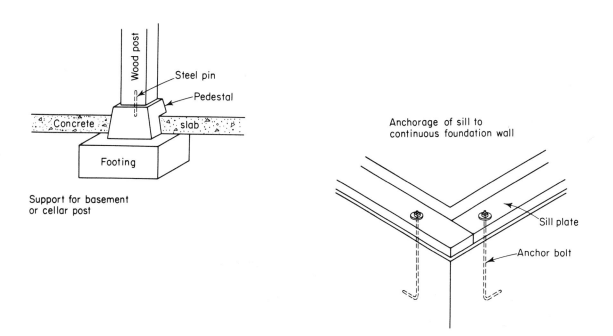

Support for basement or cellar post

Anchorage of sill to continuous foundation wall

Fig. 4-12.   Structural details.

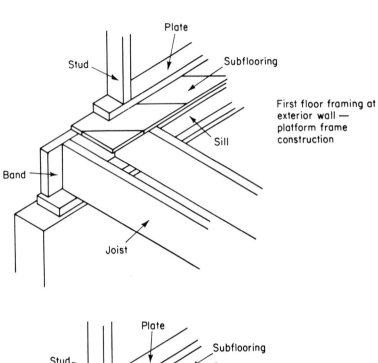

First floor framing at exterior wall — platform frame construction

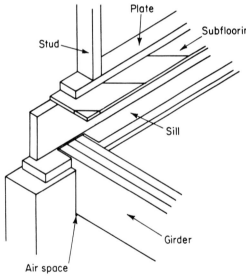

First floor framing at girder and exterior wall — platform frame construction

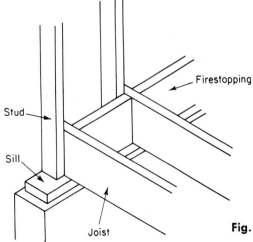

First floor framing at exterior wall — balloon frame construction

Fig. 4-13. Structural details.

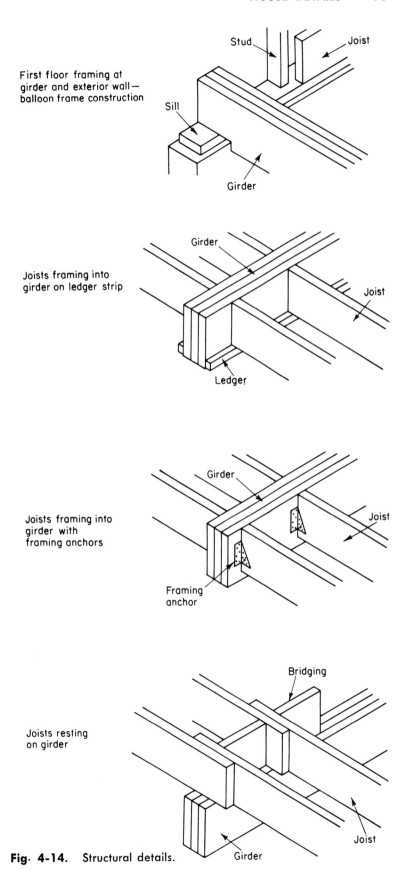

First floor framing at
girder and exterior wall—
balloon frame construction

Joists framing into
girder on ledger strip

Joists framing into
girder with
framing anchors

Joists resting
on girder

Fig. 4-14.   Structural details.

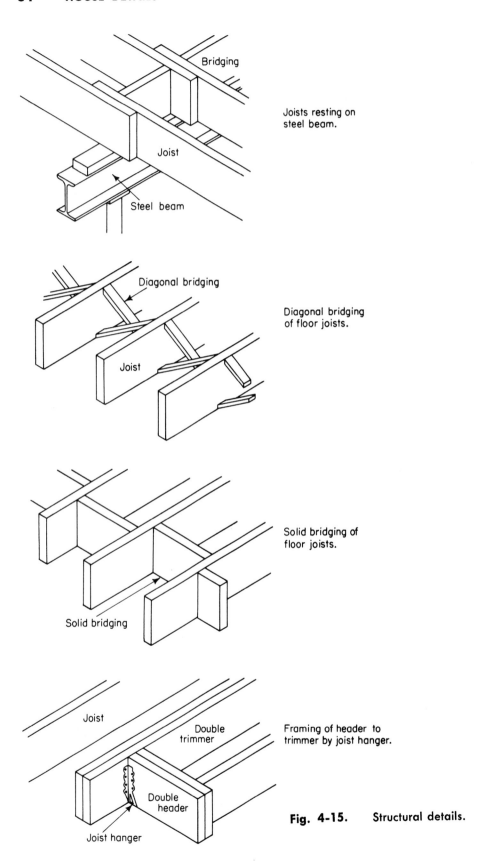

Joists resting on steel beam.

Diagonal bridging of floor joists.

Solid bridging of floor joists.

Framing of header to trimmer by joist hanger.

Fig. 4-15.   Structural details.

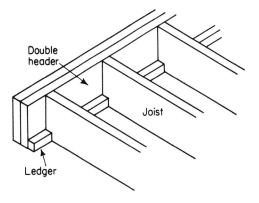

Framing of tail joists
to header on ledger strip.

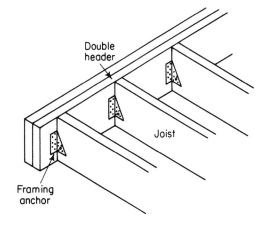

Framing of tail joists
to header by framing anchors.

Double joists under
non-bearing partitions.

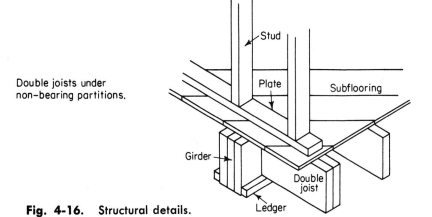

Fig. 4-16. Structural details.

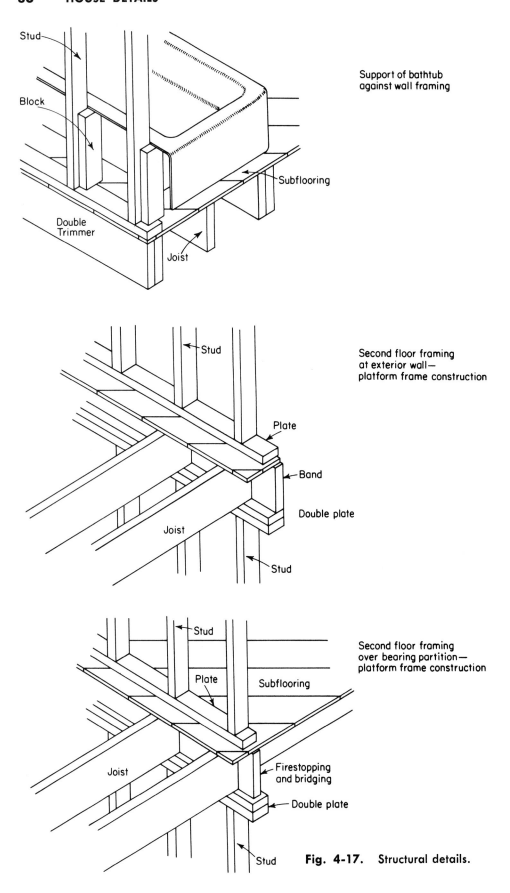

Support of bathtub
against wall framing

Second floor framing
at exterior wall—
platform frame construction

Second floor framing
over bearing partition—
platform frame construction

Fig. 4-17.   Structural details.

Second floor framing
at exterior wall —
balloon frame construction

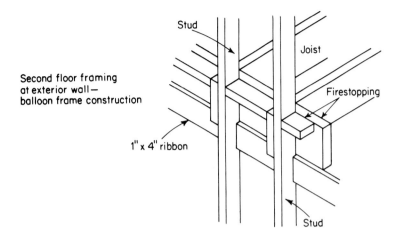

1" x 4" ribbon

Second floor framing
over bearing partition —
balloon frame construction

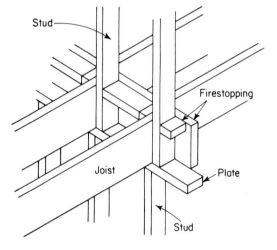

Attachment of non—bearing
partition to floor framing

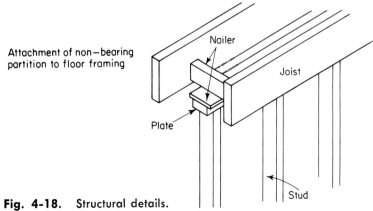

Fig. 4-18.   Structural details.

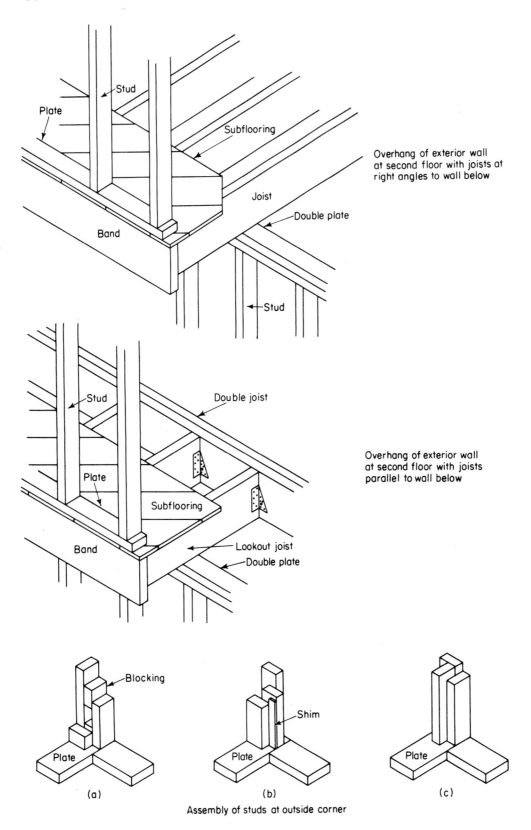

Fig. 4-19.   Structural details.

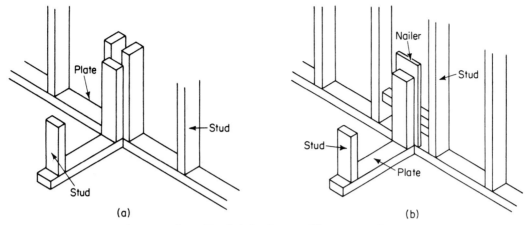

(a)   (b)

Assembly of studs where partition meets wall

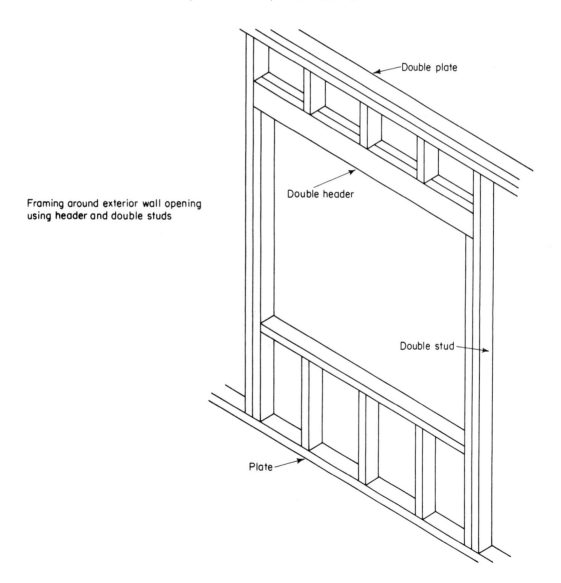

Framing around exterior wall opening
using **header** and double studs

Fig. 4-20. Structural details.

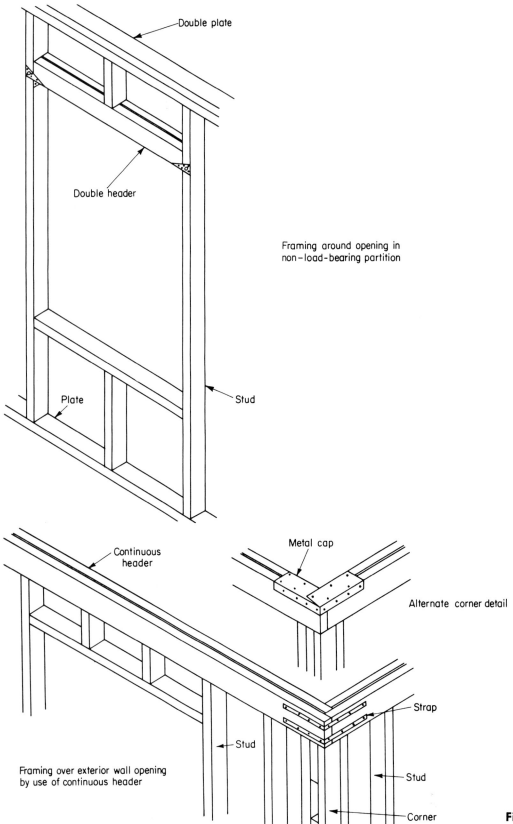

Double plate

Double header

Framing around opening in
non-load-bearing partition

Plate

Stud

Continuous
header

Metal cap

Alternate corner detail

Strap

Stud

Framing over exterior wall opening
by use of continuous header

Stud

Corner

Fig. 4-21.
Structural details.

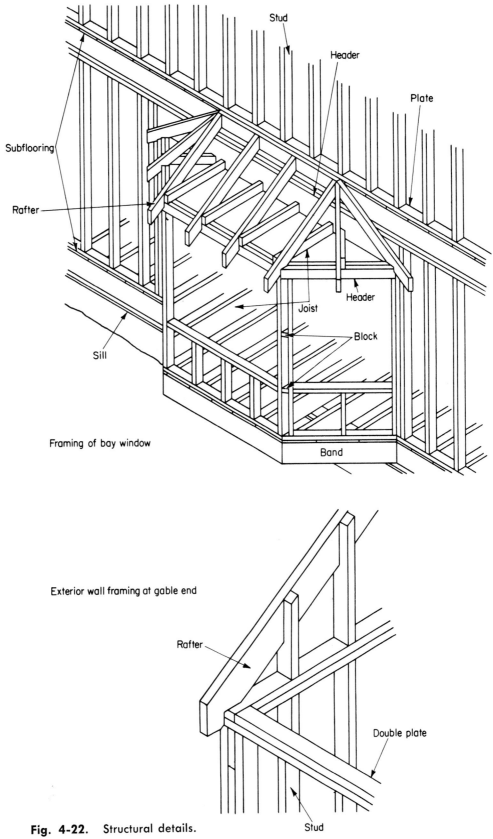

Framing of bay window

Exterior wall framing at gable end

Fig. 4-22. Structural details.

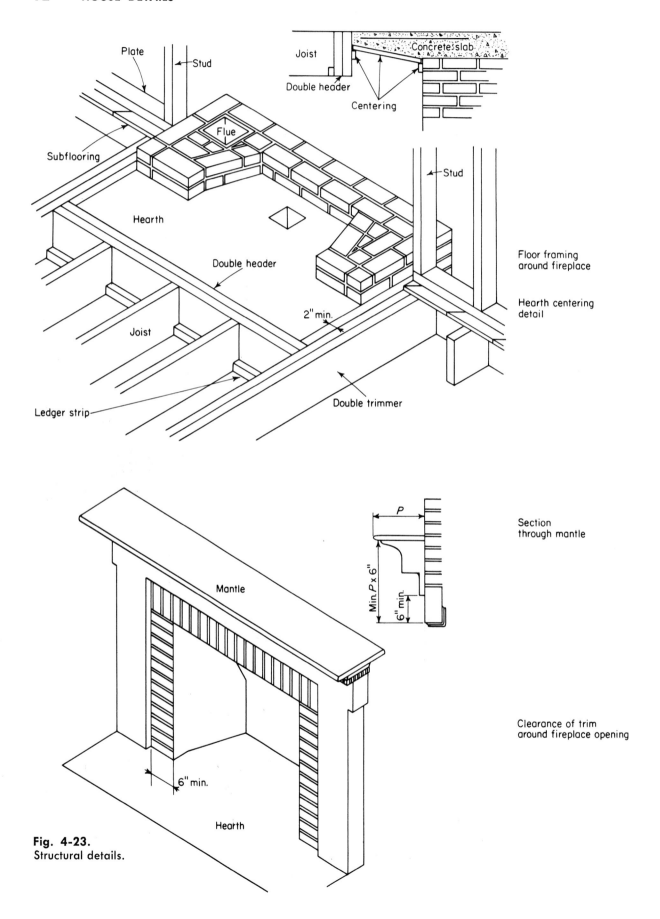

Fig. 4-23.
Structural details.

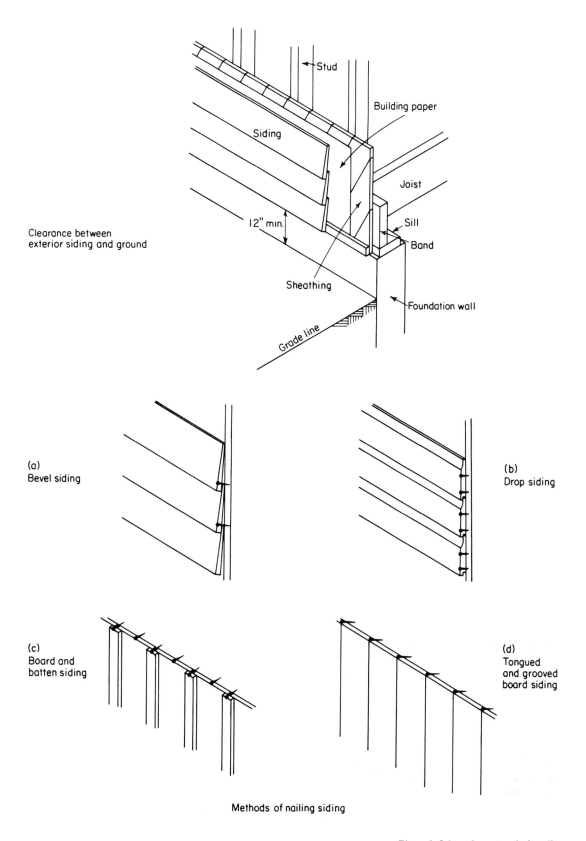

Stud

Building paper

Siding

Joist

Clearance between
exterior siding and ground

12" min.

Sill

Band

Sheathing

Foundation wall

Grade line

(a)
Bevel siding

(b)
Drop siding

(c)
Board and
batten siding

(d)
Tongued
and grooved
board siding

Methods of nailing siding

Fig. 4-24. Structural details.

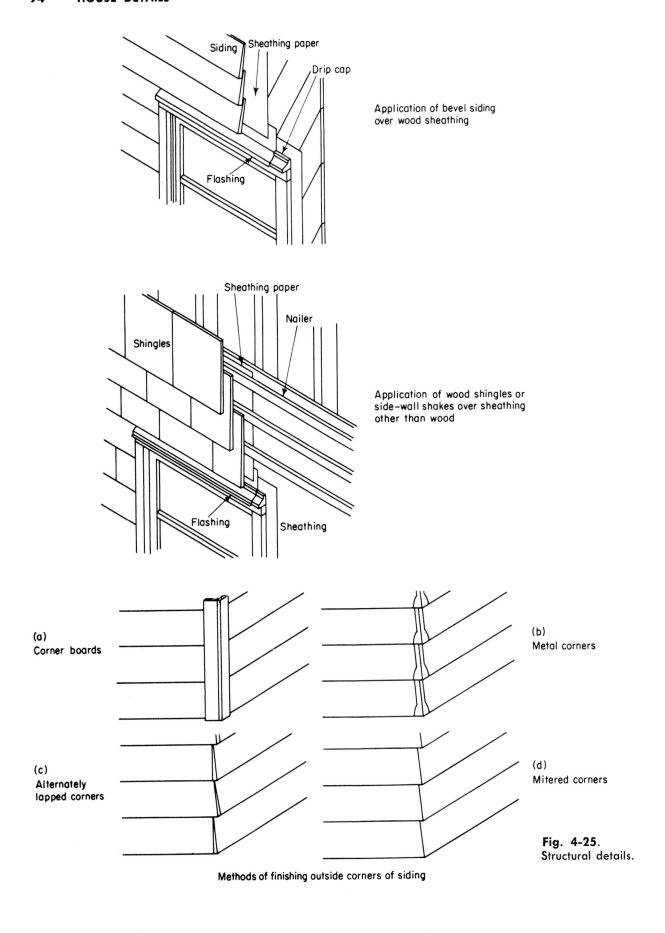

Siding   Sheathing paper

Drip cap

Application of bevel siding
over wood sheathing

Flashing

Sheathing paper

Nailer

Shingles

Application of wood shingles or
side-wall shakes over sheathing
other than wood

Flashing   Sheathing

(a)
Corner boards

(b)
Metal corners

(c)
Alternately
lapped corners

(d)
Mitered corners

Fig. 4-25.
Structural details.

Methods of finishing outside corners of siding

ASSIGNMENT:

Draw a plan and two elevations of each of the following three drawings:

1. Joists resting on a steel beam. (*See* Fig. 4.15.)

2. Assembly of studs at outside corners [*See* Fig. 4.19(a), (b) & (c).]

3. Floor framing around fireplace. (*See* Fig. 4.23.)

ROOF TRUSSES (AUSTRALIA)

Examine the 27½° pitch roof truss designed to span 32'-0" (see Fig. 4.26). The main chord of the truss is secured with timber connectors, and the other members are fastened with bolted mild steel gussets. The following specifications are noted on the original dwg:

½" ø m.s. (*mild steel*) bolts to be used throughout

x indicates positions where timber connectors are used with bolts

a indicates pair of 8" × 9" × ⅛" m.s. plates

b indicates pair of 10" × 9" × ⅛" m.s. plates

c indicates pair of 12" × 9" × ⅛" m.s. plates

Shown above the bottom chord of the dwg are two 7" × 1½" h.b. (hanging beams) which are secured to the ceiling joists to stiffen the whole ceiling assembly and prevent sags or cracks. Running longitudinally to the trusses are two underpurlins to each top chord, and the trusses or rafters are placed 2'-0" o.c. (on center). Several trusses to any one roof add great strength and rigidity to support the roofing which, in Australia, is usually of masonry tile. The total weight of a masonry tile roof for an ordinary house would be between 20 and 30 tons.

Fig. 4-26. Roof truss supporting concrete roof tiles.

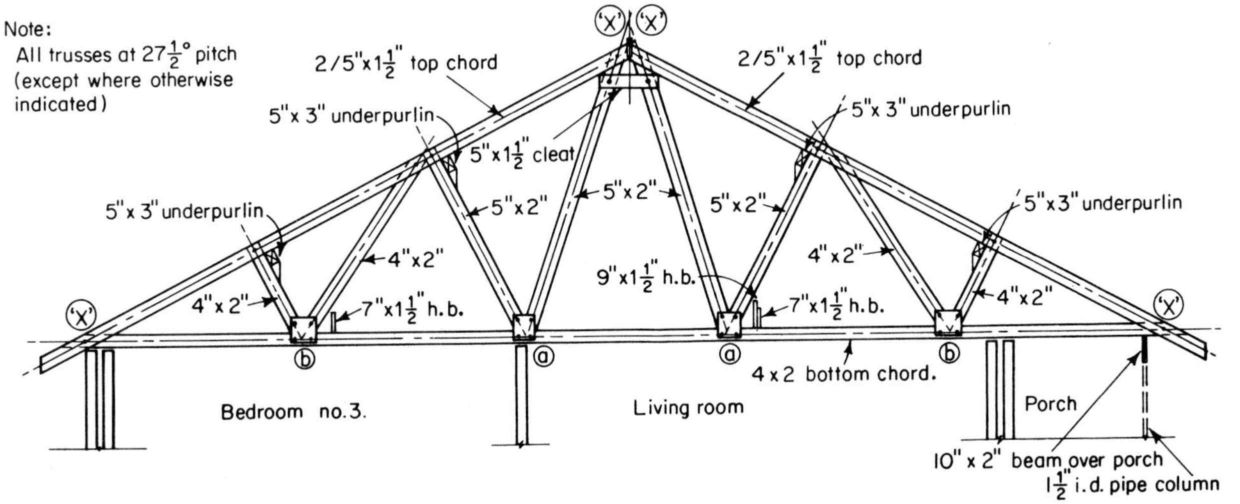

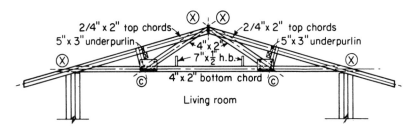

Fig. 4-27. Roof truss supporting corrugated iron roofing.

The 15° pitch roof truss shown at Fig. 4.27 is designed to span 16'-0" and to support a corr (corrugated) iron roof. This is a simple and strong roof truss for the span and superimposed roof load. The corr iron gives very great rigidity to the assembly. The more a roof is broken up into hips and valleys, the fewer trusses can be used. It is common practice in some areas to use half-trusses, especially for the valleys which are the weakest parts of the roof.

Where trusses for housing roofs are made on jigs, roofed areas are rapidly completed, enabling inside work to proceed irrespective of weather conditions.

TECO ROOF TRUSSES (SPLIT RING TYPE) AMERICAN

The following information and design of light roof trusses is published by permission of the Timber Engineering Company, Washington, D. C.

Design

The standard TECO ring type roof truss consists of a combination of 2 × 4's and 2 × 6's joined together with ½" bolts and TECO split ring connectors. Designed for a spacing of 24" o.c., the truss will easily accommodate spans ranging from 20'-0" to 32'-0" and slopes from $\frac{4}{12}$ to $\frac{11}{12}$. Greater spans can be built with a slightly different arrangement of members.

The key to the economy and efficiency of the TECO ring type truss is the split ring connector, which is placed in conforming grooves made in adjoining members of the truss. Through the use of this special type of fastener only one-half the number of connections are needed, compared to joints made with plywood gussets. Each split ring is equivalent in strength to approximately five ½" bolts or ten 20d nails. Requiring a minimum of members to fabricate and handle, it is the simplest pitched truss for spans up to 32'-0"; there are only four basic members involved!

The TECO split ring system is widely known and accepted by both national and local inspecting agencies. Complete typical design information for a variety of slopes and spans is available without charge from the Timber Engineering Company.

At Fig. 4.28 is shown dwg No. 600B of a Trussed Rafter slope 5 in 12.

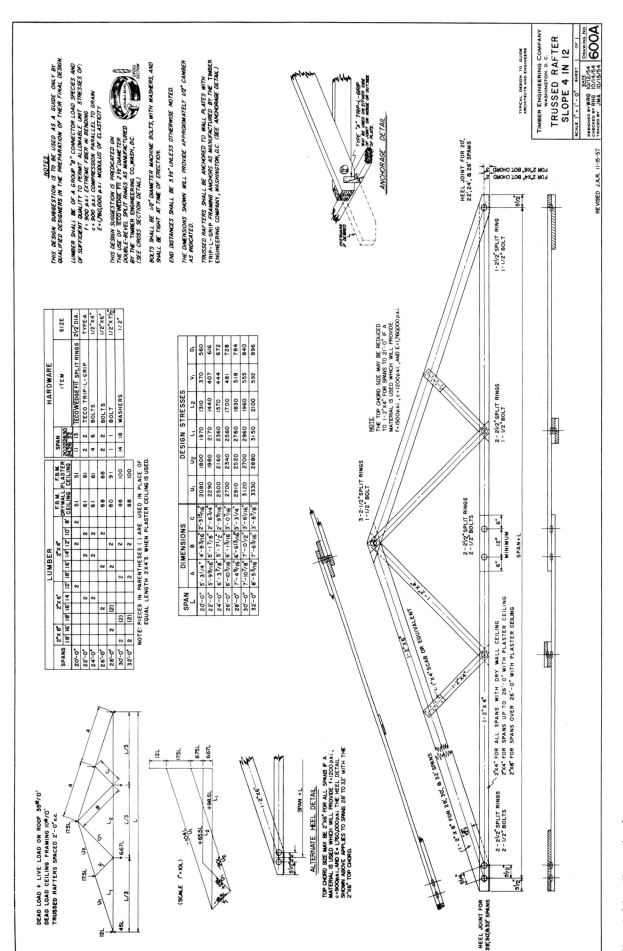

Fig. 4-28. Trussed rafter.

Notes:

LUMBER: — CONSTRUCTION GRADE SPRUCE OR EQUIVALENT.

NAILS: — ALL NAILS TO BE COMMON STEEL WIRE.
— ALL ROWS OF NAILS TO BE STAGGERED IN DIRECTION OF GRAIN TO KEEP SPLITTING TO A MINIMUM.
— NAILS MAY BE CLINCHED OR UNCLINCHED.
— SOLID BLOCKING TO BE USED UNDER GUSSET PLATES DURING NAILING.

PLYWOOD: — 1/2" SHEATHING GRADE DOUGLAS FIR THROUGHOUT.
— GRAIN DIRECTION OF PLYWOOD FACES TO BE PARALLEL TO BOTTOM CHORD EXCEPTING PLATES JOINING WEB TO TOP CHORD AT QUARTER POINTS.

GENERAL: — TO ENSURE MAXIMUM STIFFNESS, THE UPPER CHORDS MUST BE IN GOOD BEARING CONTACT AT PEAK.
— TRUSSES WITH SPANS DIFFERENT THAN THOSE LISTED MAY BE USED PROVIDED THE NAILING IS NOT LESS THAN THAT SHOWN FOR THE NEXT LARGER SPAN.

Nailing Schedule:

ROOF SNOW LOAD	SLOPE	SPAN "L" ft.	SPAN "L" in.	JOINT LOCATION 1	2	3	4	5	6
22.5	4:12	16	4	9	8	3	2	3	5
		18	4	10	9	3	2	3	5
		20	4	11	10	3	3	4	6
		22	4	12	11	4	3	4	7
		24	4	13	12	4	3	4	8
		26	4	14	13	4	4	5	9
		28	4	15	14	5	4	5	9
22.5	5:12	16	4	7	7	2	2	3	5
		18	4	8	8	3	2	3	5
		20	4	9	9	3	2	4	6
		22	4	10	10	3	3	4	7
		24	4	11	10	4	3	5	7
		28	4	12	12	4	4	5	8
30	4:12	16	4	10	9	3	2	4	7
		18	4	11	10	4	3	4	7
		20	4	13	12	4	3	5	9
		22	4	15	14	5	4	6	10
		24	4	17	16	5	4	6	11
		26	4	19	17	6	5	7	12
		28	4	20	18	6	5	7	12
30	5:12	16	4	10	9	2	2	4	6
		18	4	11	10	3	2	4	8
		20	4	13	12	4	3	5	8
		22	4	15	14	4	3	5	10
		24	4	16	15	5	4	6	10
37.5	4:12	16	4	14	13	3	3	6	11
		18	4	16	14	4	3	7	12
		20	4	17	16	5	4	8	13
		22	4	19	18	5	4	8	16
		24	4	22	20	6	5	10	17
		28	4	24	22	7	5	10	18
37.5	5:12	16	4	14	13	3	2	5	9
		18	4	16	14	4	3	6	10
		20	4	17	17	4	3	7	11
		22	4	20	19	5	4	7	12
		24	4	22	20	6	4	8	13
		28	4	24	22	7	5	9	15

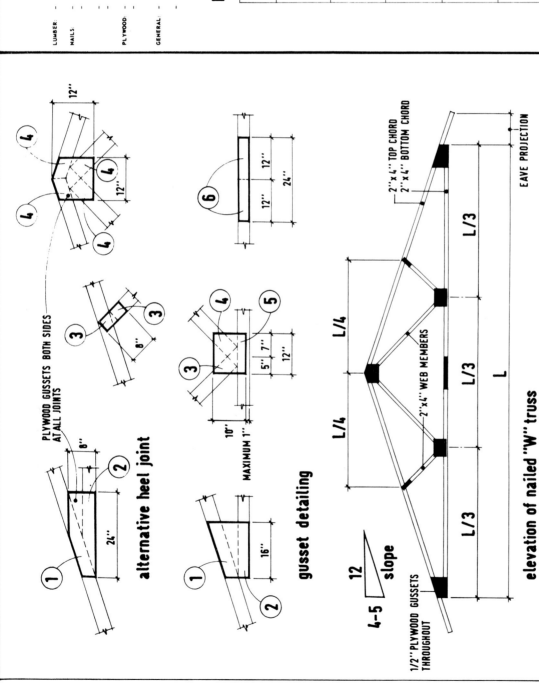

PLYWOOD GUSSETS BOTH SIDES AT ALL JOINTS

alternative heel joint

MAXIMUM 1"

gusset detailing

4–5 slope   12

1/2" PLYWOOD GUSSETS THROUGHOUT

2"x4" TOP CHORD
2"x4" BOTTOM CHORD
2"x4" WEB MEMBERS
EAVE PROJECTION

elevation of nailed "W" truss

BUILDER'S BULLETIN NUMBER 177 PREPARED JOINTLY BY:

DIVISION OF BUILDING RESEARCH - NRC   FOREST PRODUCTS LABORATORIES OF CANADA   CENTRAL MORTGAGE & HOUSING CORPORATION

SLOPES: 4/12 and 5/12	SPANS: 16'-4" to 28'-4"	GUSSETS: 1/2" plywood
		NAILED "W" TRUSS DESIGN: 2/66

Fig. 4-29. Nailed "W" truss design.

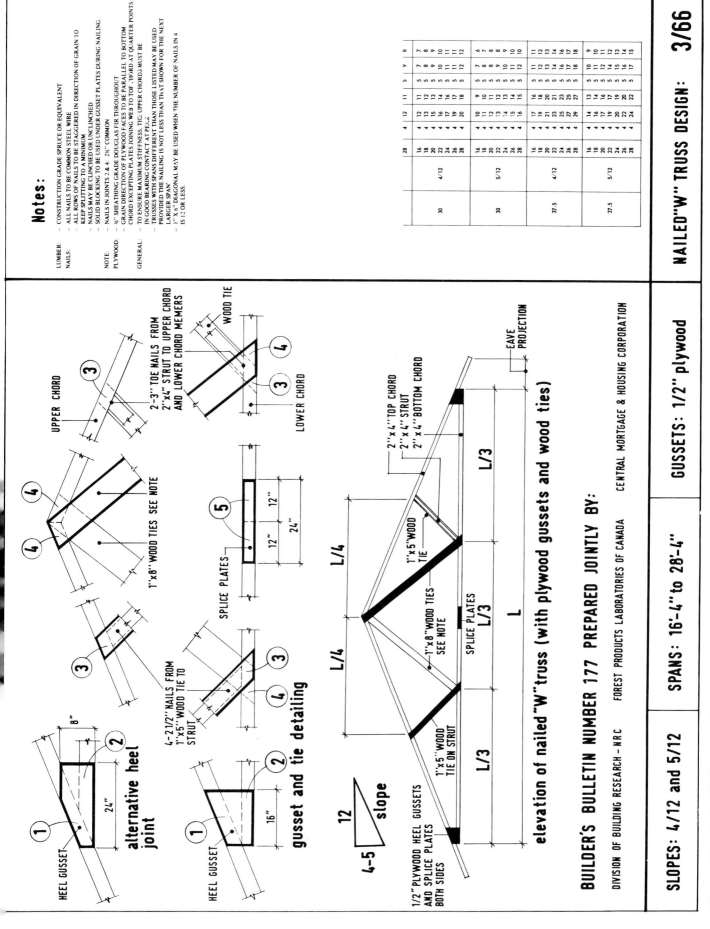

Notes:

LUMBER: – CONSTRUCTION GRADE SPRUCE OR EQUIVALENT

NAILS: – ALL NAILS TO BE COMMON STEEL WIRE
– ALL ROWS OF NAILS TO BE STAGGERED IN DIRECTION OF GRAIN 10
– KEEP SPLITTING TO A MINIMUM
– NAILS MAY BE CLINCHED OR UNCLINCHED

NOTE: – SOLID BLOCKING TO BE USED UNDER GUSSET PLATES DURING NAILING.
– NAILS IN JOINTS 2 & 4: 2½" COMMON

PLYWOOD: – ½" SHEATHING GRADE DOUGLAS FIR THROUGHOUT
– GRAIN DIRECTION OF PLYWOOD FACES TO BE PARALLEL TO BOTTOM CHORD EXCEPTING PLATES JOINING WEB TO TOP CHORD AT QUARTER POINTS.

GENERAL: – TO ENSURE MAXIMUM STIFFNESS, THE UPPER CHORDS MUST BE IN GOOD BEARING CONTACT AT PEAK
– TRUSSES WITH SPANS DIFFERENT THAN THOSE LISTED MAY BE USED PROVIDED THE NAILING IS NOT LESS THAN THAT SHOWN FOR THE NEXT LARGER SPAN
– 1" X 6" DIAGONAL MAY BE USED WHEN THE NUMBER OF NAILS IN 4 IS 12 OR LESS.

			28	4	12	11	5	9	8
30	4/12	16	28	4	12	11	5	7	7
		18	18	4	12	12	5	8	8
		20	20	4	15	13	5	8	9
		22	22	4	16	14	5	10	10
		24	24	4	17	16	5	11	11
		26	26	4	19	17	5	11	11
		28	28	4	20	18	5	12	12
30	5/12	16	16	4	10	9	5	7	6
		18	18	4	11	10	5	8	7
		20	20	4	12	11	5	8	8
		22	22	4	13	12	5	9	9
		24	24	4	14	13	5	10	10
		26	26	4	15	14	5	11	10
		28	28	4	16	15	5	12	10
37.5	4/12	16	16	4	17	16	5	11	11
		18	18	4	19	18	5	12	13
		20	20	4	21	20	5	13	14
		22	22	4	23	21	5	14	16
		24	24	4	25	23	5	16	17
		26	26	4	27	25	5	17	18
		28	28	4	29	27	5	18	18
37.5	5/12	16	16	4	14	13	5	10	9
		18	18	4	16	14	5	12	11
		20	20	4	17	16	5	14	12
		22	22	4	19	17	5	14	13
		24	24	4	20	19	5	15	14
		26	26	4	22	20	5	16	14
		28	28	4	24	22	5	17	15

HEEL GUSSET

① ② 8" 24" **alternative heel joint**

① ② 16" **gusset and tie detailing**

12 4-5 **slope**

1/2" PLYWOOD HEEL GUSSETS AND SPLICE PLATES BOTH SIDES

UPPER CHORD ③ ④ ④ ④

1"x8" WOOD TIES SEE NOTE

2–3" TOE NAILS FROM 2"x4" STRUT TO UPPER CHORD AND LOWER CHORD MEMERS ③ ④ WOOD TIE LOWER CHORD

4–2 1/2" NAILS FROM 1"x5" WOOD TIE TO STRUT ③ ④

SPLICE PLATES ⑤ 12" 12" 24"

1"x5" WOOD TIE ON STRUT

1"x8" WOOD TIES SEE NOTE

SPLICE PLATES

2"x4" TOP CHORD 2"x4" STRUT 2"x4" BOTTOM CHORD

1"x5" WOOD TIE

L/4 L/4 L/3 L/3 L/3 L/3 L EAVE PROJECTION

elevation of nailed "W" truss (with plywood gussets and wood ties)

BUILDER'S BULLETIN NUMBER 177 PREPARED JOINTLY BY:

DIVISION OF BUILDING RESEARCH – NRC   FOREST PRODUCTS LABORATORIES OF CANADA   CENTRAL MORTGAGE & HOUSING CORPORATION

SLOPES: 4/12 and 5/12 | **SPANS: 16'-4" to 28'-4"** | **GUSSETS: 1/2" plywood**

NAILED "W" TRUSS DESIGN: 3/66

Fig. 4-30. Nailed "W" truss design.

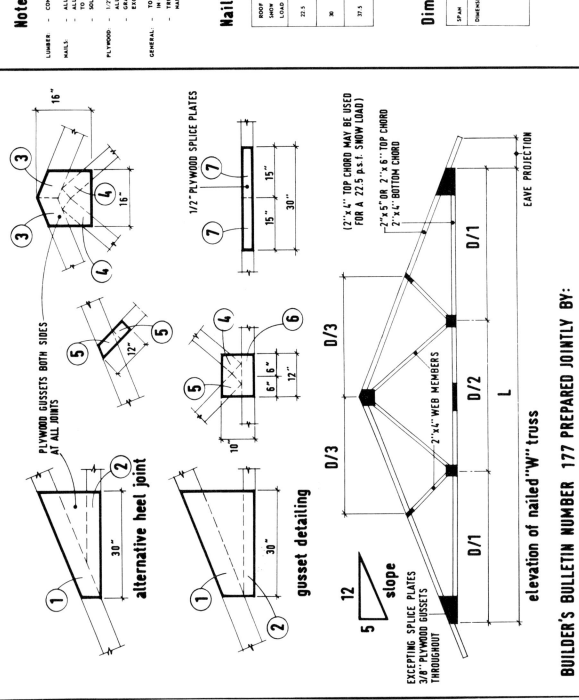

Notes:

LUMBER: – CONSTRUCTION GRADE SPRUCE OR EQUIVALENT.

NAILS: – ALL NAILS TO BE COMMON STEEL WIRE.
– ALL ROWS OF NAILS TO BE STAGGERED AND CLINCHED PERPENDICULAR TO DIRECTION OF PLYWOOD FACE.
– SOLID BLOCKING TO BE USED UNDER GUSSET PLATES DURING NAILING.

PLYWOOD: – 1/2" SHEATHING GRADE DOUGLAS FIR AT CENTRE SPLICE BOTTOM CHORD.
ALL OTHER LOCATIONS TO BE 3/8" THICK PLYWOOD OF THE SAME GRADE.
GRAIN DIRECTION OF PLYWOOD FACES TO BE PARALLEL TO BOTTOM CHORD EXCEPTING PLATES JOINING WEB TO TOP CHORD AT QUARTER POINTS.

GENERAL: – TO ENSURE MAXIMUM STIFFNESS, THE UPPER CHORDS MUST BE IN GOOD BEARING CONTACT AT PEAK.
– TRUSSES WITH SPANS BETWEEN THOSE LISTED MAY BE USED PROVIDED THE NAILING IS NOT LESS THAN THAT SHOWN FOR THE LARGER SPAN.

Nailing Schedule:

ROOF SNOW LOAD	SLOPE	SPAN ft.	"L" in.	1	2	3	4	5	6	7
22.5	5/12	30	4	12	12	4	4	3	4	7
		32	4	13	12	4	4	3	4	8
30	5/12	30	4	15	14	5	5	4	5	10
		32	4	16	15	5	5	4	5	11
37.5	5/12	30	4	18	17	5	5	4	5	12
		32	4	19	18	6	6	5	6	13

Dimension Schedule:

SPAN		L = 30'-4"	L = 32'-4"
DIMENSIONS	D/1	10'-10"	11'-7"
	D/2	8'-8"	9'-2"
	D/3	6'-9"	7'-2"

PLYWOOD GUSSETS BOTH SIDES AT ALL JOINTS

16"
16"
16"

1/2" PLYWOOD SPLICE PLATES

15"
15"
30"

(2"x 4" TOP CHORD MAY BE USED FOR A 22.5 p.s.f. SNOW LOAD)

2"x 5" OR 2"x 6" TOP CHORD
2"x 4" BOTTOM CHORD

D/1
D/3
D/2
D/3
D/1
L
EAVE PROJECTION

2"x 4" WEB MEMBERS

30"
alternative heel joint

30"

12"
10"
6" 6"
12"

gusset detailing

12
5
slope

EXCEPTING SPLICE PLATES
3/8" PLYWOOD GUSSETS
THROUGHOUT

elevation of nailed "W" truss

BUILDER'S BULLETIN NUMBER 177 PREPARED JOINTLY BY:

DIVISION OF BUILDING RESEARCH – N R C   FOREST PRODUCTS LABORATORIES OF CANADA   CENTRAL MORTGAGE & HOUSING CORPORATION

SLOPE: 5/12 only	SPANS: 30'-4" to 32'-4"	GUSSETS: 3/8"-1/2" plywood	NAILED "W" TRUSS DESIGN: 6/66

Fig. 4-31.   Nailed "W" truss design.

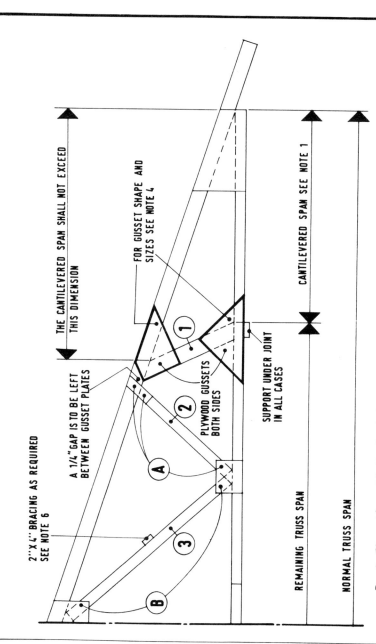

Reinforcing Requirements:

1. THE CANTILEVERED SPAN IS NOT TO EXCEED 6'–8" FOR TRUSSES WITH 2"×6" OR 2"×5" TOP CHORDS, OR 5'–4" FOR TRUSSES WITH 2"×4" TOP CHORDS.

2. THE ADDITIONAL WEB MEMBER (MEMBER 1) SHOULD BE OF THE SAME LUMBER SIZE AS THE TOP CHORD.

3. GUSSET PLATES AND NAILING REQUIRED FOR ADDITIONAL MEMBER (MEMBER 1) SHOULD BE EQUIVALENT TO THOSE AT THE HEEL JOINT.

4. THE SHAPE AND SIZE OF GUSSET PLATES SHOULD BE CHOSEN WITH REGARD TO THE SPACE LIMITATIONS AND REQUIRED NAILING AREA FOR INDIVIDUAL DESIGNS.

5. NUMBER OF NAILS AT CONNECTIONS FOR MEMBER 2 (JOINT A) TO BE INCREASED TO THAT USED FOR MEMBER 3 (JOINT B).

6. FOR TRUSSES HAVING ROOF SLOPES OF 5/12 AND GREATER LATERAL BRACING SHOULD BE PROVIDED FOR MEMBER 3 (LATERAL BRACING CAN BE ACHIEVED BY TYING TOGETHER THE MID-POINTS OF MEMBERS 3 OF THE CANTILEVERED TRUSSES USED, WITH A 2"×4" EXTENDING TO AT LEAST TWO NORMALLY SUPPORTED TRUSSES)

General Notes:

IF DESIRED, BOTH ENDS CAN BE CANTILEVERED, PROVIDING THE ABOVE PROCEDURE IS FOLLOWED FOR EACH END.

THE CANTILEVER DETAIL MAY BE USED FOR MOST TRUSS DESIGNS WHEN WEB MEMBERS ARE NOMINAL 2" OR THICKER.

THE CANTILEVER DETAIL SHALL NOT BE USED WITH TRUSS DESIGN 3.66.

8/66

2"×4" BRACING AS REQUIRED SEE NOTE 6

THE CANTILEVERED SPAN SHALL NOT EXCEED THIS DIMENSION

A 1/4" GAP IS TO BE LEFT BETWEEN GUSSET PLATES

FOR GUSSET SHAPE AND SIZES SEE NOTE 4

PLYWOOD GUSSETS BOTH SIDES

SUPPORT UNDER JOINT IN ALL CASES

REMAINING TRUSS SPAN

NORMAL TRUSS SPAN

CANTILEVERED SPAN SEE NOTE 1

Part Elevation Of Typical Truss Showing Cantilever Detail

BUILDER'S BULLETIN NUMBER 177 PREPARED JOINTLY BY:

DIVISION OF BUILDING RESEARCH – NRC   FOREST PRODUCTS LABORATORIES OF CANADA   CENTRAL MORTGAGE & HOUSING CORPORATION

METHOD OF REINFORCING CANTILEVERED NAILED "W" TRUSSES WITH PLYWOOD GUSSETS

CANTILEVER DESIGN:

Fig. 4-32.   Cantilevered "W" truss.

NAILED "W" TRUSS DESIGNS (CANADIAN)

The preceding three "W" Truss Designs, Figs. 4.29, 4.30, and 4.31, and the Cantilever Designed Truss, Fig. 4.32, were prepared jointly by the Division of Building Research of the Forest Products Laboratories of Canada, and the Central Mortgage & Housing Corporation, and are published by permission. An addendum states: Please revise the notes "Nails" on each design to read:

"All nails to be 3″ common steel wire except where otherwise permitted."

INTERSECTING HIP ROOF OF EQUAL PITCH

Fig. 4.33 shows the plan of an intersecting hip roof of equal pitch and is reproduced by courtesy of the *Canadian Builder*.

A most important consideration when designing such roofs is the wet snow load that may be imposed on the framing. In every part of the earth's surface, local climatic conditions must be taken into account.

For a full treatise on Roof Framing for small buildings, see Wass & Sanders, *Building Construction: Roof Framing* (Englewood Cliffs, N. J.: Prentice-Hall, Inc., 1960).

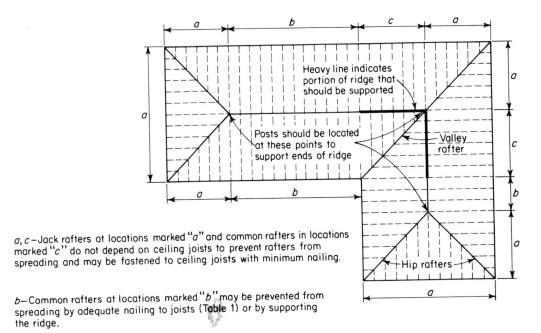

a, c—Jack rafters at locations marked "a" and common rafters in locations marked "c" do not depend on ceiling joists to prevent rafters from spreading and may be fastened to ceiling joists with minimum nailing.

b—Common rafters at locations marked "b" may be prevented from spreading by adequate nailing to joists (Table 1) or by supporting the ridge.

Schematic diagram of typical rafter layout (broken lines)

Fig. 4-33.   Intersecting roof of equal pitch.

ASSIGNMENT:

Make a tracing of the intersecting roof of equal pitch shown at Fig. 4.33 and indicate on the dwg where you would consider placing a truss or trusses and a half-truss to meet heavy snow conditions. The roof has a one-third pitch.

5 POST AND BEAM CONSTRUCTION

In this chapter we are going to study a post and beam glu-lam (wood glue laminated) modular constructed two-story home with double garage. Extracts from the original seven architectural and 36 detail dwgs are published by courtesy and permission of Mr. Alton McCaul Bowers, Architect, Calgary, Alberta.

The house is built in a cul-de-sac and has a flat roof with lower and upper floor and a front entrance with double garage facing north. From the front, the house looks like a single-story home (the lower floor at the north end is below ground level) and the sunny southern part is sheltered by the garage facing north on the left and a retaining wall for earth on the right. The orientation is important, for temperatures register 40° below zero in this area in the winter.

Before closely examining the dwgs, *locate and remember the compass point,* and then leisurely glance thru the plans and elevations to get a concept of the size and shapes of rooms and the outside appearance of the home.

At Fig. 5.1 are shown the site and the plot plan with the city supplied legal description, earth elevations, property line pegs, and future grade lines. For an understanding of this home, it is necessary to locate from the dwgs the existing and new grades and to visualize the contour of the land. The natural fall of the land is from north (front) to south. Although the front of the house gives the appearance of a single-story home, it has two floors of almost the same floor areas. You should understand something about land leveling, cut and fill. Research this subject.

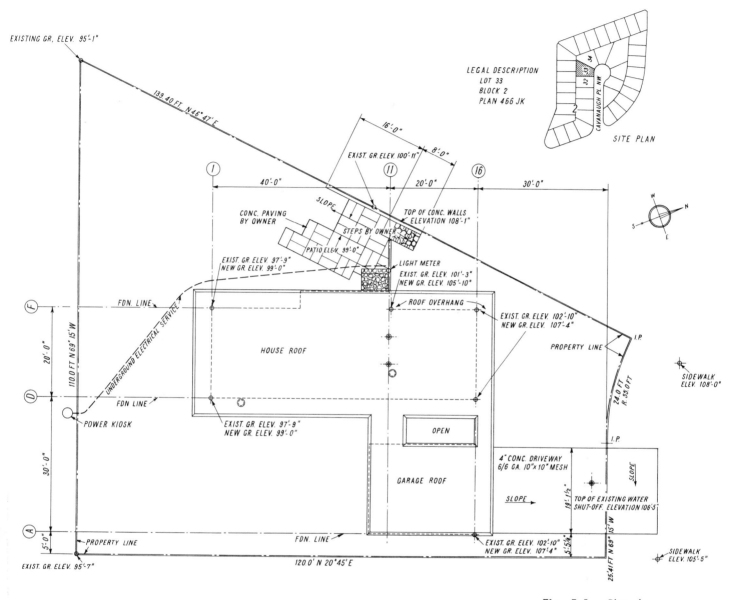

Fig. 5-1. Plot plan.

For a treatment of earthwork and land leveling, see Chapter 10 of Alonzo Wass, *Building Construction Estimating* (Englewood Cliffs, N.J.: Prentice-Hall, Inc., 1963).

At Fig. 5.2 is shown the Foundation and Footing Plan. Let us examine the dwg in clockwise fashion, starting at the top left. The detail dwgs are shown in the text in the order in which the sec (section) numbers are located on our examination of the dwg sheets. On the original architectural sheet they appear consecutively. Sec 10/7 means the tenth detail dwg on architectural sheet seven.

1: The 4'-0" modular spacings are shown on lines 1 thru 16; the longest wall is 60'-0".

2: Col (column) line 1 indicates the elevation of the top of concrete wall

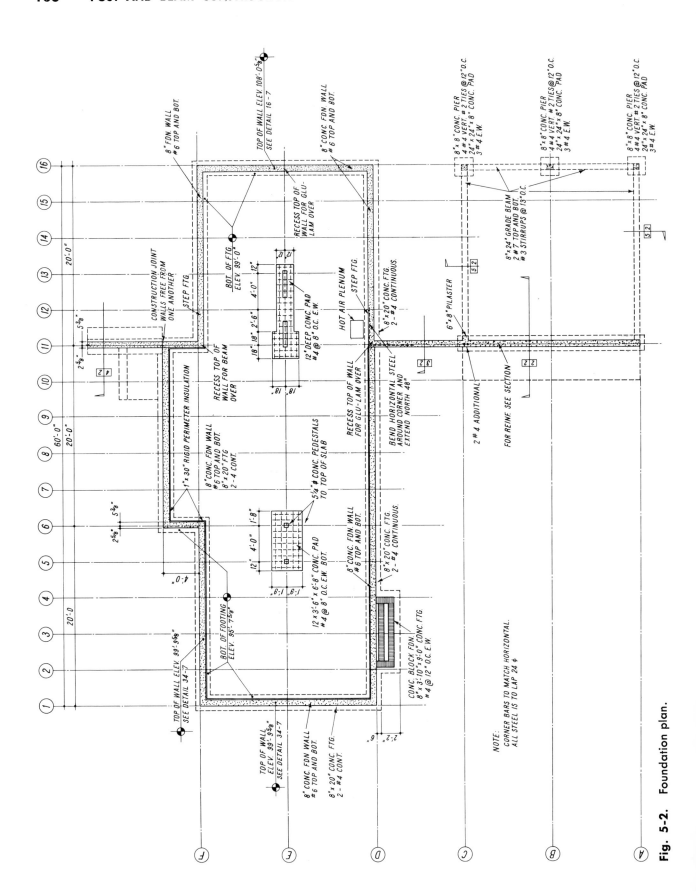

Fig. 5-2. Foundation plan.

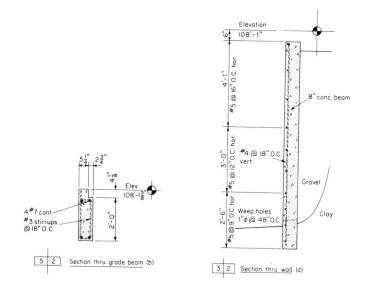

Elevation
108'-1"

6"

4'-1"

#5 @ 16" O.C. hor.

8" conc. beam

3'-0"

#4 @ 18" O.C. vert.

#5 @ 12" O.C. hor.

Gravel

2'-6"

#5 @ 9" O.C. hor.

Weep holes
1"φ @ 48" O.C.

Clay

3 | 2   Section thru wall (d)

5¼" 2¾"

4⅛"

Elev.
108'-1⅝"

4 #7 cont.

#3 stirrups
@ 18" O.C.

2'-0"

5 | 2   Section thru grade beam (b)

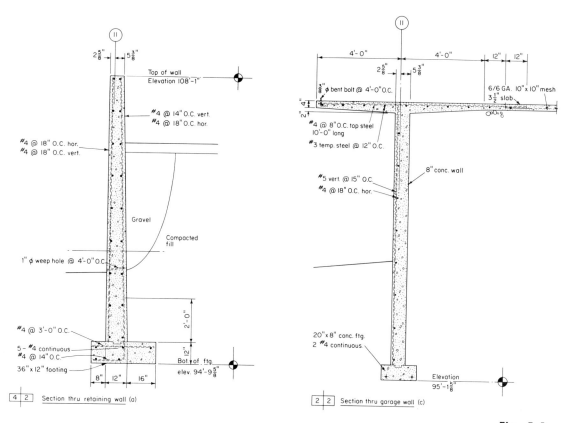

11

2⅝" 5⅜"

Top of wall
Elevation 108'-1"

#4 @ 14" O.C. vert.
#4 @ 18" O.C. hor.

#4 @ 18" O.C. hor.
#4 @ 18" O.C. vert.

Gravel

Compacted
fill

1" φ weep hole @ 4'-0" O.C.

#4 @ 3'-0" O.C.

5 - #4 continuous
#4 @ 14" O.C.

36" x 12" footing

8" 12" 16"

2'-0"

12"

Bot. of ftg.
elev. 94'-9⅝"

4 | 2   Section thru retaining wall (a)

11

4'-0" 4'-0" 12" 12"

2⅝" 5⅜"

⅜" φ bent bolt @ 4'-0" O.C.

6/6 GA. 10" x 10" mesh
3½" slab

#4 @ 8" O.C. top steel
10'-0" long

#3 temp. steel @ 12" O.C.

#5 vert. @ 15" O.C.
#4 @ 18" O.C. hor.

8" conc. wall

20" x 8" conc. ftg.
2 #4 continuous

Elevation
95'-1⅝"

2 | 2   Section thru garage wall (c)

Fig. 5-3.

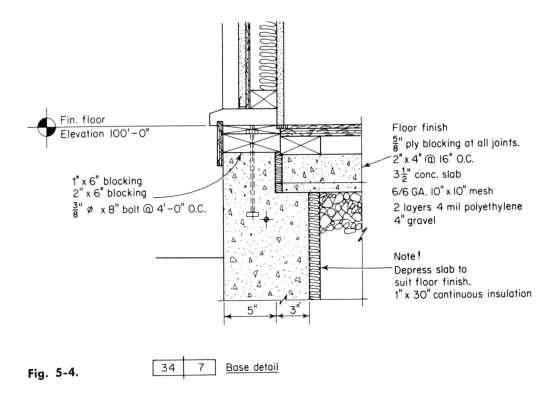

Fin. floor
Elevation 100'-0"

1" x 6" blocking
2" x 6" blocking
$\frac{3}{8}$" ∅ x 8" bolt @ 4'-0" O.C.

Floor finish
$\frac{5}{8}$" ply blocking at all joints.
2" x 4" @ 16" O.C.
$3\frac{1}{2}$" conc. slab
6/6 GA. 10" x 10" mesh
2 layers 4 mil polyethylene
4" gravel

Note!
Depress slab to
suit floor finish.
1" x 30" continuous insulation

5"   3"

Fig. 5-4. | 34 | 7 | Base detail

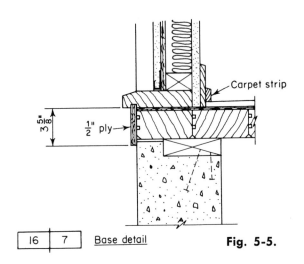

Carpet strip

$3\frac{5}{8}$" $\frac{1}{2}$" ply

| 16 | 7 | Base detail   **Fig. 5-5.**

as 99'-9¾". This is from an assumed first floor finish of 100'-0". Detail dwg is shown at Fig. 5.4. *This is a very important detail showing the lower concrete floor and the anchored sole plate.*

3: Col line 6 determines the 4'-0" modular offset of the W (west) wall.

4: Col line 11 determines the position and the width of the retaining wall. Ask yourself, "Why is it necessary to have a retaining wall here?" Detail dwg 4/2 is shown at Fig. 5.3(a).

5: Near to col line 12 is positioned the concrete wall construction joint.

6: Col line 15 indicates the 8" thickness of the fdn (foundation) wall.

7: Col line 16 determines detail 16/7 shown at Fig. 5.5, also the elevation and thickness of the concrete wall. Note the differences in elevations at Steps 2 and 6. The lower floor portion of the house is below ground level.

8: Locate the reinforced concrete ftg pads at the garage, supporting concrete piers which in turn support the grade beam. See sec 5/2 at Fig. 5.3(b). All this underpinning is below ground level.

9: The garage wall sec 2/2 is shown at Fig. 5.3(c). Note the additional vertical reinforcing at the intersection.

10: An extension of the garage wall sec at 3/2 is shown at Fig. 5.3(d).

11: An important structural detail is shown where the horizontal reinforcing is bent around the corner from the house wall toward the garage wall.

12: Notice that the continuous concrete reinforced ftg size is notated in several places.

14: Carefully examine all the internal ftg sizes and all notations. Dwgs must be sufficiently notated without being cluttered.

At Fig. 5.6 is shown that part of the lower floor plan bounded by column lines D-E-F on the "S" wall and thru col lines 1 and 11 on the "W" wall. Here is a pleasing example of modular post and beam construction at competitive cost with traditional construction. Let us examine this dwg as we did the last.

1: Col line 1 indicates the corner glu-lam column sec 1/7 shown at Fig. 5.7.

2: Col line 3 indicates a window mullion. You should learn the technical names of architectural details. Sec 10/7 is shown at Fig. 5.8.

3: Col line 6 indicates a point where two windows adjoin at right angles. Sec 35/7 is shown at Fig. 5.9.

4: Between col lines 10 and 11 is shown door opening D1. All door openings are identified on plan by a ringed letter and number and dwgs of them are shown (together with each type required) on the door schedules of one of the architectural dwg sheets. Quite frequently other than stock types of doors are required. This is important detailing. Someday it may be your job to count the doors, draw them, and make a notation of the quantity of each type required. These are important details for estimating costs.

5: Locate sec 22/7, which indicates a window jamb intersecting a concrete wall. It is shown at Fig. 5.10.

6: Sec 21/7 indicates a door and window jamb intersecting a typical inside wall and is shown at Fig. 5.11.

7: Locate several glu-lam columns. They are all $5\frac{1}{4}'' \times 5\frac{1}{4}''$ and they support glu-lam beams $5\frac{1}{4}'' \times 13''$.

8: The plan of the stone chimney should be read with the elevations and dim details; these are shown in Chapter 8. Sec 8/7 is shown in detail at Fig. 5.12.

9: Sec 11/7 indicates jamb to typical wall intersection. Note that the wood framing is 2×3 against traditional wall of 2×4. See Fig. 5.13.

10: Carefully examine the internal notations. The rooms are identified with framed numbers, such as 103. First floor numbers in North America are numbered in the 100 series, the second floor in the 200 series, and so on. This is not so in many other countries, where the floor at ground level is called the ground floor, the next above is the first floor, and so on. A Room Finish Schedule is given on one of the architectural dwg sheets.

11: *Notice that some of the walls at the north end of this floor are concrete and underground*; the remainder are wood framed. The underground room (not shown on these extracts) is for recreation.

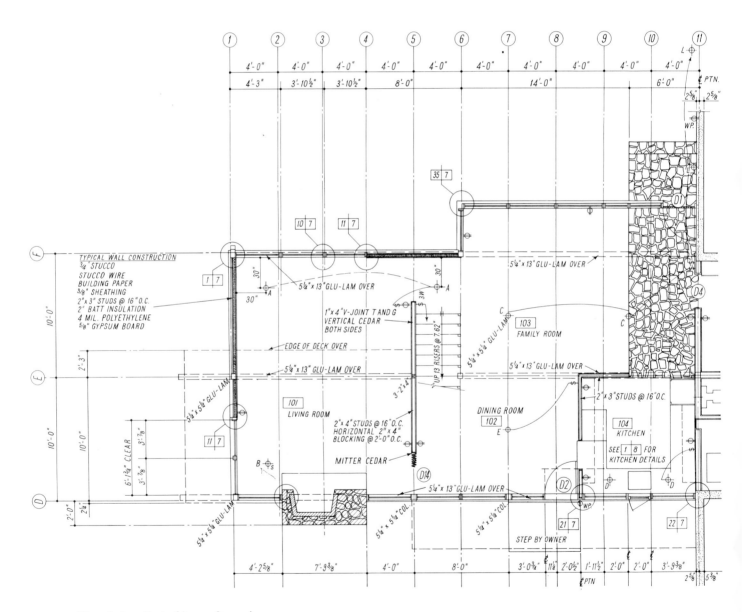

Fig. 5-6. Part of lower floor plan.

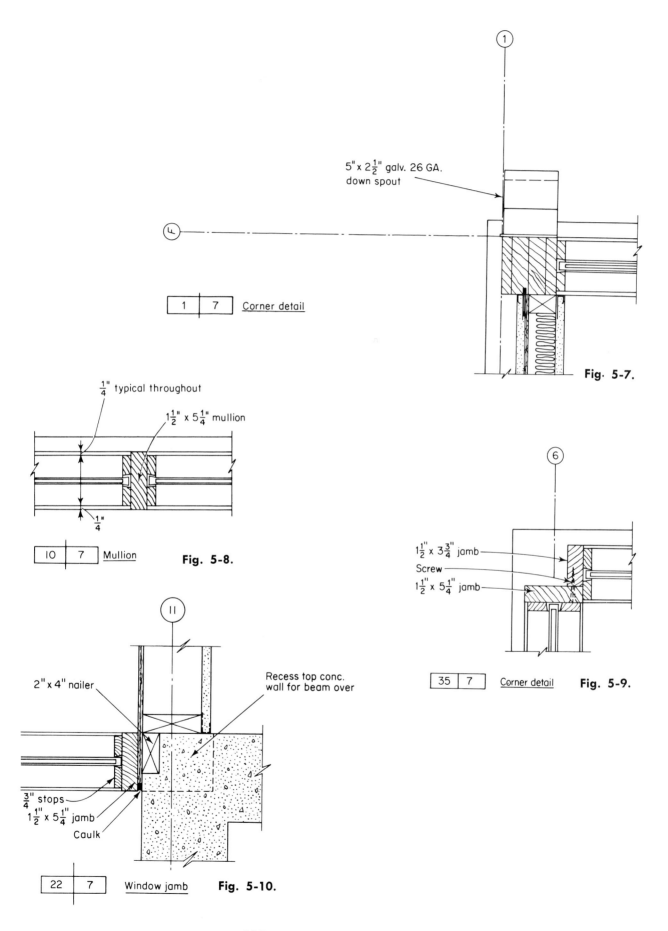

5" x 2$\frac{1}{2}$" galv. 26 GA.
down spout

| 1 | 7 | Corner detail |

Fig. 5-7.

$\frac{1}{4}$" typical throughout

1$\frac{1}{2}$" x 5$\frac{1}{4}$" mullion

$\frac{1}{4}$"

| 10 | 7 | Mullion |

Fig. 5-8.

1$\frac{1}{2}$" x 3$\frac{3}{4}$" jamb
Screw
1$\frac{1}{2}$" x 5$\frac{1}{4}$" jamb

| 35 | 7 | Corner detail |

Fig. 5-9.

2" x 4" nailer

Recess top conc.
wall for beam over

$\frac{3}{4}$" stops
1$\frac{1}{2}$" x 5$\frac{1}{4}$" jamb
Caulk

| 22 | 7 | Window jamb |

Fig. 5-10.

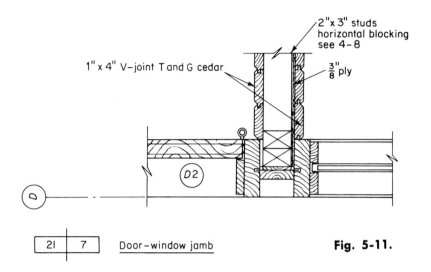

1" x 4" V-joint T and G cedar

2" x 3" studs
horizontal blocking
see 4-8

$\frac{3}{8}$" ply

| 21 | 7 |

Door-window jamb   **Fig. 5-11.**

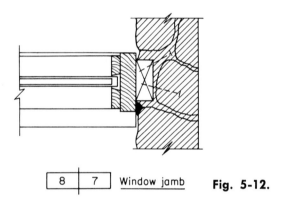

| 8 | 7 |

Window jamb   **Fig. 5-12.**

Typical wall construction

$\frac{3}{4}$" stucco
stucco wire
building paper
$\frac{3}{8}$" sheathing
2" x 3" studs @ 16"O.C.
2" batt insulation
4 mil. polyethylene
interior finish

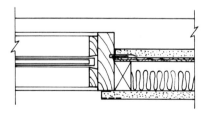

| 11 | 7 |

Jamb   **Fig. 5-13.**

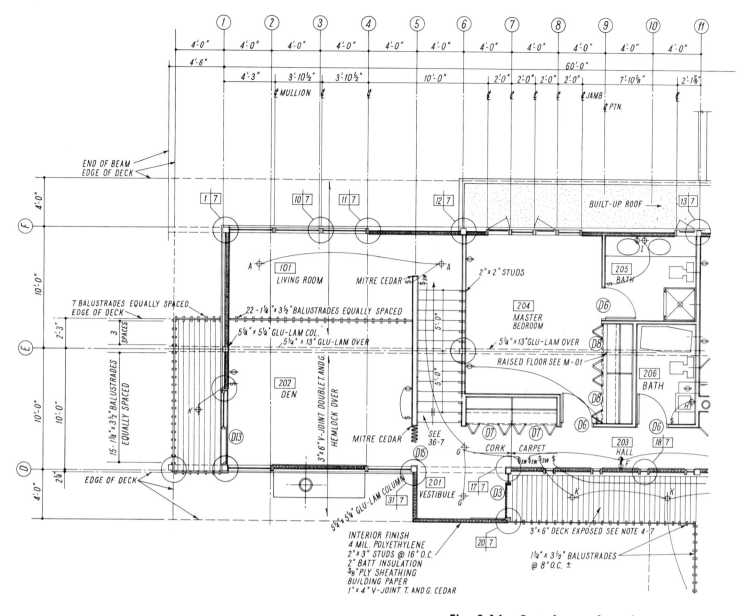

Fig. 5-14. Part of upper floor plan.

At Fig. 5.14 is shown that part of the upper floor plan located immediately over the last plan dwg. Let us examine it. Many of the section marks on this dwg have already been dealt with.

1: *Notice that all the walls on this floor are wood framed.*

2: Sec 12/7 indicates a glu-lam column intersecting three walls and is shown at Fig. 5.15.

3: Sec 13/7 indicates a glu-lam column at a door jamb at an intersection of an outside and an inside wall. We can learn a great amount about the materials used and the method of construction from such dwgs. See Fig. 5.16.

4: Sec 18/7 indicates a horizontal section of a window and wall jambs and is shown at Fig. 5.17.

5: Sec 17/7 indicates the intersection of a window jamb to a glu-lam column and a return typical wall and is shown at Fig. 5.18.

6: Sec 20/7 indicates a door jamb detail to a vestibule wall and is shown at Fig. 5.19.

7: Sec 31/7 indicates an entrance corner detail and is shown at Fig. 5.20.

113

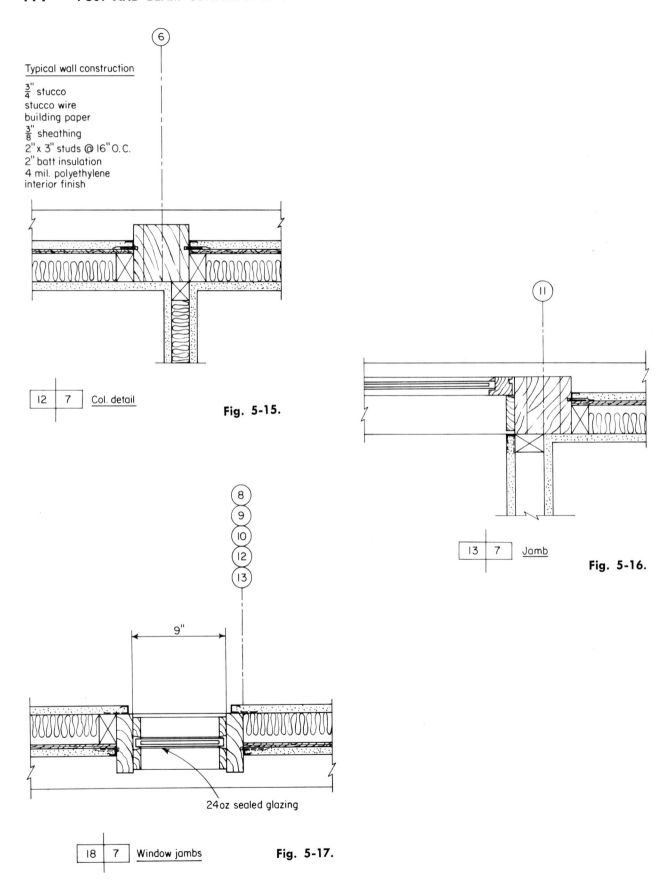

Typical wall construction

$\frac{3}{4}$" stucco
stucco wire
building paper
$\frac{3}{8}$" sheathing
2" x 3" studs @ 16" O.C.
2" batt insulation
4 mil. polyethylene
interior finish

| 12 | 7 | Col. detail |

Fig. 5-15.

| 13 | 7 | Jamb |

Fig. 5-16.

9"

24oz sealed glazing

| 18 | 7 | Window jambs |

Fig. 5-17.

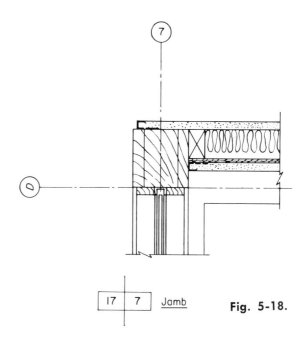

17	7	Jamb

Fig. 5-18.

1" x 4" V—joint T and G cedar
horizontal blocking @ 24" O.C.

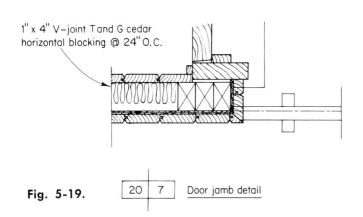

Fig. 5-19.

20	7

Door jamb detail

Entrance corner detail

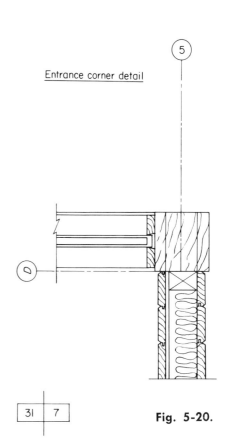

31	7

Fig. 5-20.

At Fig. 5.21 is shown the north (front) elevation with its Bi-Fold garage doors. Note the underpinning to the garage and also to the below ground concrete wall of a Games Room which is not shown on our restricted plan dwgs.

At Fig. 5.22 is shown the south elevation with its 8" concrete garage wall and sealed glazing above. This is 40'-0" north of the house wall. Check on Fig. 5.2, page 106. The two-story house wall is for the living room and also the upper floor of the den, room 202. Note the balustrades on the decking of the den. Examine this part of the bldg very carefully by checking the plans and the elevations. It is very important that you understand the structural details for this part of the house. The upper floor is directly accessible from the sidewalk of the street without steps.

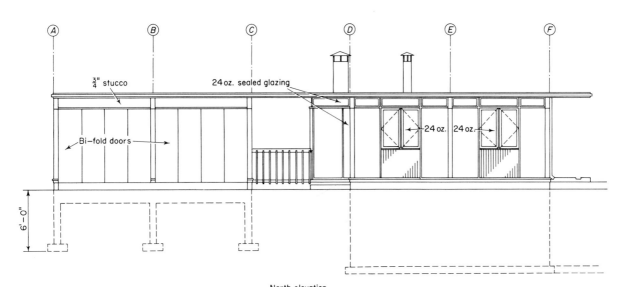

North elevation

Fig. 5-21.

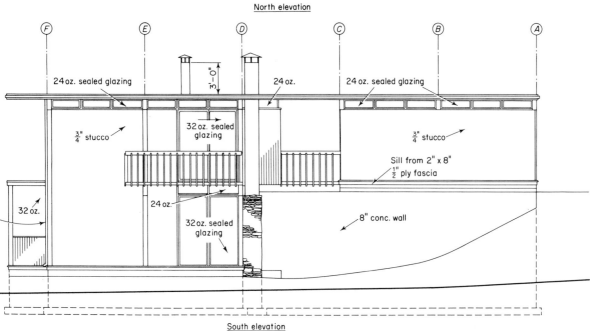

South elevation

Fig. 5-22.

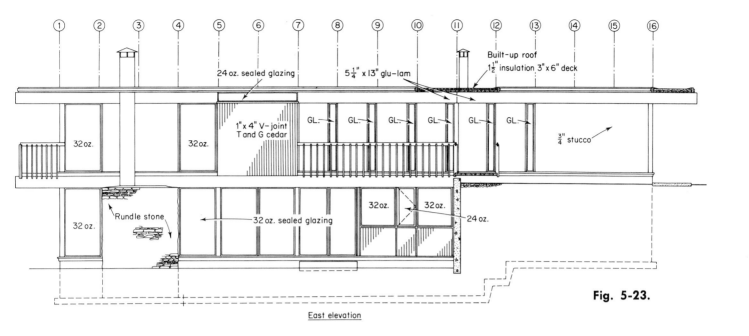

Fig. 5-23.

East elevation

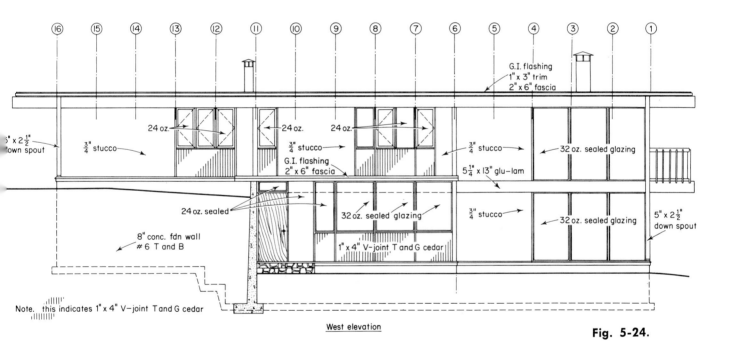

West elevation

Fig. 5-24.

At Fig. 5.23 is shown the east elevation with the concrete garage wall; all the remainder of the house from col lines 1 thru 11 correspond with the portion of the restricted plans shown. This elevation also shows the chimney, built with local Rundel stone. Note the balcony extension from the den, room 202. Visible from the balustrades of the den is the living room below. See plan, page 110.

At Fig. 5.24 is shown the west elevation with the retaining wall section. Time should be profitably spent studying the plans and the four elevations. You may locate any point on either the plans or the elevations from the col lines. Note very carefully the glu-lam framing, the floors, and the roofing for this home and relate all these to the detail dwgs.

117

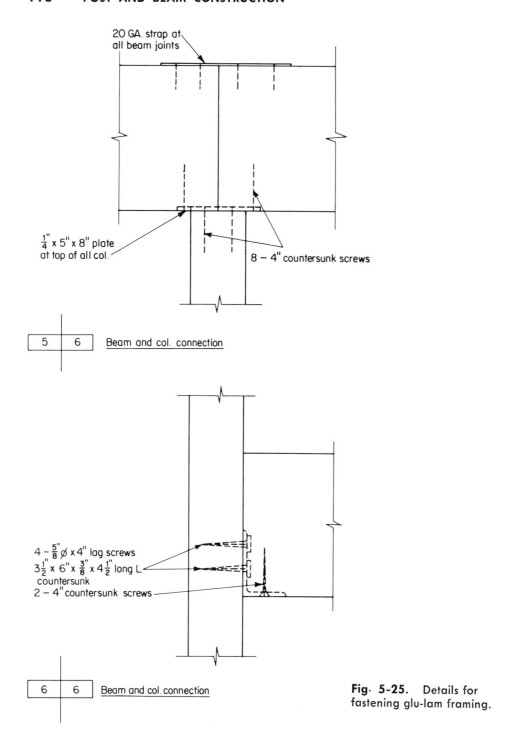

20 GA. strap at all beam joints

$\frac{1}{4}$" x 5" x 8" plate at top of all col.

8 – 4" countersunk screws

| 5 | 6 | Beam and col. connection

4 – $\frac{5}{8}$" ∅ x 4" lag screws

$3\frac{1}{2}$" x 6" x $\frac{3}{8}$" x $4\frac{1}{2}$" long L countersunk

2 – 4" countersunk screws

| 6 | 6 | Beam and col. connection

Fig. 5-25. Details for fastening glu-lam framing.

Sec 5/6 and 6/6 show the fastening devices for the glu-lam framing. They are efficient, simple, and easy to assemble. It is such construction details that keep bldg costs to a minimum. See Fig. 5.25.

Sec 1/6 shows a building section between col lines D-E-F. There is a lot of detail on this dwg from the underpinning to the roof. Note the floor levels and the glu-lam beams; examine the detail thoroughly, and then locate it on the plan. See Fig. 5.26.

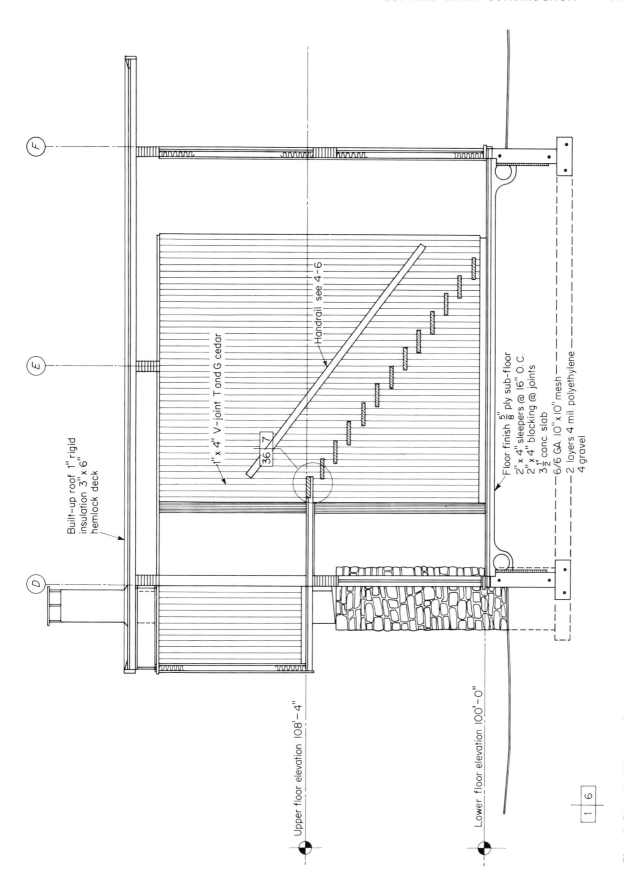

Built-up roof 1" rigid
insulation 3" x 6"
hemlock deck

Handrail see 4–6

1" x 4" V-joint T and G cedar

36 7

Floor finish $\frac{5}{8}$" ply sub-floor
2" x 4" sleepers @ 16" O. C.
2" x 4" blocking @ joints
$3\frac{1}{2}$" conc. slab
6/6 GA. 10" x 10" mesh
2 layers 4 mil polyethylene
4 gravel

Upper floor elevation 108'–4"

Lower floor elevation 100'–0"

1 6

Fig. 5-26. Building section.

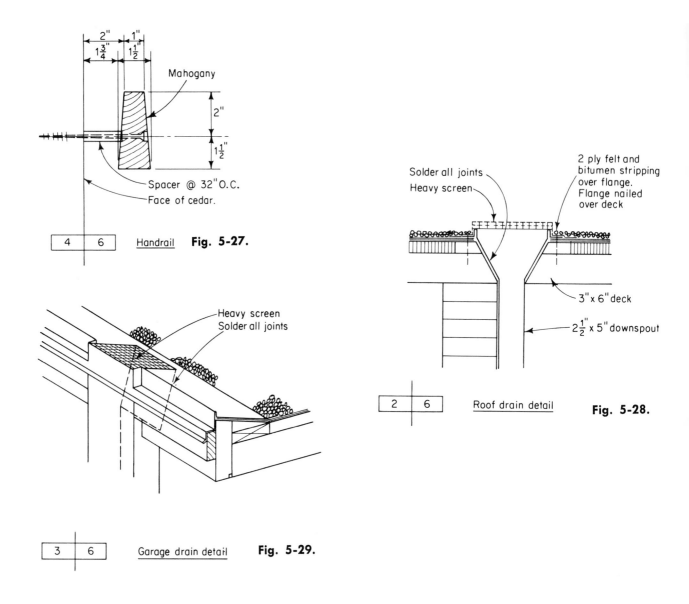

2"
1¾"
1"
1½"

Mahogany

2"

1½"

Spacer @ 32" O.C.
Face of cedar.

| 4 | 6 |

Handrail **Fig. 5-27.**

Heavy screen
Solder all joints

| 3 | 6 |

Garage drain detail **Fig. 5-29.**

Solder all joints
Heavy screen

2 ply felt and
bitumen stripping
over flange.
Flange nailed
over deck

3" x 6" deck

2½" x 5" downspout

| 2 | 6 |

Roof drain detail **Fig. 5-28.**

Sec 4/6 shows the stair handrail. This is a small but important item; it is contrary to the Building Code to erect a staircase without a handrail. Consider the quantities and types of hardware for a hospital block. Some day it may be your job to detail some of this very expensive material. See Fig. 5.27.

Sec 2/6 shows a typical down spout with a heavy screen. Birds nesting in sewer vent pipes have been known to be the direct cause of some very serious sewer gas explosions. It is a detail to remember that could affect public health and safety. Study your local Building Code. See Fig. 5.28.

Sec 3/6 shows a typical garage roof drain which is also provided with a heavy screen. See Fig. 5.29.

Secs 24/7 and 25/7 respectively show the entrance base and head details up to and including the G.I. flashing for the roof. Note the floor and roof timber construction. See Fig. 5.30.

Secs 15/7 and 16/7 respectively show the wall base and head detail; without such details it would be impossible to build the home. Note the double T & G (tongue and groove) floor and roof decking. See Fig. 5.31.

120

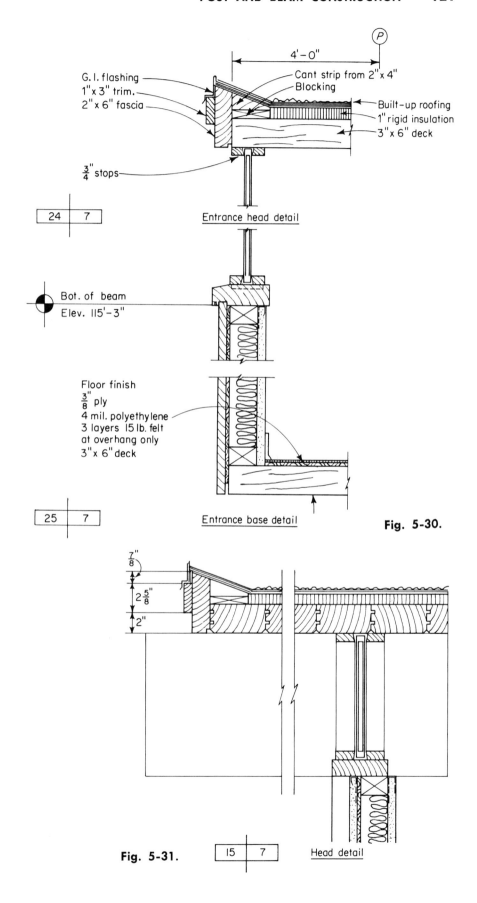

G. I. flashing
1" x 3" trim.
2" x 6" fascia

Cant strip from 2" x 4"
Blocking
Built-up roofing
1" rigid insulation
3" x 6" deck

4'-0"

$\frac{3}{4}$" stops

24 | 7

Entrance head detail

Bot. of beam
Elev. 115'-3"

Floor finish
$\frac{3}{8}$" ply
4 mil. polyethylene
3 layers 15 lb. felt
at overhang only
3" x 6" deck

25 | 7

Entrance base detail

Fig. 5-30.

$\frac{7}{8}$"

$2\frac{5}{8}$"

2"

Fig. 5-31.

15 | 7

Head detail

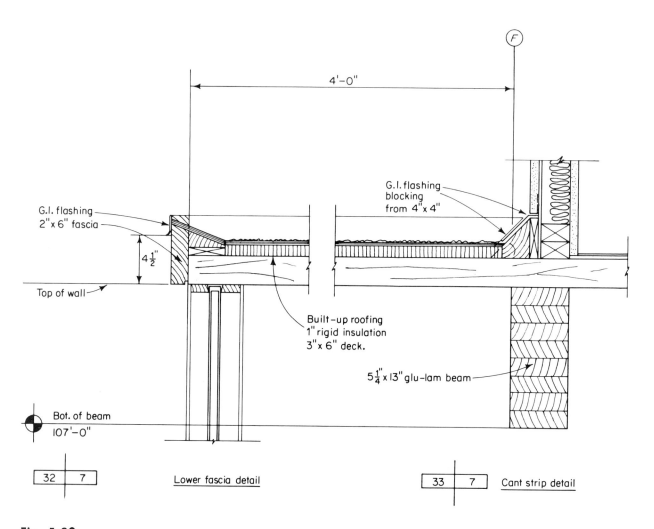

G.I. flashing
2"x 6" fascia

4½"

Top of wall

4'-0"

F

G.I. flashing
blocking
from 4"x 4"

Built-up roofing
1" rigid insulation
3"x 6" deck.

5¼"x 13" glu-lam beam

Bot. of beam
107'-0"

| 32 | 7 |

Lower fascia detail

| 33 | 7 |

Cant strip detail

Fig. 5-32.

Secs 32/7 and 33/7 respectively show the lower fascia and the roof cant strip detail. See Fig. 5.32.

Review this chapter. It is deserving of careful study not only for the structural details but also for the positioning of the house. It faces north, with the lower floor below ground at the front and the garage and retaining walls making an excellent break from winter's below zero temperatures.

ASSIGNMENT:

A. *Resolve in the following order.*
1. Using a scale of ½" to 1'-0", draw the plot plan.
2. Locate and show all existing grade elevations in black.
3. Below the existing grade elevations show all new elevations in red.
4. Draw east-west grid lines thru existing elevations.
5. Draw a straight line of similar length to the eastern boundary to represent grade level 100'-0".

6. Draw on this line in black a profile of the existing grade elevations.

7. Impose on this line in red the new grade elevations.

8. Repeat for the other three boundary lines.

B. Using 150 words or less, state why the contour of the land was changed.

C. Using plans shown at Figs. 5.6 and 5.14 on pages 110 and 113 and elevations shown at Figs. 5.22 and 5.23 pages 116 ando 117, make a freehand, southeast perspective sketch of the house.

6 CURTAINWALLS

In this chapter we are going to study curtainwall details. It is most important to keep abreast with this ever evolving concept of multi-story or single-story wall construction. Manufacturers research proceeds unremittingly, and office files should be kept up to date with released information. Critical points for detailing are: sufficient strength in framing members, anchorage, and joint sealers; the last presents the greatest problem.

The following material was obtained from Ceco Steel Products and is published with permission.

Fig. 6.1 shows a section numbered elevation and detail dwgs of panel arrangements, ventilating areas, fixed windows, and steel standardized sections which are readily available. Almost limitless treatment of vertical and horizontal sight lines is obtainable with structural members.

Mullions (intermediate perpendicular members) are constructed to carry the weight of the curtainwall system and also to withstand wind loads of either 15 p.s.f. or 20 p.s.f. as specified. Porcelain steel panels of the box or laminated type are manufactured with current specifications of the Porcelain Enamel Institute.

MULTISTORY CONSTRUCTION

Examine Figs. 6.2 and 6.3 and note:
(a) sect 1 shows a roof and head assembly of the curtainwall with the insulation panel well bedded with caulking compound. The wall can be anchored to any type of roof or flat arch.

MULTI-STORY CONSTRUCTION

Aluminum / Grid-type / Series 1100

Installation details • Quarter-size

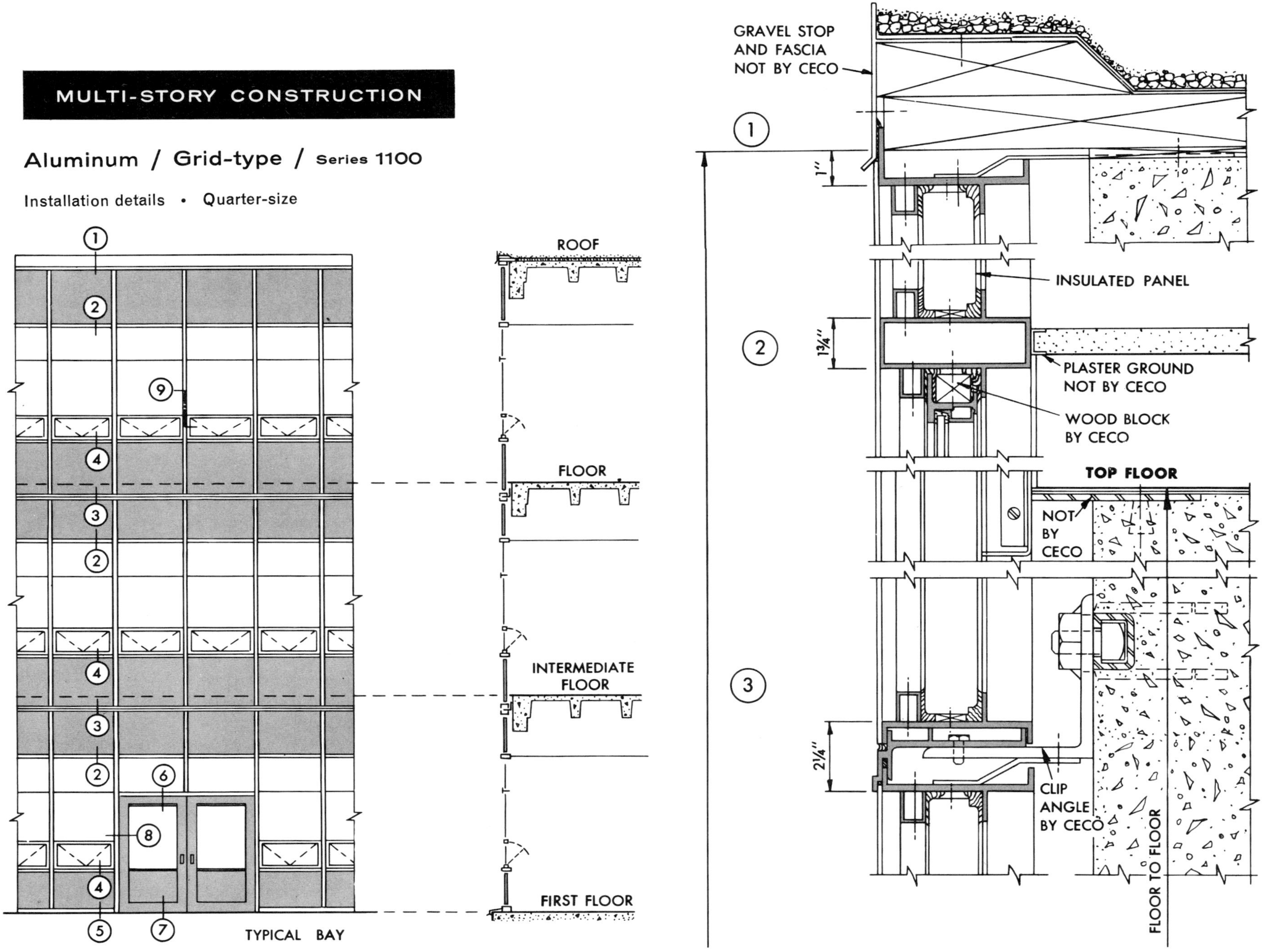
1
2
9
4
3
2
4
3
2
6
8
4
5
7
TYPICAL BAY
ROOF
FLOOR
INTERMEDIATE FLOOR
FIRST FLOOR
GRAVEL STOP AND FASCIA NOT BY CECO
1
1"
2
1¾"
INSULATED PANEL
PLASTER GROUND NOT BY CECO
WOOD BLOCK BY CECO
TOP FLOOR
NOT BY CECO
3
2¼"
CLIP ANGLE BY CECO
FLOOR TO FLOOR

Fig. 6-1.

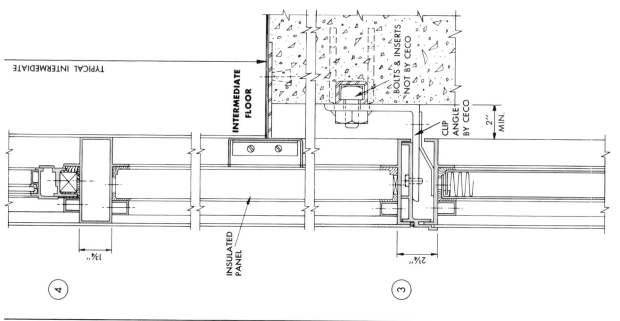

TYPICAL INTERMEDIATE

INTERMEDIATE FLOOR

BOLTS & INSERTS NOT BY CECO

CLIP ANGLE BY CECO

2" MIN.

INSULATED PANEL

1⅜"

2¼"

④

③

OPENING DIMENSION

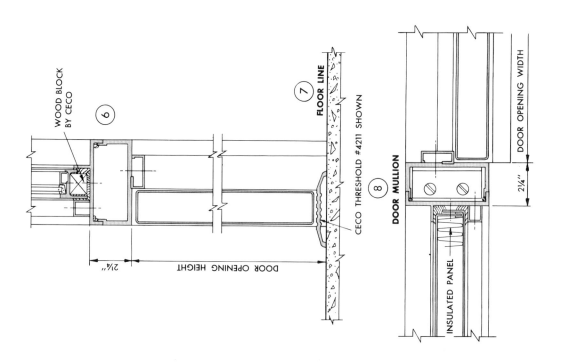

WOOD BLOCK BY CECO

⑥

2¼"

DOOR OPENING HEIGHT

FLOOR LINE

CECO THRESHOLD #4211 SHOWN

⑦

DOOR MULLION

⑧

DOOR OPENING WIDTH

2¼"

INSULATED PANEL

Fig. 6-2.

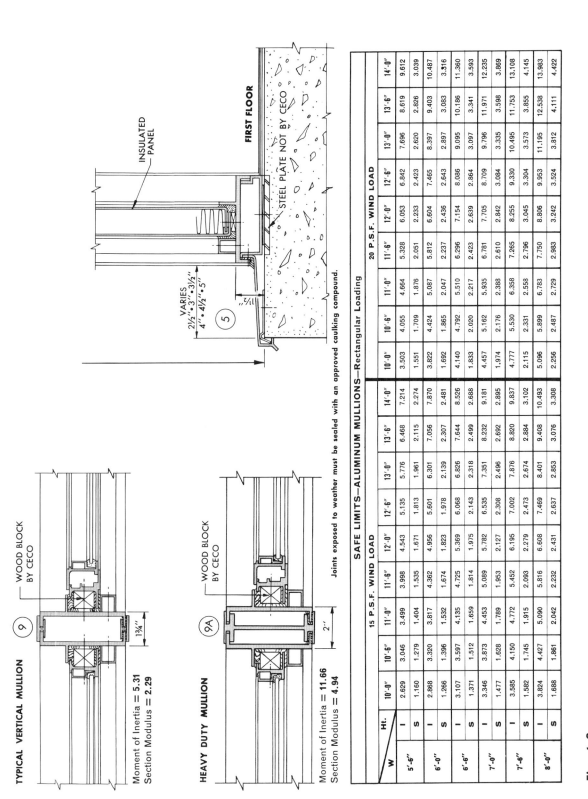

TYPICAL VERTICAL MULLION ⑨

WOOD BLOCK BY CECO

1¾"

Moment of Inertia = 5.31
Section Modulus = 2.29

HEAVY DUTY MULLION ⑨ᴬ

WOOD BLOCK BY CECO

2"

Moment of Inertia = 11.66
Section Modulus = 4.94

INSULATED PANEL

FIRST FLOOR

STEEL PLATE NOT BY CECO

VARIES
2½"•3"•3½"
4"•4½"•5"

1½"

⑤

Joints exposed to weather must be sealed with an approved caulking compound.

SAFE LIMITS—ALUMINUM MULLIONS—Rectangular Loading

W	Ht.	15 P.S.F. WIND LOAD									20 P.S.F. WIND LOAD								
		10'-0"	10'-6"	11'-0"	11'-6"	12'-0"	12'-6"	13'-0"	13'-6"	14'-0"	10'-0"	10'-6"	11'-0"	11'-6"	12'-0"	12'-6"	13'-0"	13'-6"	14'-0"
5'-6"	I	2.629	3.046	3.499	3.998	4.543	5.135	5.776	6.468	7.214	3.503	4.055	4.664	5.328	6.053	6.842	7.696	8.619	9.612
	S	1.160	1.279	1.404	1.535	1.671	1.813	1.961	2.115	2.274	1.551	1.709	1.876	2.051	2.233	2.423	2.620	2.826	3.039
6'-0"	I	2.868	3.320	3.817	4.362	4.956	5.601	6.301	7.056	7.870	3.822	4.424	5.087	5.812	6.604	7.465	8.397	9.403	10.487
	S	1.266	1.396	1.532	1.674	1.823	1.978	2.139	2.307	2.481	1.692	1.865	2.047	2.237	2.436	2.643	2.897	3.083	3.316
6'-6"	I	3.107	3.597	4.135	4.725	5.369	6.068	6.826	7.644	8.526	4.140	4.792	5.510	6.296	7.154	8.086	9.095	10.186	11.360
	S	1.371	1.512	1.659	1.814	1.975	2.143	2.318	2.499	2.688	1.833	2.020	2.217	2.423	2.639	2.864	3.097	3.341	3.593
7'-0"	I	3.346	3.873	4.453	5.089	5.782	6.535	7.351	8.232	9.181	4.457	5.162	5.935	6.781	7.705	8.709	9.796	11.971	12.235
	S	1.477	1.628	1.789	1.953	2.127	2.308	2.496	2.692	2.895	1.974	2.176	2.388	2.610	2.842	3.084	3.335	3.598	3.869
7'-6"	I	3.585	4.150	4.772	5.452	6.195	7.002	7.876	8.820	9.837	4.777	5.530	6.358	7.265	8.255	9.330	10.495	11.753	13.108
	S	1.582	1.745	1.915	2.093	2.279	2.473	2.674	2.884	3.102	2.115	2.331	2.558	2.796	3.045	3.304	3.573	3.855	4.145
8'-0"	I	3.824	4.427	5.090	5.816	6.608	7.469	8.401	9.408	10.493	5.096	5.899	6.783	7.750	8.806	9.953	11.195	12.538	13.983
	S	1.688	1.861	2.042	2.232	2.431	2.637	2.853	3.076	3.308	2.256	2.487	2.729	2.983	3.242	3.524	3.812	4.111	4.422

Fig. 6-3.

(b) sect 2 shows a horizontal member of a window frame. Observe the wood strip under the insulated panel and above the glass.

(c) sect 3 shows the curtainwall assembly anchored to a floor. The total depth of sects 2 and 3 are different. Note why!

(d) sect 4 shows the btm rail of the ventilator sash.

(e) sect 5 shows the first floor sill assembly and the notation of the variants.

(f) sect 6 and 7 show the door frame head, with the door section below. Pay special attention to the thorough caulking of the transom window (over the door). The threshold is shown below the door and there are variants.

(g) sect 8 shows a door mullion accommodating an insulated panel and hinged door.

(h) sect 9 shows a typical mullion and sect 9A shows a heavy duty mullion. The type selected for any project would meet the engineering requirements of any structure in its particular climatic area.

All principal sects of aluminum curtainwalls are extruded from aluminum alloy having a tensile strength of not less than 22,000 p.s.i.

All sects of steel curtainwall are fabricated from hot rolled new billet steel.

These dwgs present a maximum of readily assimilated detail clarity with a minimum but sufficiency of words. *They are worthy of emulation.*

HEAD AND SILL CONDITIONS

Fig. 6.4 shows the head and sill closures for insulated panels. An important point for detailing and specification writing is the notation of continuous steel angles (miscellaneous metal work). This is usually shown as a schedule on architectural dwgs. *The detailing of miscellaneous metal work on all dwgs is most important* and amounts to a very considerable expense in construction costs. Note carefully the provision allowed for expansion on all curtainwall systems.

STEEL MULLIONS

Figs. 6.5 and 6.6 show steel mullion details and a table of safe limit with rectangular loading.

ASSIGNMENT:

Research six different types of curtainwalls, obtain manufacturers' literature, state which type you prefer, and give your reasons.

HEAD AND SILL CONDITIONS

Steel

Installation details • Quarter-size

The head and sill closures shown on these pages are typical of the conditions often encountered in actual construction. As head and sill closures are such an important part of a successful curtainwall, they should receive the same care in design and installation as the vertical mullion anchors. Each building design should be reviewed and analyzed as to conditions encountered and a decision made as to whether the head and sill closures are to be set before or after the mullions and windows. Head and sill conditions are modified to fit each situation. Head

closures are designed to be flexible, with consideration given to two important points—adjustment so the closures can be positioned correctly and provision for vertical expansion of the curtainwall system.

Head and sill closures should be installed in accordance with the curtainwall manufacturer's instructions, because the final position of the closures must be straight, level and in alignment with anchors and sub-sills below. Consult the Ceco district office for further information.

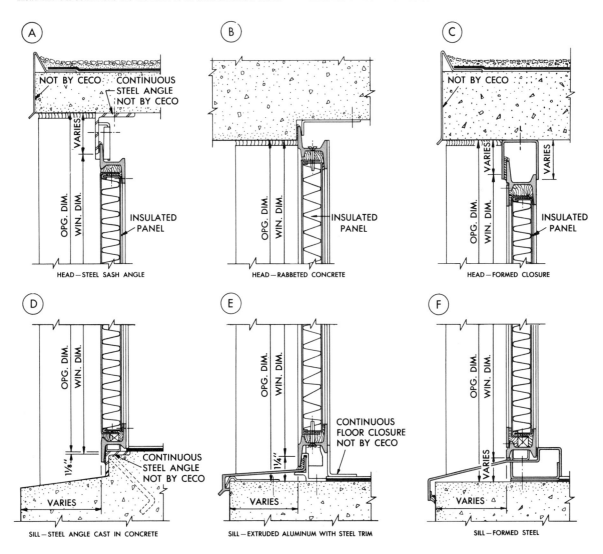

Fig. 6-4.

129

MULLION DETAILS

Steel Mullions

Half-size sections

The tables on the facing page show safe limits based on a horizontal load of 15 and 20 lbs. per sq. ft. and maximum deflection of 1/175 of span. In some areas, 15 lbs. per sq. ft. is adequate for one-story buildings. Mullion heights listed in the tables are established conservative dimensions for the center-to-center widths shown. Any departure from these schedules should be submitted to company engineers for specific job load calculations. Heights given in these tables are for single spans unsupported between anchorages.

In using the tables, obtain the moment of inertia (I) and the section modulus (S) for the width and height required. Then select a mullion detail with I and S factors of equal or higher capacity. For instance, mullion C2 accommodates the 12'-0" height and the 4'-0" width at 20 P.S.F. wind load because the C2 I and S are greater than 1.513 and .864, respectively.

Black areas in the details have been used in determining moments of inertia (I) and section modulus (S).

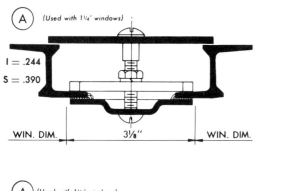

(A) (Used with 1¼" windows)

I = .244
S = .390

WIN. DIM. — 3⅛" — WIN. DIM.

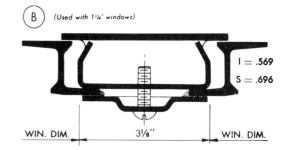

(B) (Used with 1¼" windows)

I = .569
S = .696

WIN. DIM. — 3⅛" — WIN. DIM.

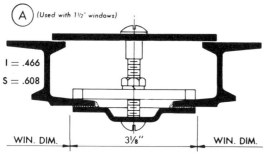

(A) (Used with 1½" windows)

I = .466
S = .608

WIN. DIM. — 3⅛" — WIN. DIM.

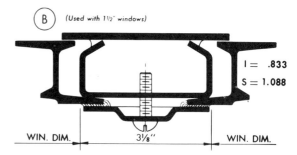

(B) (Used with 1½" windows)

I = .833
S = 1.088

WIN. DIM. — 3⅛" — WIN. DIM.

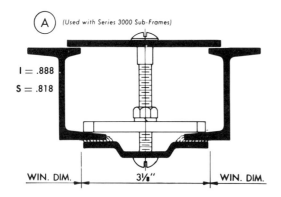

(A) (Used with Series 3000 Sub-Frames)

I = .888
S = .818

WIN. DIM. — 3⅛" — WIN. DIM.

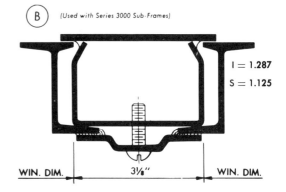

(B) (Used with Series 3000 Sub-Frames)

I = 1.287
S = 1.125

WIN. DIM. — 3⅛" — WIN. DIM.

Fig. 6-5.

SAFE LIMITS—STEEL MULLIONS—Rectangular Loading

W.	HT.	15 P.S.F. WIND LOAD									20 P.S.F. WIND LOAD														
		8'-0"	8'-6"	9'-0"	9'-6"	10'-0"	10'-6"	11'-0"	11'-6"	12'-0"	8'-0"	8'-6"	9'-0"	9'-6"	10'-0"	10'-6"	11'-0"	11'-6"	12'-0"	12'-6"	13'-0"	13'-6"	14'-0"	14'-6"	15'-0"
3'-6"	I	.293	.352	.418	.492	.574	.664	.763	.872	.991	.392	.470	.558	.656	.766	.886	1.019	1.164	1.323	1.496	1.682	1.884	2.101	2.335	2.585
	S	.250	.283	.317	.353	.392	.432	.474	.518	.564	.336	.379	.425	.473	.525	.578	.635	.694	.756	.820	.887	.956	1.029	1.103	1.181
3'-9"	I	.314	.377	.448	.527	.615	.711	.818	.935	1.062	.420	.504	.598	.703	.821	.950	1.092	1.248	1.418	1.603	1.803	2.019	2.252	2.502	2.770
	S	.268	.303	.340	.379	.420	.463	.508	.555	.604	.359	.406	.455	.507	.562	.619	.680	.743	.809	.878	.949	1.024	1.101	1.181	1.264
4'-0"	I	.335	.402	.478	.562	.656	.759	.873	.997	1.133	.448	.537	.638	.750	.876	1.014	1.165	1.332	1.513	1.710	1.924	2.155	2.403	2.670	2.956
	S	.286	.323	.362	.404	.448	.493	.542	.592	.645	.384	.433	.486	.541	.600	.661	.726	.793	.864	.937	1.014	1.093	1.176	1.261	1.350
4'-6"	I	.377	.453	.538	.632	.738	.854	.982	1.122	1.275	.504	.604	.718	.844	.985	1.140	1.311	1.498	1.702	1.923	2.164	2.423	2.702	3.002	3.324
	S	.322	.364	.408	.454	.504	.555	.609	.666	.725	.432	.487	.546	.609	.675	.744	.816	.892	.972	1.054	1.140	1.230	1.323	1.419	1.518
5'-0"	I	.419	.503	.597	.703	.820	.949	1.091	1.247	1.416	.558	.669	.794	.934	1.090	1.261	1.450	1.657	1.883	2.128	2.394	2.681	2.990	3.323	3.678
	S	.358	.404	.453	.505	.560	.617	.677	.740	.806	.480	.541	.607	.676	.750	.826	.907	.991	1.080	1.171	1.267	1.366	1.470	1.576	1.687

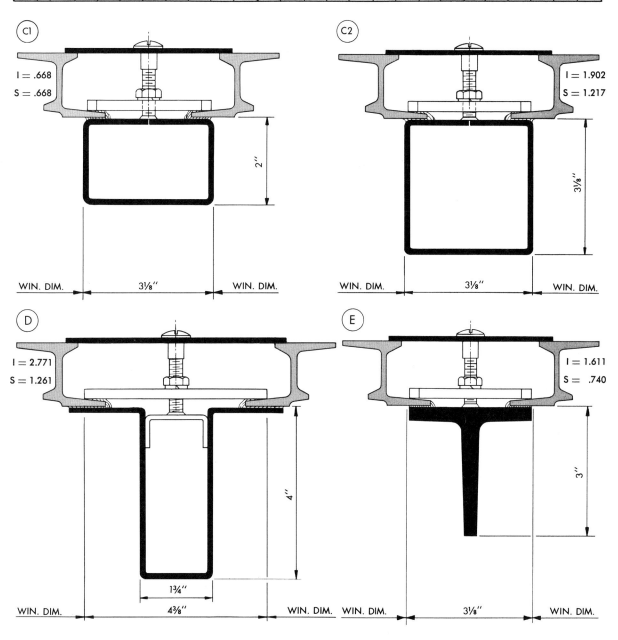

C1
I = .668
S = .668
2"
WIN. DIM.   3⅛"   WIN. DIM.

C2
I = 1.902
S = 1.217
3⅛"
WIN. DIM.   3⅛"   WIN. DIM.

D
I = 2.771
S = 1.261
4"
1¾"
WIN. DIM.   4⅜"   WIN. DIM.

E
I = 1.611
S = .740
3"
WIN. DIM.   3⅛"   WIN. DIM.

Fig. 6-6.

WINDOWS FOR AN ADMINISTRATION OFFICE

The following material was supplied by, and is published with the permission of, Mr. H. F. Malkin, Principal Architect, and Mr. J. Griffiths, Assistant Director, Administration and Finance, Public Buildings Department, Adelaide, South Australia.

Plan and elevation

Fig. 6.7 shows part plan and elevation of office windows. *Note:*

(a) *plan* dimension lines c to c (center to center)
(b) standard 5'-7¼" width of door and window centers
(c) timber threshold (See Fig. 6.12, sect 2/4)
(d) 12" × 12" steel fireproofed col. Trace grids M and 7
(e) sect mark 1/41 (See Fig. 6.8)
   sect mark 2/41 (See Fig. 6.11)
   sect mark 3/41 (See Fig. 6.8)
(f) *elevation* F.F.L. (finished floor level) 254.65'
(g) sect mark 4/41 horizontal thru bookcase (See Fig. 6.10)
(h) sect marks 5/41, 6/41, and 7/41. Sect thru window sill and crash bar. See Fig. 6.9 (9/41)

Window vertical sections

Fig. 6.8 shows two vertical window sections. Read with Fig. 6.7. *Note:*

(a) sect 1/41 of typical wall and bookcase
(b) floor assembly and dim
(c) walls have black vitrolite base panels under and ½" polished plate glass over
(d) sect 3/41 of sliding door with plate glass throughout
(e) the aligning of crash bar of door and panels. *This is very important detailing.*
(f) 1'-3¼" overall to col.

Door vertical sections

Fig. 6.9 shows sect thru sliding door. Read with Fig. 6.7. *Note:*

(a) the floor assembly covers the following trades: concrete layer, carpenter, painter, metal worker, glazier, plasterer, and carpet layer; the latter is not in the original contract. *Study this dwg: a detailer must be very knowledgeable in his field, he must have an intimate knowledge of trades, and he must keep abreast with new materials and technologies.*

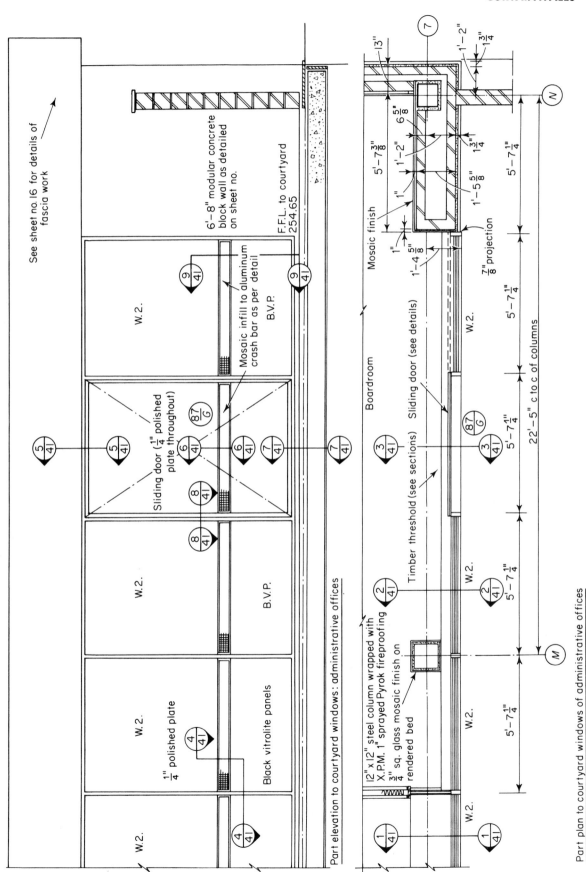

See sheet no.16 for details of fascia work

6'-8" modular concrete block wall as detailed on sheet no.

Mosaic infill to aluminum crash bar as per detail

B.V.P.

F.F.L. to courtyard 254.65

Sliding door ($\frac{1}{4}$" polished plate throughout)

W. 2.

$\frac{87}{G}$

W. 2.

B.V.P.

$\frac{1}{4}$" polished plate

Black vitrolite panels

W. 2.

Part elevation to courtyard windows: administrative offices

Mosaic finish

5'-7$\frac{3}{8}$"

13"

1'-2"

$\frac{3}{4}$"

1'-2"

6$\frac{5}{8}$"

1$\frac{3}{4}$"

1"

1'-5$\frac{5}{8}$"

5'-7$\frac{1}{4}$"

N

1"

1'-4$\frac{5}{8}$"

$\frac{7}{8}$" projection

Boardroom

Sliding door (see details)

W. 2.

5'-7$\frac{1}{4}$"

22'-5" c to c of columns

$\frac{87}{G}$

5'-7$\frac{1}{4}$"

Timber threshold (see sections)

12"×12" steel column wrapped with X.P.M. 1" sprayed Pyrok fireproofing $\frac{3}{4}$" sq. glass mosaic finish on rendered bed

W. 2.

5'-7$\frac{1}{4}$"

W. 2.

M

W. 2.

5'-7$\frac{1}{4}$"

W. 2.

Part plan to courtyard windows of administrative offices

Fig. 6-7.

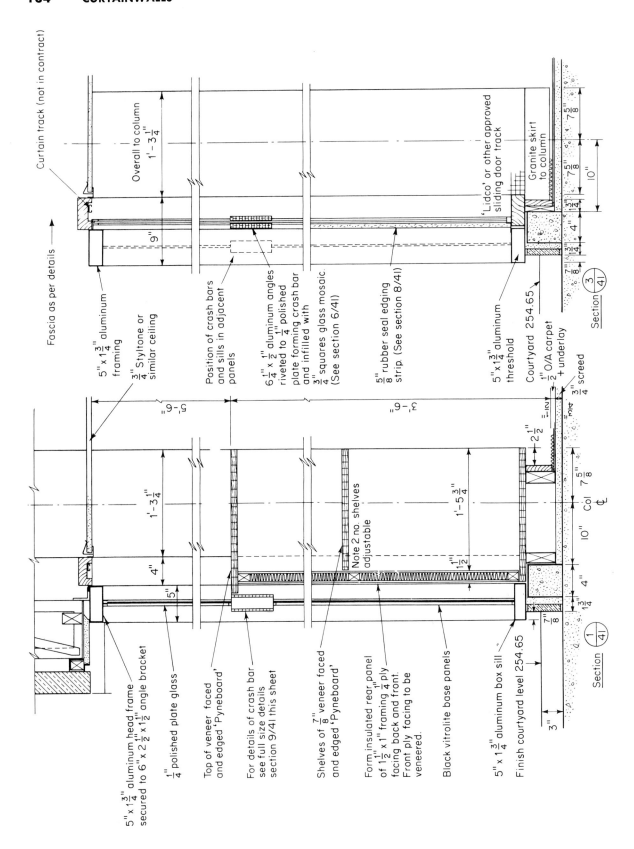

Curtain track (not in contract)

Fascia as per details

Overall to column 1'-3¼"

9"

'Lidco' or other approved sliding door track

Granite skirt to column

10"

7⅝" 7⅝" 7⅝"

3¾"

4"

¾"

7⅛"

Section 3/41

5" x 1¾" aluminum framing

¾" Styltone or similar ceiling

Position of crash bars and sills in adjacent panels

6¼" x ½" aluminum angles riveted to ¼" polished plate forming crash bar and infilled with ¾" squares glass mosaic. (See section 6/41)

⅝" rubber seal edging strip. (See section 8/41)

5" x1¾" aluminum threshold

Courtyard 254.65

½" O/A carpet + underlay

¾" screed

5'-6"

3'-6"

1'-3¼"

4"

5"

Note 2 no. shelves adjustable

1-5¾"

1½"

2½"

7⅝"

Col ₵

10"

4"

1¾"

7⅛"

Section 1/41

5" x 1¾" aluminum head frame secured to 6" x 2½" x 1½" angle bracket

¼" polished plate glass

Top of veneer faced and edged 'Pyneboard'

For details of crash bar see full size details section 9/41 this sheet

Shelves of ⅞" veneer faced and edged 'Pyneboard'

Form insulated rear panel of 1½" x 1" framing ¼" ply facing back and front. Front ply facing to be veneered.

Black vitrolite base panels

5" x 1¾" aluminum box sill

Finish courtyard level 254.65

3"

Fig. 6-8. Vertical window sections.

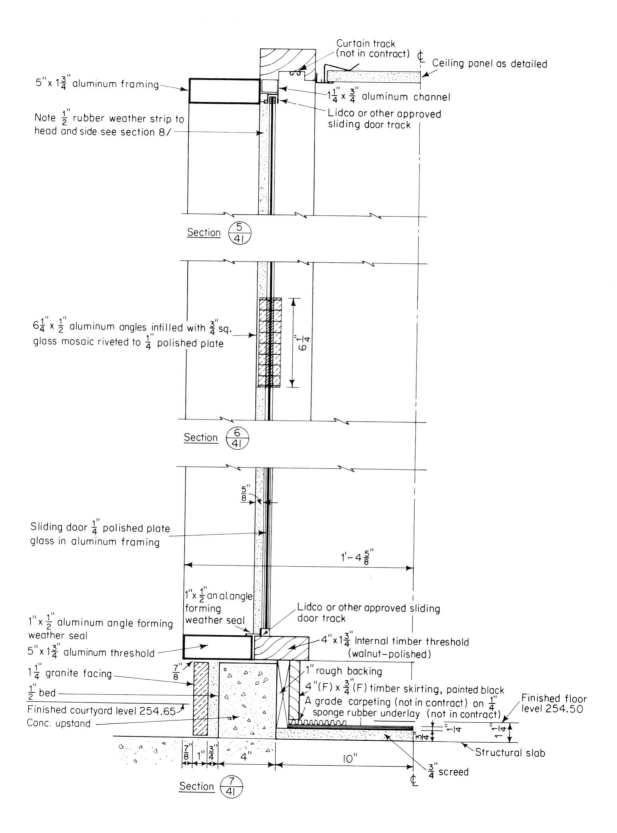

5" x 1¾" aluminum framing

Note ½" rubber weather strip to head and side see section 8/

Curtain track (not in contract)

Ceiling panel as detailed

1¼" x ¾" aluminum channel

Lidco or other approved sliding door track

Section 5/41

6¼" x ½" aluminum angles infilled with ¾" sq. glass mosaic riveted to ¼" polished plate

6¼"

Section 6/41

5/8"

Sliding door ¼" polished plate glass in aluminum framing

1'–4 5/8"

1" x ½" an al.angle forming weather seal

1" x ½" aluminum angle forming weather seal

5" x 1¾" aluminum threshold

Lidco or other approved sliding door track

4" x 1¾" Internal timber threshold (walnut–polished)

1¼" granite facing

½" bed

Finished courtyard level 254.65

Conc. upstand

7/8"

1" rough backing

4"(F) x ¾"(F) timber skirting, painted black

A grade carpeting (not in contract) on ¼" sponge rubber underlay (not in contract)

Finished floor level 254.50

Structural slab

7/8" 1" ¾" 4" 10"

¾" screed

Section 7/41

Fig. 6-9. Sliding door section.

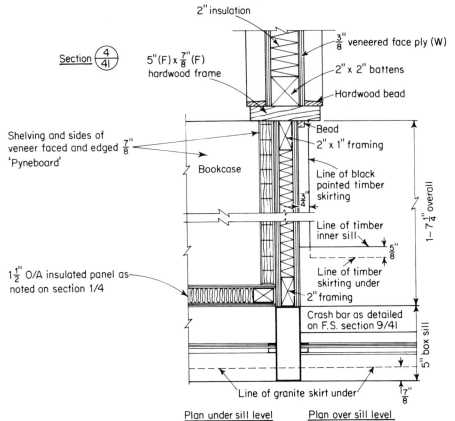

Section $\dfrac{4}{41}$

2" insulation

$\dfrac{3}{8}$" veneered face ply (W)

5"(F) x $\dfrac{7}{8}$"(F) hardwood frame

2" x 2" battens

Hardwood bead

Shelving and sides of veneer faced and edged $\dfrac{7}{8}$" 'Pyneboard'

Bead

2" x 1" framing

Bookcase

Line of black painted timber skirting

$\dfrac{3}{4}$"

$1-7\dfrac{1}{4}$" overall

Line of timber inner sill

$\dfrac{5}{8}$"

Line of timber skirting under

$1\dfrac{1}{2}$" O/A insulated panel as noted on section 1/4

2" framing

Crash bar as detailed on F.S. section 9/41

5" box sill

$\dfrac{7}{8}$"

Line of granite skirt under

Plan under sill level   Plan over sill level   **Fig. 6-10.**

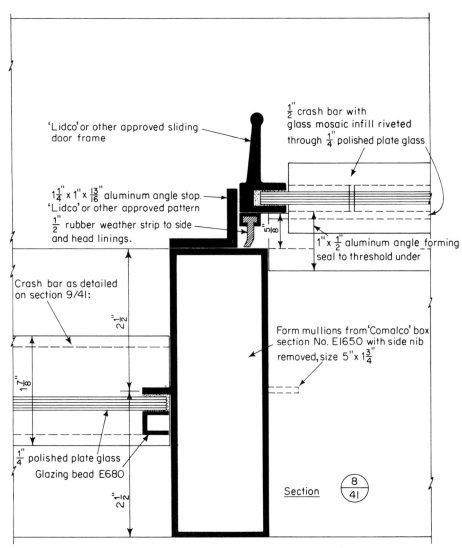

'Lidco' or other approved sliding door frame

$\dfrac{1}{2}$" crash bar with glass mosaic infill riveted through $\dfrac{1}{4}$" polished plate glass

$1\dfrac{1}{4}$" x 1" x $\dfrac{13}{16}$" aluminum angle stop. 'Lidco' or other approved pattern

$\dfrac{1}{2}$" rubber weather strip to side and head linings.

$\dfrac{5}{8}$"

1" x $\dfrac{1}{2}$" aluminum angle forming seal to threshold under

Crash bar as detailed on section 9/41:

$2\dfrac{1}{2}$"

Form mullions from 'Comalco' box section No. E1650 with side nib removed, size 5" x $1\dfrac{3}{4}$"

$1\dfrac{7}{8}$"

$\dfrac{1}{4}$" polished plate glass

Glazing bead E680

$2\dfrac{1}{2}$"

Section $\dfrac{8}{41}$

Fig. 6-11.

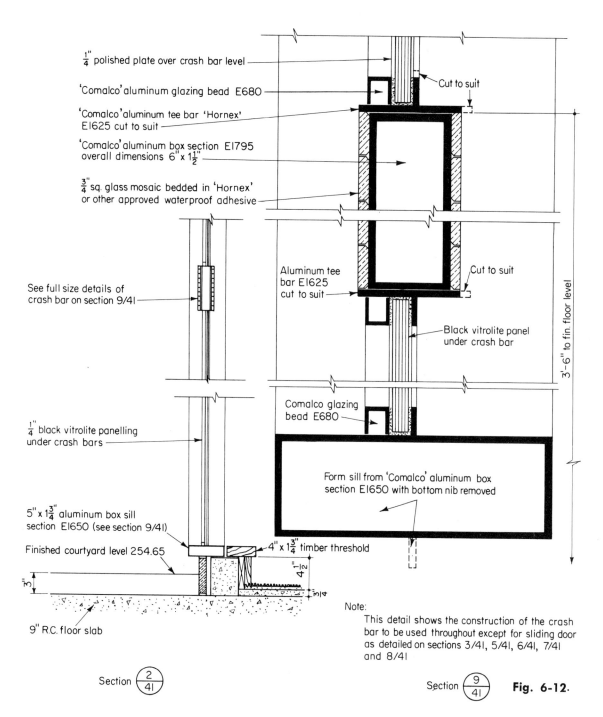

¼" polished plate over crash bar level

'Comalco' aluminum glazing bead E680

'Comalco' aluminum tee bar 'Hornex' E1625 cut to suit

'Comalco' aluminum box section E1795 overall dimensions 6" x 1½"

¾" sq. glass mosaic bedded in 'Hornex' or other approved waterproof adhesive

Cut to suit

See full size details of crash bar on section 9/41

Aluminum tee bar E1625 cut to suit

Cut to suit

Black vitrolite panel under crash bar

¼" black vitrolite panelling under crash bars

Comalco glazing bead E680

Form sill from 'Comalco' aluminum box section E1650 with bottom nib removed

5" x 1¾" aluminum box sill section E1650 (see section 9/41)

Finished courtyard level 254.65

4" x 1¾" timber threshold

9" R.C. floor slab

3'-6" to fin. floor level

Note:
This detail shows the construction of the crash bar to be used throughout except for sliding door as detailed on sections 3/41, 5/41, 6/41, 7/41 and 8/41

Section 2/41

Section 9/41   **Fig. 6-12.**

Wall horizontal sections

Fig. 6.10 shows two horizontal wall sections. Read with Fig. 6.7

Door jamb section

Fig. 6.11 shows a section thru the door jamb and sliding door. Read with Fig. 6.7.

Floor assembly and crash bar vertical sections

Fig. 6.12 shows floor asembly and crash bar section. *Note:*
(a) sect 4/41 floor assembly and relate 4″ × 1¾″ timber threshold to plan line on sect 2/41 of Fig. 6.7.

(b) sect 9/41 shows large detail of crash bar; the original was drawn to full size.

Examine these details very carefully. They are excellent, and the more they are studied the more apparent is the commendable detailing.

GLIDING DOOR PERMA-SHIELD

The following material is from the Anderson Corporation and is published with permission.

Fig. 6.13 shows the details for gliding doors. Part of the suggested specifications are as follows:

(a) Exterior surfaces of frame, entire surface of door panels are covered with white rigid vinyl (PVC). Wood core is treated with a toxic water repellent preservative. PVC screen head channel applied. Extruded anodized aluminum sill facing with PVC thermal barrier, stainless steel cap applied over operating door track.

(b) Door panels, 7⅞" thick, stop glazed with polished plate insulating glass, or tempered insulating glass. Left or right hand operating (viewed from outside) as specified, triple door right hand only.

(c) Weatherstripping, a combination of rigid vinyl (PVC), polypropylene woven pile, and flexible vinyl.

Examine the structural details for installation of these units in wood frame, brick veneer, or concrete block walls. The wood frame opening is supported by wood beams. The brick veneer is supported with an angle iron and wood beams, and the concrete block opening is supported by reinforcing rods placed in the concrete core of the arch blocks during construction. See the details and notice the clearance allowed between the head of the window and the rough opening in every case. *This is important.*

GLIDING PATIO WALL

Fig. 6.14 shows details for a gliding patio wall with hinged door, a combination that gives walk-out convenience with all-weather comfort. Note the sect references on the elevation, and commencing with A-A read all the details in alphabetical order and study the sections. Pay careful attention to the differences in the sill details of B-B and D-D and also to the alignment of the heads of the windows and door heads. The whole ensemble presents an excellence in detailing with no trace of extraneous matter.

FLEXIVENT WINDOWS

Fig. 6.15 shows a flexivent window detail. These sashes are manufactured in a number of sizes and combinations from a single sash to nine sashes in one frame. Where sashes are used in a combination of, say, two wide and

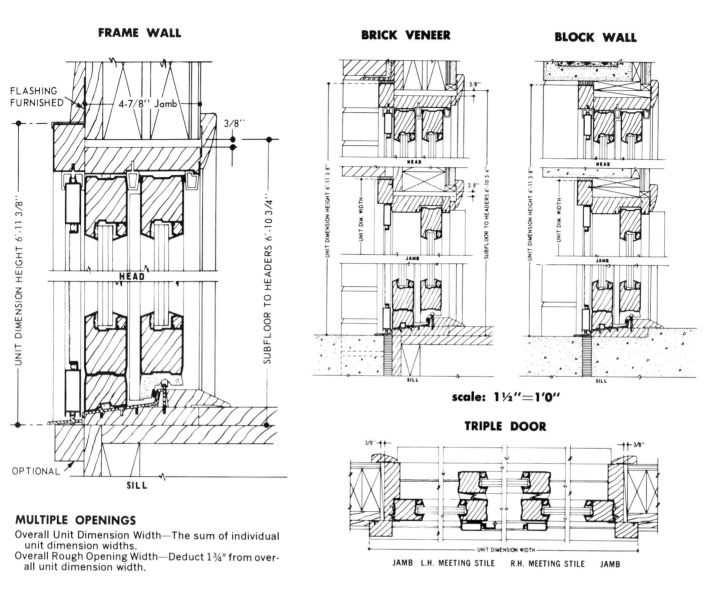

FRAME WALL

FLASHING FURNISHED

4-7/8" Jamb

3/8"

UNIT DIMENSION HEIGHT 6'-11 3/8"

SUBFLOOR TO HEADERS 6'-10 3/4"

HEAD

OPTIONAL

SILL

BRICK VENEER

3/8"

3/8"

UNIT DIMENSION HEIGHT 6'-11 3/8"

UNIT DIM. WIDTH

SUBFLOOR TO HEADERS 6'-10 3/4"

HEAD

JAMB

SILL

BLOCK WALL

UNIT DIMENSION HEIGHT 6'-11 3/8"

UNIT DIM. WIDTH

HEAD

JAMB

SILL

scale: 1½"=1'0"

MULTIPLE OPENINGS

Overall Unit Dimension Width—The sum of individual unit dimension widths.
Overall Rough Opening Width—Deduct 1¾" from overall unit dimension width.

TRIPLE DOOR

3/8"   3/8"

UNIT DIMENSION WIDTH

JAMB   L.H. MEETING STILE   R.H. MEETING STILE   JAMB

scale: 3"=1'0"

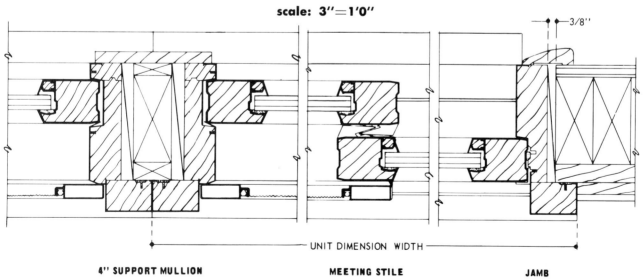

3/8"

UNIT DIMENSION WIDTH

4" SUPPORT MULLION   **MEETING STILE**   **JAMB**

Fig. 6-13.

139

Unit Sizes

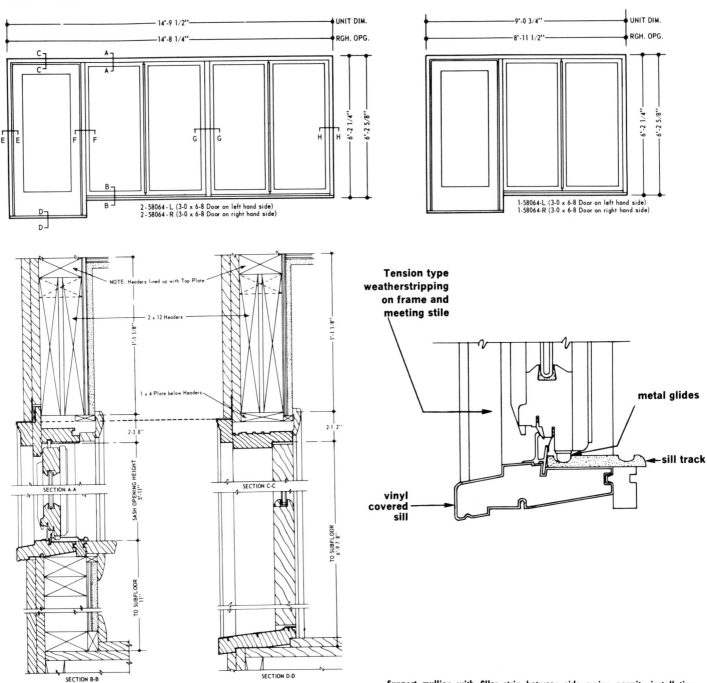

NOTE: Headers lined up with Top Plate

2 x 12 Headers

1 x 4 Plate below Headers

SECTION A-A

SECTION C-C

SECTION B-B

SECTION D-D

Vertical sections show how window and door line up on interior and exterior.

14'-9 1/2'' — UNIT DIM.
14'-8 1/4'' — RGH. OPG.

6'-2 1/4''
6'-2 5/8''

2 - 58064 - L (3-0 x 6-8 Door on left hand side)
2 - 58064 - R (3-0 x 6-8 Door on right hand side)

9'-0 3/4'' — UNIT DIM.
8'-11 1/2'' — RGH. OPG.

6'-2 1/4''
6'-2 5/8''

1-58064-L (3-0 x 6-8 Door on left hand side)
1-58064-R (3-0 x 6-8 Door on right hand side)

Tension type weatherstripping on frame and meeting stile

metal glides

sill track

vinyl covered sill

Support mullion with filler strip between side casing permits installation of Gliding Window without cutting lugs at head or sill. Use same rough openings as for single units.

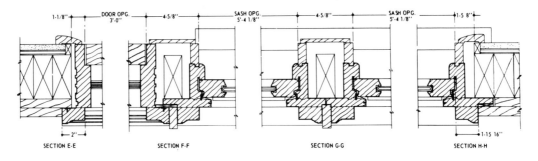

SECTION E-E

SECTION F-F

SECTION G-G

SECTION H-H

Fig. 6-14. Gliding patio wall detail.

140

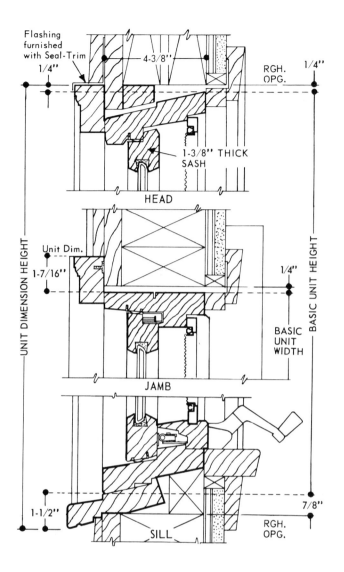

Flashing furnished with Seal-Trim

4-3/8"

1/4"

RGH. OPG.

1/4"

1-3/8" THICK SASH

HEAD

Unit Dim.
1-7/16"

1/4"

BASIC UNIT WIDTH

UNIT DIMENSION HEIGHT

BASIC UNIT HEIGHT

JAMB

1-1/2"

7/8"

RGH. OPG.

SILL

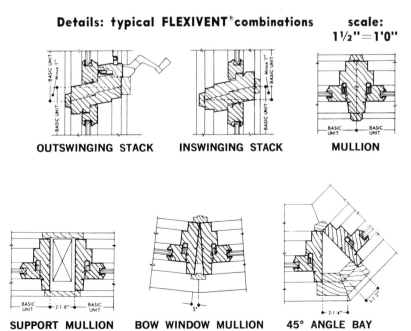

Details: typical FLEXIVENT®combinations   scale: 1½"=1'0"

BASIC UNIT — Minus 1"

BASIC UNIT

OUTSWINGING STACK

Minus 1"
BASIC UNIT

BASIC UNIT

INSWINGING STACK

BASIC UNIT

BASIC UNIT

MULLION

BASIC UNIT

2-1·8"

BASIC UNIT

SUPPORT MULLION

5°

BOW WINDOW MULLION

1·7·2"

2-1·4"

45° ANGLE BAY

Fig. 6-15. Flexivent window detail

141

three high, they are referred to on the dwgs as being stacked. See the typical flexivent vertical sections for sashes described as being outswinging stacked or inswinging stacked.

Pay special attention to the bow mullion and the 45° angle bay.

All architectural dwgs have window details. Please be reminded that they must be well done. Contractors are known to increase their bids when structural details are not readily understandable. What alternative have they?

MASONRY UNIT DETAILS 7

In this chapter we are going to examine a selection of structural details and suggested specifications for masonry unit reinforcing, control joints, adjustable wall ties, and parapet walls. The source of the following material is Dur-O-Wal National Inc.; it is published with permission.

REINFORCING IN MASONRY UNIT WALLS

Fig. 7.1 shows a selection of basic reinforcing applied to masonry unit walls. It must be clearly emphasized that apart from design, control joints, and reinforcing, the quality of mortar and workmanship is of paramount importance in controlling wall fractures. Fig. 7.1 and the accompanying data should be studied together.

REINFORCEMENT CENTERING, PLACING, SPLICING, AND SPACING

Figs. 7.2(a), 7.2(b), and 7.2(c) show how to center, place, splice, and space reinforcement in masonry unit walls. Pay very careful attention to correct lapping and extra reinforcing at openings.

As a point of departure for this discussion we list the following typical questions asked by architects:

■ **1.** "Should vertical control joints be used?"

■ **2.** "Should plaster be applied directly to concrete block in stack bond, reinforcing 16" on center?"

■ **3.** "What is the best treatment for hairline cracks in plaster that has been applied directly to concrete block?"

■ **4.** "How frequently would you recommend the use of vertical control in long block walls in excess of 12' in height?"

These questions involve many variables, and it is almost impossible to give pat answers. However, basically, all the questions deal with the problem of cracking, to which all types of masonry units are subject, in varying degrees, from the following causes acting separately or in combination:

■ **(a)** Unequal settlement or distortion of footings or structures supporting the masonry.

■ **(b)** Overstressing of masonry caused by external forces of unexpected severity, which may occasionally develop from earth pressures, earthquakes, hurricanes, etc.

■ **(c)** Abnormal distortions, especially expansion of pertinent elements such as structural frames, floors, and roofs.

■ **(d)** Volume change in masonry involving principally temperature and moisture shrinkage.

Items (a), (b), and (c) can be controlled by careful design, such as providing for adequate footings and foundations, and related design details.

The problem involved in item (d) has been summed up very well by R. E. Copeland, Consulting Engineer (formerly Director of Engineering for the National Concrete Masonry Association), in the following two paragraphs from a paper which appeared in the Journal of the American Concrete Institute.

"The subject of shrinkage and temperature stresses in masonry walls involves many separate phases, variable factors and complexities. It does not lend itself to neat mathematical solution. We know that masonry that is trying to contract due to internal changes, but is fully or partially prevented from doing so, will be stressed in tension and usually also in shear. We know that cracks form when these stresses exceed the strength of the masonry. Beyond this point we emerge into the field of theoretical speculation illumined only slightly by experimental data and systematic observation.

"The principal approaches to minimizing shrinkage and temperature cracking in concrete masonry include: (1) improving the dimensional stability of the concrete itself and of the masonry, (2) reducing residual shrinkage by the use of properly dried units, (3) controlling crack width by means of reinforcing, and (4) incorporating wall design details which allow the masonry to contract more freely and without being overstressed."

Improvement in regard to dimensional stability and residual shrinkage is definitely the responsibility of the masonry industry. Great strides have been made within the last few years and a continuing program of research is under way in this direction.

Practical experience indicates that control of crack width and the wall flexibility that allows masonry to contract more freely can both be achieved by architect and engineer in the design of a masonry wall — with a judicious use of horizontal Dur-o-wal joint reinforcement in combination with vertical control joints.

Horizontal joint reinforcement — when, where, and how much? In combination with how many control joints?

The amount of horizontal joint reinforcement to be used depends largely upon the type of mortar. When Type N mortar is used, there is a limit to the amount of stress load that mortar will carry. Wall panels designed with Type N mortar can be reinforced effectively up to the point where Standard weight Dur-o-wal is used every second course, or 16" o.c. The use of steel beyond this point would not appear to be justified. When using Type M or Type S mortar, however, the strength of the wall increases uniformly as the amount of steel increases, and Dur-o-wal can be effectively used in every course.

The effective spacing of control joints naturally also depends on type of mortar and amount of steel used. When Type N mortar is used, with Standard weight Dur-o-wal in every second course 16″ o.c., control joints should be spaced approximately 20 feet o.c. An increase of 25% in this spacing is reasonable, to allow the architect to work the control joints into his architectural treatment more readily.

When using *Type M or S* mortar, control joints should be spaced approximately 30 feet apart with reasonable allowance for architectural treatment requirements.

Within and in addition to the maximum space limitations mentioned in the preceding, control joints should be placed at points of stress concentration, such as:

1. Change in wall height.

2. Change in wall thickness.

3. At chases in walls required for pipes and columns.

4. Abutment of columns and walls.

5. Over weakened planes in foundation walls.

As far as the control joint itself is concerned, the architect is concerned with three principles:

1. The joint must cut the masonry wall completely from top to bottom, so as to form a truly stress-relieving joint.

2. It must be structurally sound in that a sufficient shear section is developed to provide for lateral stability.

3. It must be either self-sealing or one that can be very easily caulked to prevent water penetration or leakage.

Masonry manufacturers are now producing ready-made control joint units to meet all of these requirements. Another, meeting with growing nation-wide popularity is the *Rapid Control Joint*, developed by the producers of Dur-o-wal. This is a pre-molded rubber-type unit, engineered to meet the requirements with special emphasis on a complete self-sealing action.

Referring back to the four questions at the beginning of this analysis:

Should control joints be used? Yes. They are definitely helpful for the control of cracking in masonry walls, especially when used in combination with proper horizontal joint reinforcement.

Should plaster be applied directly to concrete block in stacked bond, reinforcing 16″ on center? If stacked bond walls are designed properly, there is no reason why they should not be plastered direct, the same as for running bond walls.

What is the best treatment for hairline cracks in plaster that has been directly applied to concrete block? In a survey of projects where this condition occurred, it has been noted that in all cases, sand gypsum plaster base was used. Where lightweight plaster such as Perlite or Vermiculite was used, this condition did not appear to exist. Therefore this type of plaster is recommended for direct-to-concrete use.

How frequently would you recommend the use of vertical control in long block walls in excess of 12′ in height? Walls of this height have a relatively greater resistance to cracking than average-size walls, and control joints can be spaced somewhat farther apart than normally recommended. In no case, however, should they be spaced more than 2 times the height. It is good practice to space control joints in high walls an average of 1.5 times the height.

Basic Dur-O-waL Applications

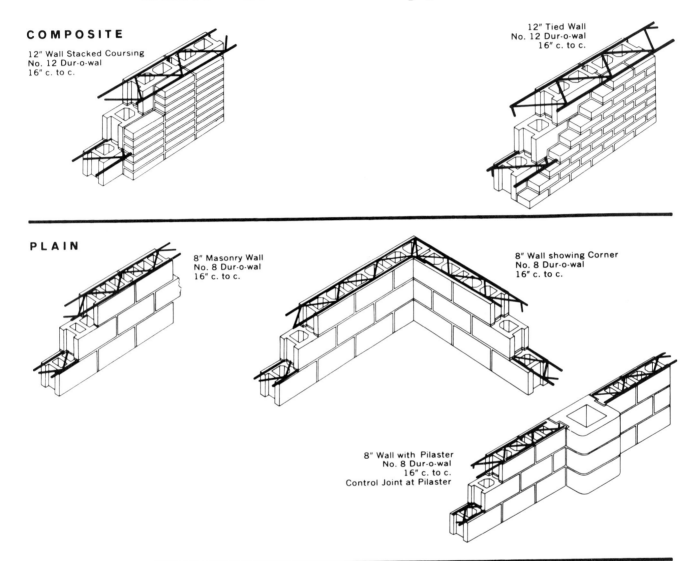

COMPOSITE

12" Wall Stacked Coursing
No. 12 Dur-o-wal
16" c. to c.

12" Tied Wall
No. 12 Dur-o-wal
16" c. to c.

PLAIN

8" Masonry Wall
No. 8 Dur-o-wal
16" c. to c.

8" Wall showing Corner
No. 8 Dur-o-wal
16" c. to c.

8" Wall with Pilaster
No. 8 Dur-o-wal
16" c. to c.
Control Joint at Pilaster

CAVITY

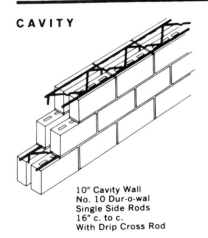

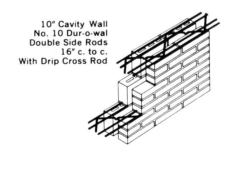

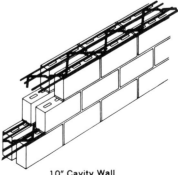

10" Cavity Wall
No. 10 Dur-o-wal
Single Side Rods
16" c. to c.
With Drip Cross Rod

10" Cavity Wall
No. 10 Dur-o-wal
Double Side Rods
16" c. to c.
With Drip Cross Rod

10" Cavity Wall
No. 10 Dur-o-wal
Double Side Rods
16" c. to c.
With Drip Cross Rod

Fig. 7-1.

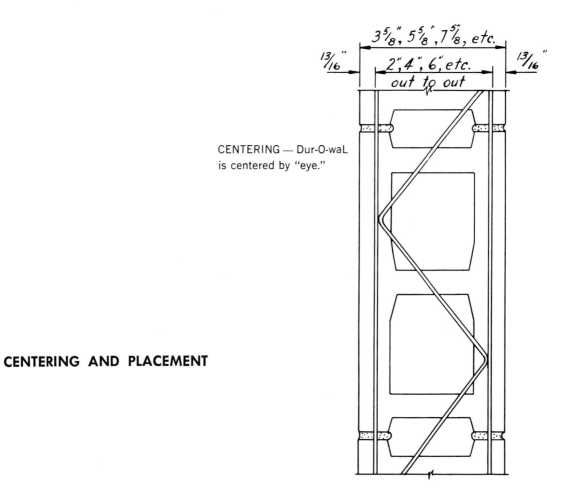

CENTERING — Dur-O-waL is centered by "eye."

CENTERING AND PLACEMENT

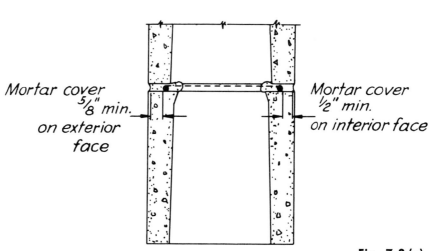

Mortar cover 5/8" min. on exterior face

Mortar cover 1/2" min. on interior face

Fig. 7-2 (a).

REINFORCEMENT SPLICES

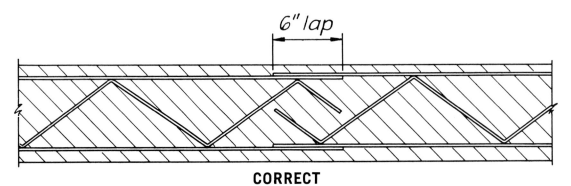

6" lap

CORRECT
The side wires are lapped 6″

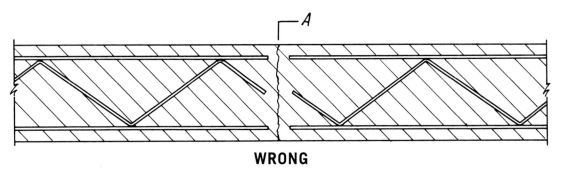

A

WRONG

The side wires are not lapped. Reinforcement is ineffective in preventing a crack from starting and opening up at A.

Proper lapping of wires at splices is essential to the continuity of the reinforcement so that tensile stress will be transmitted from one wire to the other across the splice.

Fig. 7-2 (b).

TYPICAL REINFORCEMENT SPACING

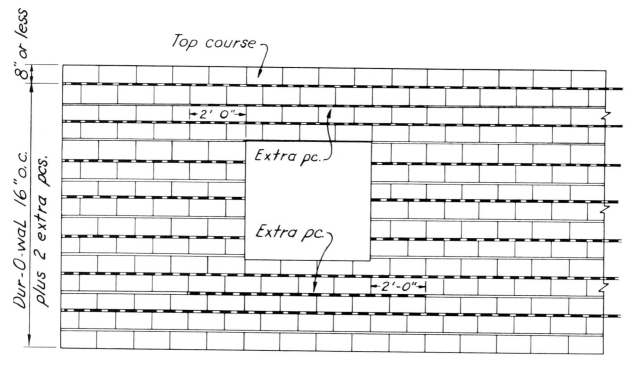

WALLS WITH OPENINGS

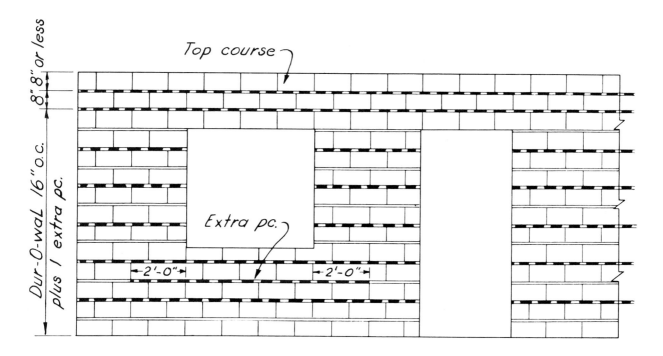

Fig. 7-2 (c).

REINFORCEMENT IN PLAN AND VERTICAL WALL SECTION

Fig. 7.3 shows a plan, elevation, and comparison table for types of ties for a cavity wall 13″ thick. Note the reinforcing lap in plan and the drip in elevation.

REINFORCING USED WITH GLASS BLOCKS

Fig. 7.4 shows the structural details for reinforcing glass block walls, together with a suggested specification. Pay special attention to the lapping of reinforcing (where unavoidable) and also to additional reinforcing below and above openings in the walls.

CONTROL JOINT FLANGE

Fig. 7.5 shows sections of wide and regular control joints with data and a picture of its application. It is very important that you keep your files up to date with control joint techniques for all kinds of structures from footing to roofings.

ADJUSTABLE WALL TIES

A relatively new product used in masonry unit walls is the adjustable wall tie. Not only does it solve the coursing problems for inside and outside wythes of differing depths, it also allows a building to be fully closed in (during cold weather) with only one wythe. This allows inside trades an earlier start and reduces construction time. *This is very important.* Figs. 7.6(a) and 7.6(b) show the dwgs and some technical data of these ties.

EXPANSION JOINTS IN MASONRY UNIT WALLS

The source of the following material is the Canadian Structural Clay Association. It is published with permission.

Fig. 7.7(a) shows four different joint fillers. The first shows 21-oz copper water stops made up with short pieces that overlap at the joints; the remainder are premolded control joints in common use.

Fig. 7.7(b) shows three hypothetical bldg line plans with lettered sections showing suggested places for expansion joints. The structural dwgs for the letters are shown at Figs. 7.8 and 7.9.

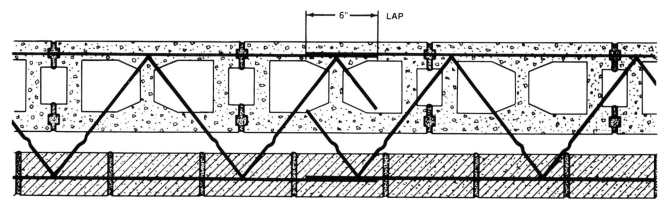

Codes generally call for a minimum of one 3/16″ dia.
tie for each 3 to 4½ sq. ft. of wall. Dur-o-wal exceeds
this requirement and provides maximum anchorage with
positive and uniform spacing of ties. It also reinforces
the masonry longitudinally.

Comparison Table—Various Type Cavity Wall Ties

Type	Spacing	Cross Sectional Area of Ties per sq. ft. Wall
Z-Ties, ³⁄₁₆″ dia.	1 for each 3 sq. ft. 1 for each 4½ sq. ft.	.0092 sq. in. .0061 sq. in.
Rectangular ties, two ³⁄₁₆″ dia.	1 for each 3 sq. ft. 1 for each 4½ sq. ft.	.0184 sq. in. .0122 sq. in.
U-Ties, two ³⁄₁₆″ dia.	1 for each 3 sq. ft. 1 for each 4½ sq. ft.	.0184 sq. in. .0122 sq. in.
Dur-o-wal, No. 9 gauge	**Spaced 16 in. o.c. vertically**	.0196 sq. in.

Dur-o-wal for Cavity Walls is furnished with steel side rods and galvanized cross rod or with
all galvanized steel rods.

NOTE: All Dur-O-waL for cavity walls is furnished with or without drip.

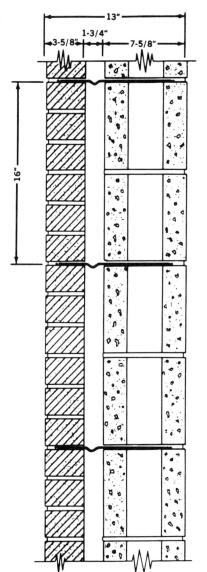

Fig. 7-3.

RECOMMENDATION AND DESCRIPTION

Standard Weight Dur-o-wal No. 3-S is recommended for glass block reinforcement. It is manufactured with a No. 9 gauge trussed designed Cross Rod butt welded to No. 9 gauge deformed Side Rods. Double mortar locks at each weld add greatly to the tensile load carrying capacity of the assembly. All rods are in a single plane thus assuring a neat, tight mortar joint.

SUGGESTED GENERAL SPECIFICATION

Glass block panel reinforcement shall be Dur-o-wal (or approved equal) with deformed side rods and trussed designed cross rod and shall comply with material requirements of ASTM Standard A 82 for cold drawn steel wire for concrete reinforcement. Reinforcement shall extend from end to end of mortar joints but not across expansion joints, with any unavoidable joints spliced by lapping the reinforcement not less than 6 inches. Dur-o-wal shall be spaced not more than 2 feet apart vertically. In addition reinforcement shall be placed in the joint immediately below and above any openings within a panel. The reinforcement assembly shall consist of two parallel longitudinal galvanized, deformed steel wires, No. 9 gauge, spaced approximately 2 inches apart, and having butt welded thereto No. 9 gauge trussed designed cross wire at intervals not exceeding 8 inches, or the equivalent approved by the building official.

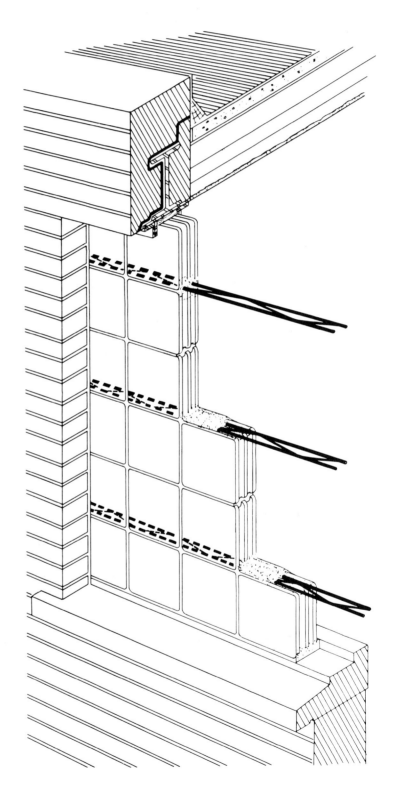

Fig. 7-4.

Wide Flange and Regular Rapid Control Joint

QUICKEST, MOST EFFECTIVE MEANS TO A YEAR-ROUND WEATHER SEAL

The Wide Flange Rapid Control Joint has been engineered by the makers of Dur-O-waL to provide a complete answer to the control joint problem. Flexible neoprene flanges, that take care of the full working thickness of a concrete block, expand and contract with the joint — to make up a quickly installed control structure that lets a wall "breathe," yet keeps itself sealed tight. Caulking is not always necessary in standard concrete block construction. The neoprene compound used is resistant to flex-cracking, weather, heat and cold. Not harmed by oil or solvents. The concave edge allows easy compression.

The Regular (narrow flange) Rapid Control Joint is recommended by construction engineers for various special needs. Both types of Rapid Control Joint fit neatly and quickly into the grooves of metal sash jamb block.

Effect of control joint spacing — Regular or Wide Flange Rapid Control Joint when used in design of masonry walls and in combination with Dur-O-waL Truss Design masonry wall reinforcement, should be spaced approximately 20 feet c. to c. for average height walls, and not to exceed 2 times wall height for high walls. Incorporated within limitations of this spacing, control joints should also be placed at points of great stress concentration such as — *change in wall heights; change in wall thickness; at chases in wall required for pipes, vents and columns; abutment of columns and wall, and over weakened planes in foundation walls.*

For control joint to perform adequately, the following three principles should be considered:

1- The joint must cut the masonry wall completely from top to bottom, so as to form a truly stress relieving joint.

2- It must be structurally sound in that a sufficient shear section is developed to provide for lateral stability.

3- It must be either self-sealing or one that can be easily caulked to prevent moisture penetration or leakage.

Shear Strength — In tests at Armour Research Foundation the ultimate transverse shear strength of Rapid Control Joints was over 4700 lbs. per lineal foot of joint.

GENERAL SPECIFICATIONS:

Regular
Wide Flange } Rapid Control Joint shall be placed in masonry walls as noted on plans.

PRODUCT SPECIFICATION:
Regular Rapid Control Joint

Rubber material for shear section shall meet requirements of ASTM D735

Wide Flange Rapid Control Joint

Rubber material for shear section shall meet requirements of ASTM D735 Neoprene compound for flange resistance of these materials to lateral forces.

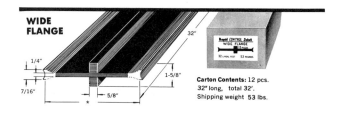

WIDE FLANGE

1/4"
7/16"
1-5/8"
5/8"
32"

Carton Contents: 12 pcs. 32" long, total 32'. Shipping weight 53 lbs.

*Available in 6⅞" and 4⅞" widths.

REGULAR

1-9/16"
1"
5/8"
5/16"
5/8"
32"

Carton Contents: 12 pcs. 32" long, total 32'. Shipping weight 31 lbs.

The Rapid Control Joint comes in sections, four block courses in depth. Quickly, easily installed, it saves time and money.

Fig. 7-5.

ADJUSTABLE WALL TIES*

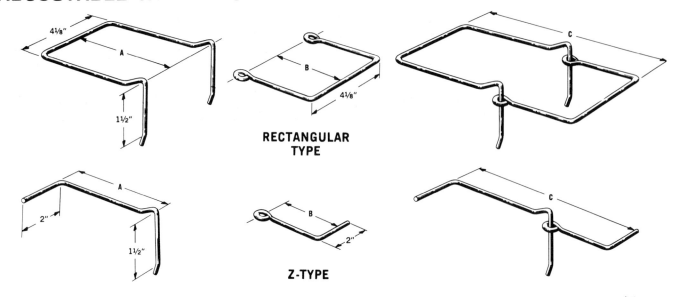

RECTANGULAR TYPE

Z-TYPE

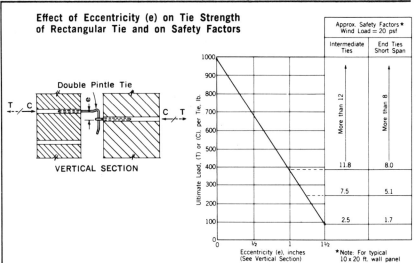

ADJUSTABLE WALL TIE SELECTION TABLE			
TIE NUMBER RECT. OR Z-TYPE	PINTLE SECTION A Dimension (In.)	EYE SECTION B Dimension (In.)	FULL TIE LENGTH C Dimension (In.)
#6	3¼	2¾	6
#7	4¾	2¾	7½
#8	5¼	2¾	8
#8A	3¼	4¾	8
#9	4¾	4¾	9½
#10	5¼	4¾	10

Effect of Eccentricity (e) on Tie Strength of Rectangular Tie and on Safety Factors

GENERAL DESCRIPTION

Material — Dur-O-waL Adjustable Wall Ties are manufactured from 3/16 in. diameter, high tensile, cold drawn steel wire which conforms to material requirements of ASTM A82.

Shape — Dur-O-waL Adjustable Wall Ties are available in either the Z-Type or the Rectangular Type. Sizes are available as shown in the Selection Table at top of page.

Finish — Unless otherwise specified, all ties will have zinc coating (galvanized) which conforms to ASTM A116 Class 1. Other weights of zinc coating and other types of finishes can be furnished on request.

FUNCTIONS AND APPLICATIONS

Labor Savings — Enables the contractor to adopt labor saving construction techniques.

Solution to Coursing Problems — Especially adaptable to job conditions where the facing and backing do not course out level at proper intervals or where it is desir-

able to build one wythe ahead of the other.

Increased Productivity — Enables mason to concentrate on one wythe of wall to any given height before changing to other wythe, resulting in increased productivity.

Ease of Inspection — Architect or building inspector can see if the ties are being installed as specified.

Eliminates Bending of Ties — Eliminates mason's problem of bending and reshaping rigid ties when misalignment occurs.

Anchoring Intersecting Walls — Provides a means of anchoring intersecting walls.

Speeds Up Construction — The inside wythe of the wall can be built to enclose or partially enclose the building so work can start inside. The exterior wythe can be tied in later.

RECOMMENDED SPACING

Rectangular Type Adjustable Wall Ties should be spaced

Fig. 7-6 (a).

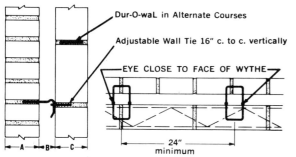

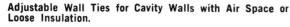

| OVERALL WALL WIDTH (In.) | WIDTH OF CAVITY AND WYTHES | | | TIE NUMBER RECT. OR Z-TYPE |
	EXTERIOR A (In.)	CAVITY B (In.)	BACKUP C (In.)	
10	4	2	4	#7
11	4	3	4	#8
12	4	2	6	#7
13	4	3	6	#8
14	4	2	8	#7
15	4	3	8	#8

Inserting the Pintle Section

The Pintle Section is always installed in the second wythe built. It may be inserted either up or down. Bed joints of opposing wythes must be no farther apart vertically than 1½ inches either direction.

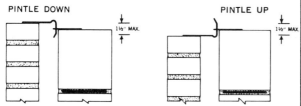

PINTLE DOWN   1½" MAX.   PINTLE UP   1½" MAX.

Adjustable Wall Ties for Faced or Composite Walls

Use Adjustable Wall Tie No. 6 for Faced or Composite Walls of all sizes.

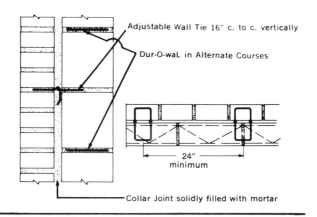

Adjustable Wall Ties for Cavity Walls with Rigid Insulation

Selection of Tie (Use Selection Table)
1. Select Eye Section long enough to extend approx. 2" into the masonry with center of eyelet at face of insulation.
2. Select Pintle Section long enough to extend approx. 2" into the masonry and reach across cavity to engage eyelet.

When properly installed, Pintle will hold insulation in place.

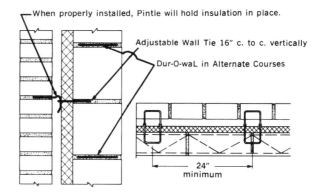

to provide one tie for every 2.66 sq. ft. of wall area, approximately 16" vertically and 24" horizontally. Z-Type Adjustable Wall Ties should be spaced to provide one such tie per 1.33 sq. ft. of wall area. This recommendation is based on research findings and engineering analysis of code requirements for wind pressures, distribution of wind loads to spans, etc. for a 10 foot by 20 foot wall panel, a 20 psf. wind load, and *all* ties at *maximum* eccentricity with a factor of safety of approximately two. (See Dur-O-waL Technical Bulletin 64-4.)

REQUIREMENTS FOR EXTRA TIES

Ties should be located within 8 in. of each side of vertical supports and control joints. Extra ties as currently required by codes should be located around openings.

Extra ties should be installed where special attention to tie location is desirable.

Extra ties are not necessary at points of support where solid bridging is used.

GENERAL SPECIFICATIONS FOR THE USE OF ADJUSTABLE WALL TIES

Wall ties shall be (Rectangular) (Z-Type) Adjustable Wall Ties as manufactured by Dur-O-waL or approved equal adjustable ties. Ties shall be spaced as noted on plans. (State finish if other than Class I galvanized.)

TECHNICAL DATA

Research — The strength of Adjustable Wall Ties was investigated in a program of tests directed by the Armour Research Foundation of the Illinois Institute of Technology. Tests indicate that Dur-O-waL Adjustable Wall Ties, used as recommended herein, adequately meet structural requirements. For an approved condensed copy of Dur-O-waL Technical Bulletin 64-4 entitled "Dur-O-waL Adjustable Wall Ties, Their Structural Properties and Recommended Use," write Dur-O-waL National, Inc., Box 368, Cedar Rapids, Iowa.

Fig. 7-6 (b).

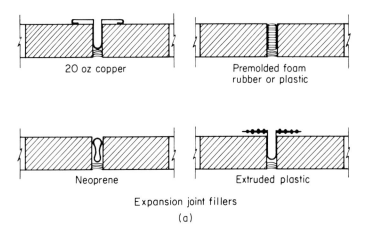

Expansion joint fillers

(a)

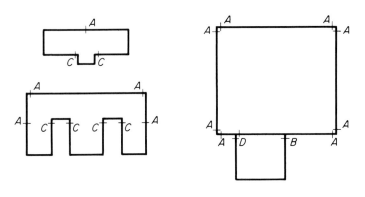

Typical expansion joint placement

(b)

Fig. 7-7.

EXPANSION JOINTS IN STRAIGHT WALLS

Fig. 7.8 shows eight expansion joints in straight walls. Note the location (Letter *A*) which is shown at Fig. 7.7(b). Pay careful attention to the treatment at pilasters and cols.

EXPANSION JOINTS AT OFFSETS AND JUNCTURE WALLS

Fig. 7.9 shows six expansion joints at the junctures of masonry unit walls. Note the location letters *C*, *B*, and *D*. Relate them to Fig. 7.7(b). The type of visible bonding desired may sometimes affect the positioning of expansion joints.

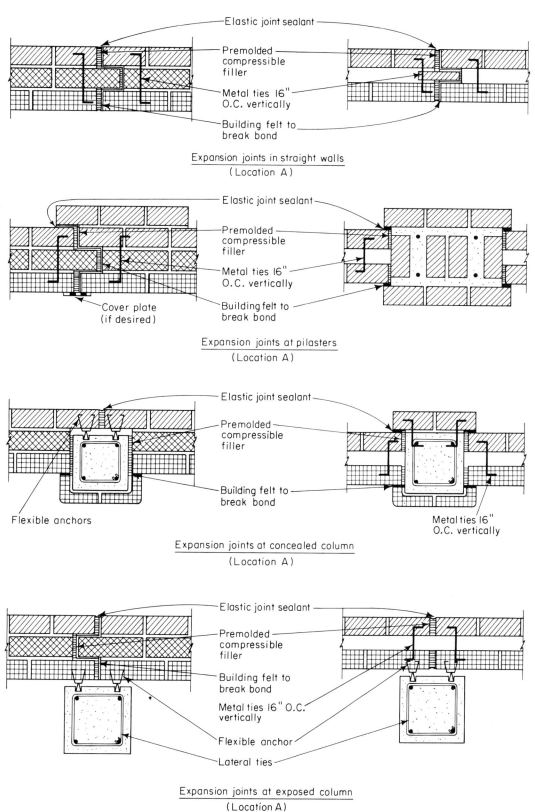

Elastic joint sealant

Premolded compressible filler

Metal ties 16" O.C. vertically

Building felt to break bond

Expansion joints in straight walls
(Location A)

Elastic joint sealant

Premolded compressible filler

Metal ties 16" O.C. vertically

Cover plate (if desired)

Building felt to break bond

Expansion joints at pilasters
(Location A)

Elastic joint sealant

Premolded compressible filler

Building felt to break bond

Flexible anchors

Metal ties 16" O.C. vertically

Expansion joints at concealed column
(Location A)

Elastic joint sealant

Premolded compressible filler

Building felt to break bond

Metal ties 16" O.C. vertically

Flexible anchor

Lateral ties

Expansion joints at exposed column
(Location A)

Fig. 7-8. Expansion joints in straight walls.

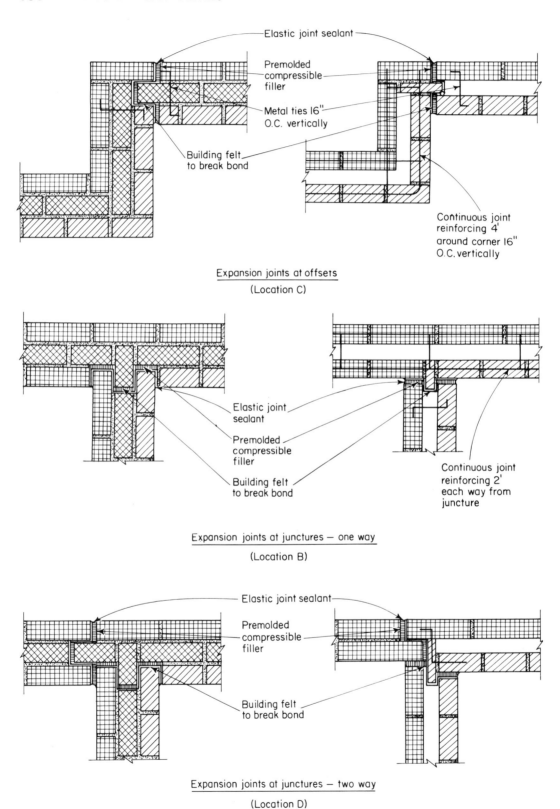

Elastic joint sealant

Premolded compressible filler

Metal ties 16" O.C. vertically

Building felt to break bond

Continuous joint reinforcing 4' around corner 16" O.C. vertically

Expansion joints at offsets
(Location C)

Elastic joint sealant

Premolded compressible filler

Building felt to break bond

Continuous joint reinforcing 2' each way from juncture

Expansion joints at junctures — one way
(Location B)

Elastic joint sealant

Premolded compressible filler

Building felt to break bond

Expansion joints at junctures — two way
(Location D)

Fig. 7-9. Expansion joints at offsets and junctures.

EXPANSION JOINTS IN SKELETON-FRAME BUILDINGS

Fig. 7.10 shows a method of detailing joints in skeleton-frame bldgs. Pay special attention to the dovetail anchors which are placed 16″ o.c. on the cols.

HORIZONTAL EXPANSION JOINTS AT SHELF ANGLE

Fig. 7.11 shows a horizontal expansion joint at a shelf angle. Such joints may be used when height or large numbers of openings occur in masonry unit walls. A 55-lb felt placed above and below the angle forms the joint; elastic section completes the joint and matches the mortar.

FLEXIBLE ANCHORAGE TO BEAMS

Fig. 7.12 shows plans and wall section anchors of masonry units to beams. The second example shows a flexible anchor hooked to an angle welded to a beam.

FLEXIBLE ANCHORAGE TO COLUMNS

Fig. 7.13 shows plan and section details of anchors of masonry units to cols. In one case, the flexible anchor is dovetailed to the conc col; the second example shows a flexible anchor welded at 8″ o.c. vertically to the steel col.

REINFORCED MASONRY UNIT LINTELS

Fig. 7.14 shows three built-in-place reinforced masonry unit lintels. Fig. 7.14(a) shows the longitudinal tensile steel and the stirrups where required. Fig. 7.14(b) shows a reinforced lintel built with special manufacturer designed units, and Fig. 7.14(c) shows a reinforced lintel built with standard masonry units, field cut to receive the reinforcing.

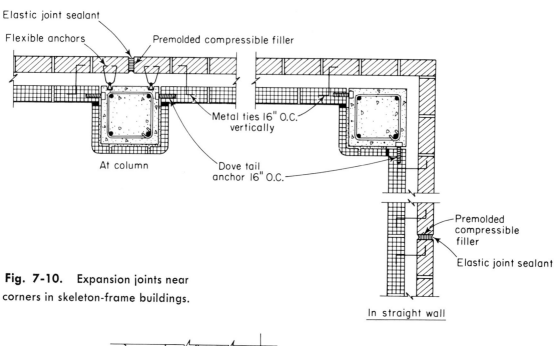

Fig. 7-10. Expansion joints near corners in skeleton-frame buildings.

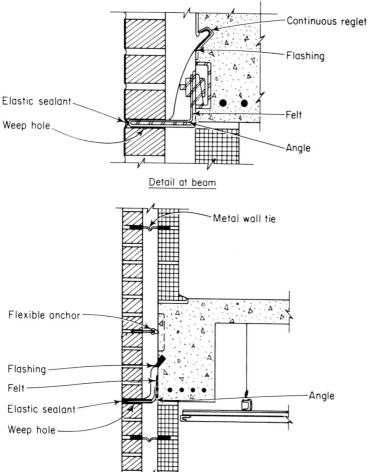

Fig. 7-11. Horizontal expansion joint at shelf angle.

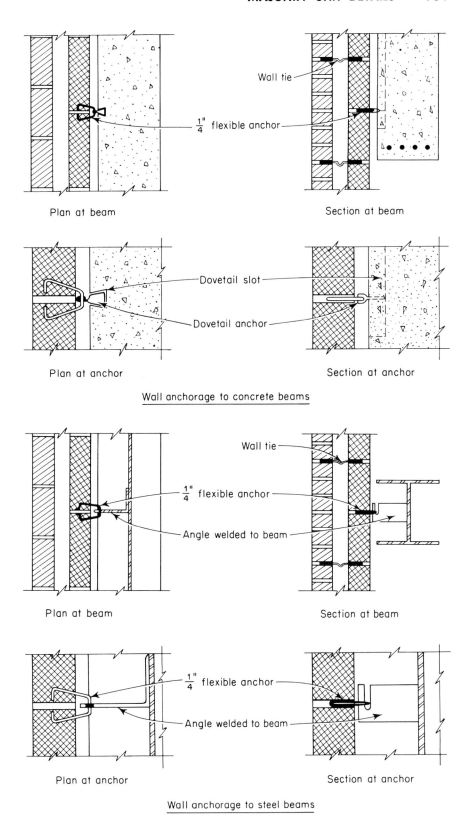

Plan at beam

Section at beam

Plan at anchor

Section at anchor

Wall anchorage to concrete beams

Plan at beam

Section at beam

Plan at anchor

Section at anchor

Wall anchorage to steel beams

Fig. 7-12. Flexible anchorage to beams.

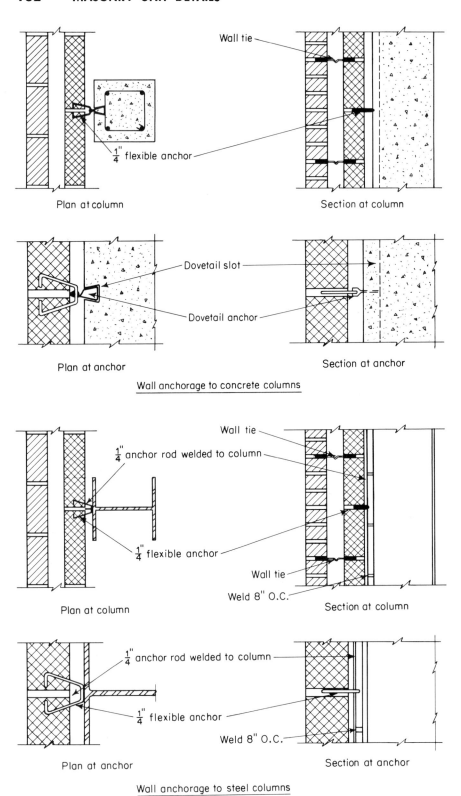

Fig. 7-13.   Flexible anchorage to columns.

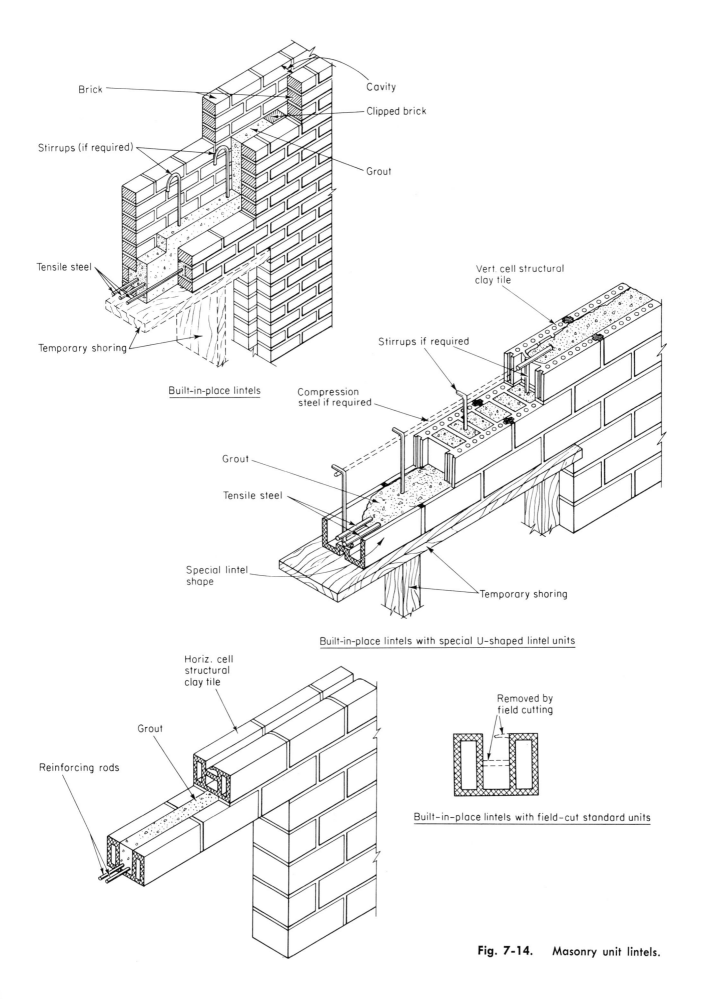

Brick

Cavity

Clipped brick

Stirrups (if required)

Grout

Tensile steel

Temporary shoring

Built-in-place lintels

Vert. cell structural clay tile

Stirrups if required

Compression steel if required

Grout

Tensile steel

Special lintel shape

Temporary shoring

Built-in-place lintels with special U-shaped lintel units

Horiz. cell structural clay tile

Grout

Reinforcing rods

Removed by field cutting

Built-in-place lintels with field-cut standard units

Fig. 7-14. Masonry unit lintels.

FIREPROOFING COLUMNS AND BEAMS WITH MASONRY UNITS

Fig. 7.15 shows details of fireproofing steel cols and beams with masonry units. Note the fire rating for each col.

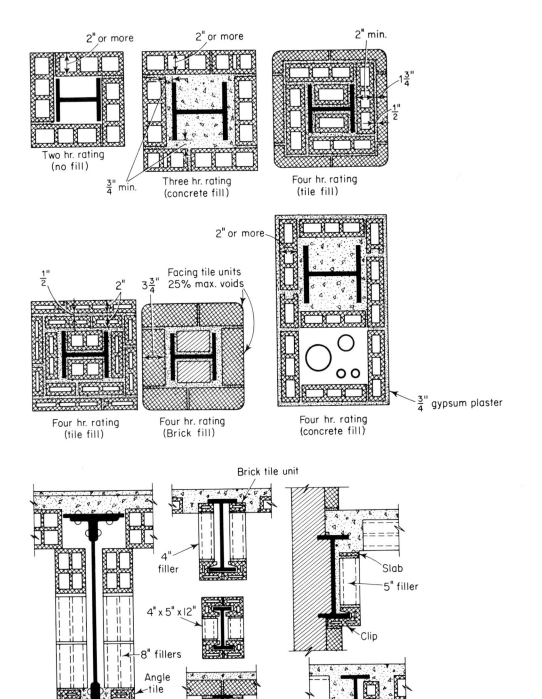

Fig. 7-15. Structural clay fire-proofing.

Fig. 7-16. Structural clay tile subfloors.

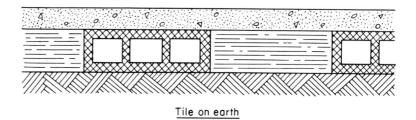

Tile on earth

Structural clay tile

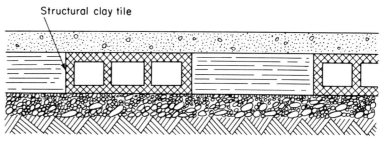

Tile on gravel fill

$1\frac{1}{2}$" to 2" conc.

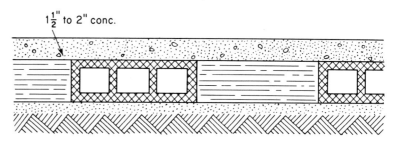

Tile on sand cushion

STRUCTURAL CLAY TILE SUB-FLOORS

The source of the following material is the Structural Clay Products Institute, Washington, D.C. It is published thru their courtesy and with the permission of the copyright holder.

Fig. 7.16 shows three situations where a typical tile and concrete sub-floor may be used for eliminating condensation and mildew.

Fig. 7.17 shows four excellent examples for anchoring ceramic veneer to masonry walls.

Fig. 7.18 shows a tile arch floor system which, although light in weight, offers great strength and fire resisting qualities.

PARAPET WALLS

Figs. 7.19 and 7.20 each show a parapet wall with flashing and counter flashing.

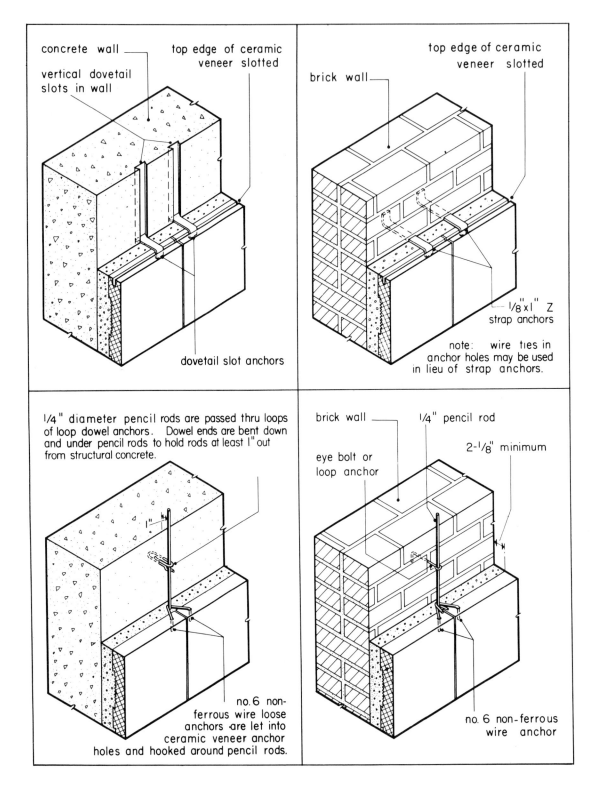

concrete wall
top edge of ceramic veneer slotted
vertical dovetail slots in wall
dovetail slot anchors

brick wall
top edge of ceramic veneer slotted
1/8" x 1" Z strap anchors
note: wire ties in anchor holes may be used in lieu of strap anchors.

1/4" diameter pencil rods are passed thru loops of loop dowel anchors. Dowel ends are bent down and under pencil rods to hold rods at least 1" out from structural concrete.
1"
no. 6 non-ferrous wire loose anchors are let into ceramic veneer anchor holes and hooked around pencil rods.

brick wall
1/4" pencil rod
2-1/8" minimum
eye bolt or loop anchor
no. 6 non-ferrous wire anchor

Fig. 7-17. Anchoring ceramic veneer to masonry walls.

Masonry wall cracks at or near the junction of parapet and roof lines are perhaps the most difficult of all types of masonry cracking to eliminate. This is due to the severe exposures to which the parapet is subjected, to its relatively light weight, and to movements between the parapet and building walls. This problem of expansion, together with flashing difficulties, means leaking, water infiltration, freezing, anchorage failure, and displacement.

Where possible, the best solution is to omit the parapet.

When a parapet is required, the most careful consideration must be given to design and construction, with very special attention given to expansion.

Since the parapet is constructed above the roof line, it is subjected to exposure on three surfaces, and special precautions should be taken to protect the masonry.

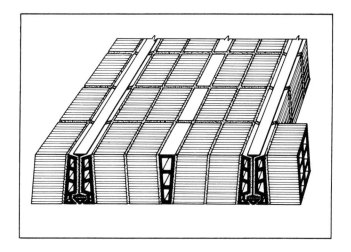

Fig. 7-19. Parapet wall.

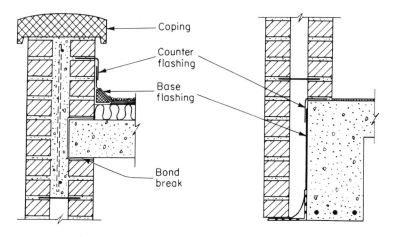

Coping

Counter flashing

Base flashing

Bond break

Fig. 7-18. Tile arch floor system.

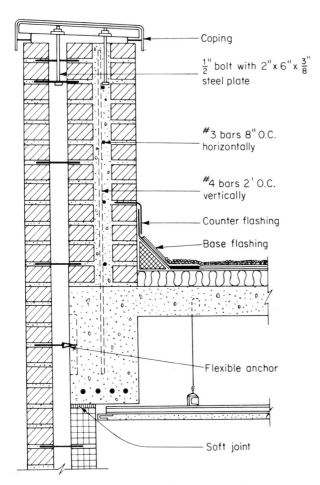

Coping

$\frac{1}{2}$" bolt with 2"x 6"x $\frac{3}{8}$" steel plate

#3 bars 8" O.C. horizontally

#4 bars 2' O.C. vertically

Counter flashing

Base flashing

Flexible anchor

Soft joint

Fig. 7-20.   Reinforced brick parapet wall.

The quality of brick or tile used should be given careful consideration. The back of the parapet wall should be built of the same well burned grade of material as the facing. The common practice of using lower grade material here, because it is hidden from general view, should be prohibited since it is frequently the cause of disintegration of the wall.

Field observations of parapet walls have in some instances disclosed cracks which may be attributed to expansion of either the wall or the roof slab. It is therefore recommended that parapet walls be reinforced both horizontally and vertically with a minimum of two ¼-in. rods horizontally on 16 in. centers and ⅜-in. rods vertically on 24 in. centers. Fig. 7.20 shows a reinforced brick parapet wall with slightly more than the minimum reinforcement.

FIREPLACES 8
AND
CHIMNEYS

In this chapter we are going to study dwgs of domestic solid-fuel-burning fireplaces and chimneys which have to comply with the local Building Code and be inspected by the Building Inspector. In unorganized territories of Canada an inspection is made by an officer of the Royal Canadian Mounted Police. Check for a comparable situation in your area.

CHIMNEY FOUNDATIONS

Foundations for free-standing fireplaces and chimneys are designed to meet known loads. Factors affecting the ftgs are as follows:

(a) The size and total height of the chimney above the fireplace hearth, including that part above the ridge of the roof.

(b) The number of fireplaces and separate flues trimmed into the chimney.

(c) The total depth of the chimney below the lowest fireplace hearth to a basement cleanout and down to the ftg.

(d) The ground and frost conditions.

The source for the following three dwgs and material is Donley's *Book of Successful Fireplaces—How to Build Them* and is published with permission.

ESSENTIALS OF DESIGN OF FIREPLACES

The four essentials for correct design of fireplaces are as follows:

(a) Proper combustion of the fuel.

(b) Delivery of all smoke and other products of combustion up the chimney.

(c) Radiation of the maximum amount of heat into the room.

(d) Simplicity in construction and fire safety.

Of these, (a) and (b) are closely related and depend mainly upon the shape and relative dimensions of the combustion chamber, the proper location of the fireplace throat and its relation to the smoke shelf, and the ratio of the flue area to fireplace opening area, (c) is dependent upon the shape and dimensions of the combustion chamber, and (d) is subject to the size and shape of the masonry units used and their ability to withstand high temperatures without warping, cracking, or deterioration.

SIZES OF FIREPLACES

Careful consideration should be given to the size of the fireplace best suited to the room in which it is located, taking into account not only its appearance but its operation as well. If it is too small, it may function properly but will not produce a sufficient amount of heat. If too large, a fire that would fill the combustion chamber would be too hot for the room. Moreover, it would require a larger chimney and induce an abnormal infiltration of air through doors and windows to supply the needs for combustion and so waste fuel.

A room with 300 square feet of floor area is well served by a fireplace with an opening 30 to 36 inches wide. For larger rooms the width may be increased, but all dimensions should be as indicated by Fig. 8.1 and the following Notes of Construction and Dimension Table.

Fireplace openings should not be too high; for the usual width of opening, the height above the hearth is seldom more than 32 inches.

FIREPLACES ON SEVERAL FLOORS

At Fig. 8.2 is shown a sketch of three fireplaces, each on a separate floor and all trimmed into one chimney stack. The dwgs show an ideal way to combine such fireplaces with each flue leading off correctly from the center of the chamber. The slope of the flue in no way impedes the discharge of smoke.

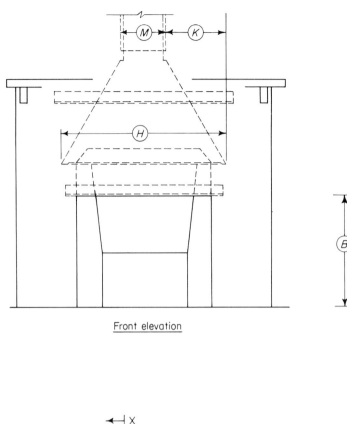

Front elevation

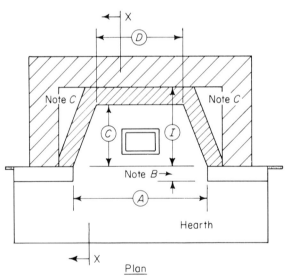

Plan

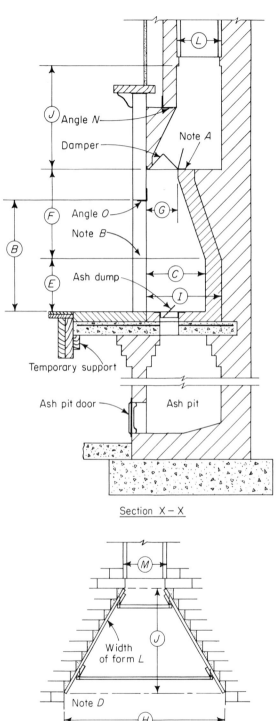

Section X–X

Fig. 8-1. Construction details of a typical fireplace.

Notes on Construction Sketch and Dimension Table

Note A—The back flange of the damper must be protected from intense heat by being fully supported by the masonry. At the same time, the damper should not be built in solidly at the ends but given freedom to expand with heat, as shown in the front elevation on the opposite page.

Note B—The drawing indicates the thickness of the brick fireplace front as four inches. However, no definite dimension can be given for this because of the various materials used—marble, stone, tile, etc., all having varying thicknesses.

Note C—The hollow, triangular spaces indicated in the plan, behind the splayed sides of the inner brickwork, should be filled to afford solid backing. If desired to locate a flue in either space, the outside dimensions of the rough brickwork should be increased.

Note D—A good way to build a smoke chamber is to erect a wooden form consisting of two sloping boards at the sides, held apart by spreaders at the top and bottom. Spreaders are nailed upward into cleats as shown. The letters H, M, and J correspond to letters in the elevation and in the Table of Dimensions. The form boards should have the same width as the flue lining. See description on Page 25.

Note E—A steel smoke chamber is made by The Donley Brothers Co. and furnished where desired.

Note F—The sectional view opposite shows the rotary control type of Donley Damper. On Page 37 are described poker control and chain control types, also description of materials and full range of sizes.

Table of Fireplace Dimensions

Finished Fireplace Opening							Rough Brickwork and Flue Size			New Flue Sizes**			Round	Old Flue Sizes			Equipment						
A	B	C	D	E	F	G	H	I	J	K	L	M		K	L	M	Hearth Assemblies	Damper Rotary No.	Damper Poker No.	Ash Dump	Ash-pit Door	N	O
24	24	16	11	14	18	8¾	32	20	19	10	8	12	8	11¾	8½	8½	72	324	224	58	12x8	A-36	A-36
26	24	16	13	14	18	8¾	34	20	21	11	8	12	8	12¾	8½	8½	72	330	230	58	12x8	A-36	A-36
28	24	16	15	14	18	8¾	36	20	21	12	8	12	10	11½	8½	13	72	330	230	58	12x8	A-36	A-36
30	29	16	17	14	23	8¾	38	20	24	13	12	12	10	12½	8½	13	72 or 84	330	230	58	12x8	A-42	A-36
32	29	16	19	14	23	8¾	40	20	24	14	12	12	10	13½	8½	13	72 or 84	333	233	58	12x8	A-42	A-42
36	29	16	23	14	23	8¾	44	20	27	16	12	12	12	15½	13	13	72 or 84	336	236	70	12x8	A-48	A-42
40	29	16	27	14	23	8¾	48	20	29	16	12	16	12	17½	13	13	72 or 84	342	242	70	12x8	A-48	A-48
42	32	16	29	14	26	8¾	50	20	32	17	16	16	12	18½	13	13	72 or 84	342	242	70	12x8	B-54	A-48
48	32	18	33	14	26	8¾	56	22	37	20	16	16	15	21½	13	13	96	348	248	70	12x8	B-60	B-54
54	37	20	37	16	29	13	68	24	45	26	16	16	15	25	13	18	96	...	254	70	12x8	B-72	B-60
60	37	22	42	16	29	13	72	27	45	26	16	20	15	27	13	18	96	...	260	70	12x8	B-72	B-66
60	40	22	42	16	31	13	72	27	45	26	16	20	18	27	18	18	96	...	260	70	12x8	B-72	B-66
72	40	22	54	16	31	13	84	27	56	32	20	20	18	33	18	18	Special	...	272	70	12x8	C-84	C-84
84	40	24	64	20	28	13	96	29	61	36	20	24	20	36	20	20	Special	384	284	70	12x8	C-96	C-96
96	40	24	76	20	28	13	108	29	75	42	20	24	22	42	24	24	Special	396	296	70	12x8	C-108	C-108

NOTES.   *Angle Sizes: A—3x3x³⁄₁₆, B—3½x3x¼, C—5x3½x⁵⁄₁₆.

**New Flue Sizes—Conform to new modular dimensional system. Sizes shown are nominal. Actual size is ½ in. less each dimension.

Note 1.—A ruler is a convenience in using this table. Select the number in the left-hand column that corresponds to your proposed width of fireplace opening. Lay the ruler on the line below it and read the figures to the right on the same line. They give you the complete recommended dimensions and installation, for the fireplace, of the chosen width of opening.

Note 2—Under the heading Equipment, the second and third columns refer to two different types of damper and are, of course, alternates. Rotary control dampers have numbers beginning with 3, poker beginning with Figure 2. An order that simply calls for a given size in inches is not sufficiently clear. Order dampers by number.

Note 3—Two sets of flue lining dimensions appear in the table above, one for the old standard sizes and another for the nominal sizes of those conforming to the new, modular standard. Round sizes are also shown. Capacity as indicated by sectional area is presented under heading, Capacity of Flue Linings. By "nominal" size is meant actual size plus half an inch for each dimension as joint space. The modular movement, as promoted by the American Standards Association and American Institute of Architects, seeks to reduce all sizes of installed materials to derivatives of a 4-inch module.

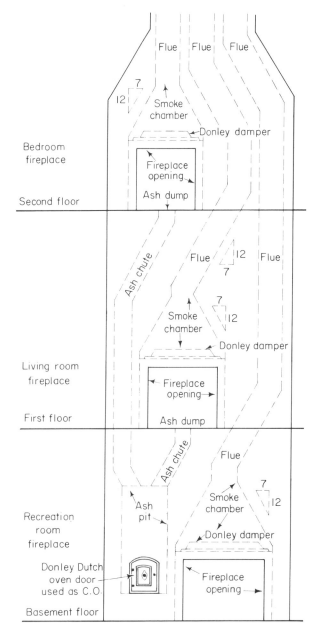

Fig. 8-2. Fireplaces on several floors. (By courtesy of Donley Brothers Company.)

FIREPLACES ON OPPOSITE SIDES OF A WALL

Fig. 8.3 shows a suggested staggered positioning of fireplaces to serve areas opposite each other: this method avoids the deep projection that would be necessary if the two fireplaces stood back to back. A brick wall-facing is shown for the fireplaces, which may be modified to suit other conditions. For a fuller treatment of conventional fireplaces, readers are recommended to study the book from which this material is drawn.

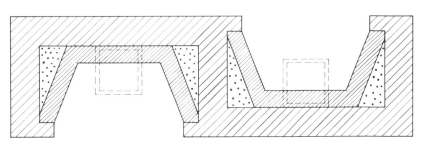

Fig. 8-3. Fireplaces on opposite sides of a wall.

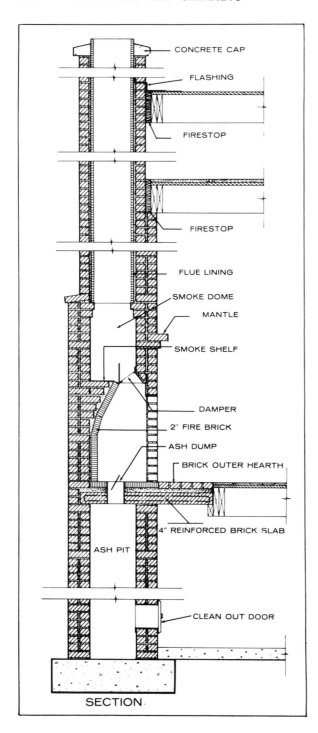

CONCRETE CAP

FLASHING

FIRESTOP

FIRESTOP

FLUE LINING

SMOKE DOME

MANTLE

SMOKE SHELF

DAMPER

2" FIRE BRICK

ASH DUMP

BRICK OUTER HEARTH

4" REINFORCED BRICK SLAB

ASH PIT

CLEAN OUT DOOR

SECTION

Fig. 8-4.

At Fig. 8.4 is shown a typical fireplace section from a basement cleanout and first floor fireplace and thru two wood floors to a concrete chimney cap. Note the hearth and inert material for a firestop. *The minimum clearance between the masonry of a chimney and combustible material is very important.* What is it in your area?

CHIMNEY FLASHINGS

Figs. 8.5, 8.6, and 8.7 show chimney flashing details and suggested specifications. They are published thru the courtesy and permission of Anaconda American Brass Limited. These dwgs are clear enough for all to understand.

Chimney flashing at ridge

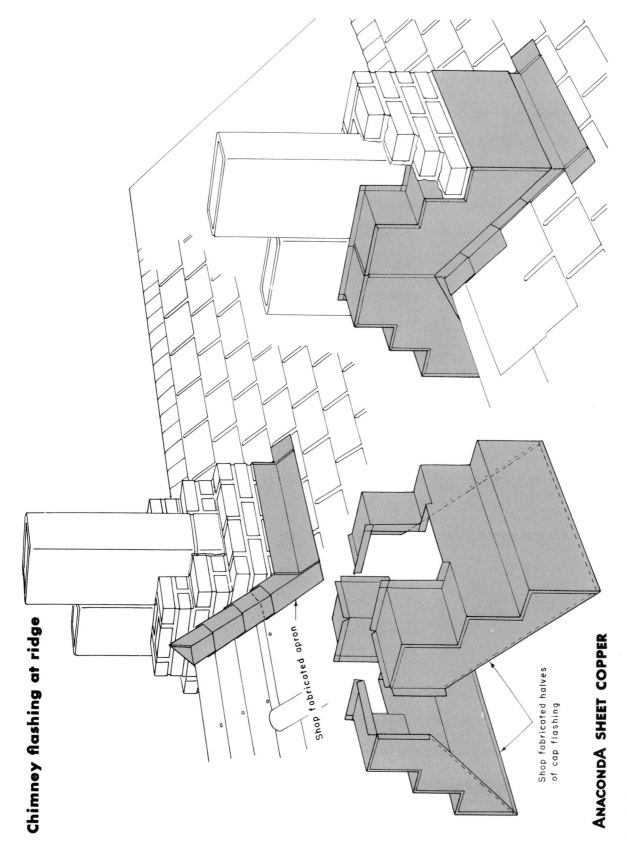

Shop fabricated apron

Shop fabricated halves of cap flashing

ANACONDA SHEET COPPER

Fig. 8-5.

Chimney flashing, architectural design

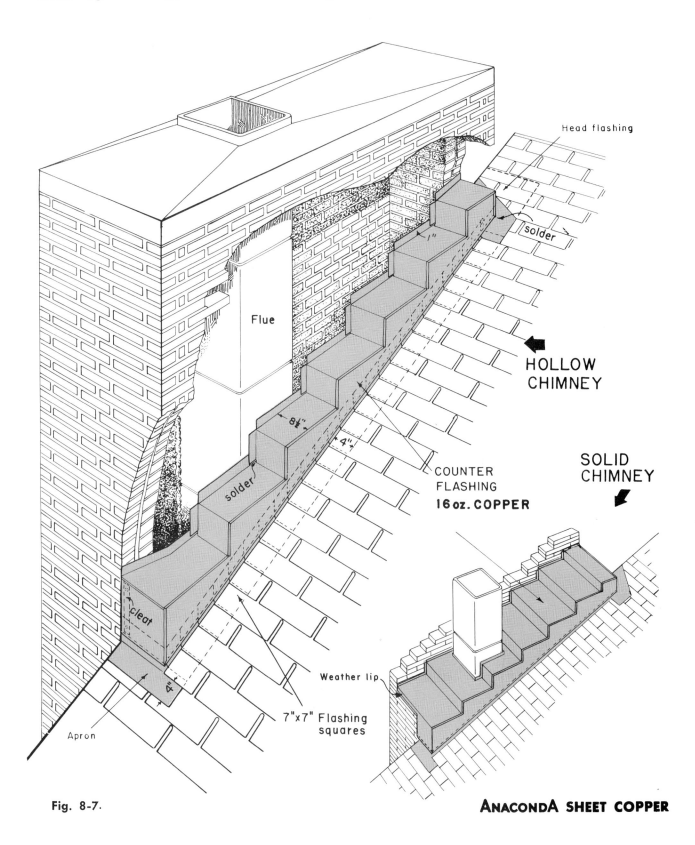

Head flashing

solder

Flue

HOLLOW
CHIMNEY

8½"

4"

solder

SOLID
CHIMNEY

COUNTER
FLASHING
16 oz. COPPER

cleat

4"

Weather lip

7"x7" Flashing
squares

Apron

Fig. 8-7.

ANACONDA SHEET COPPER

Chimney flashing in slope

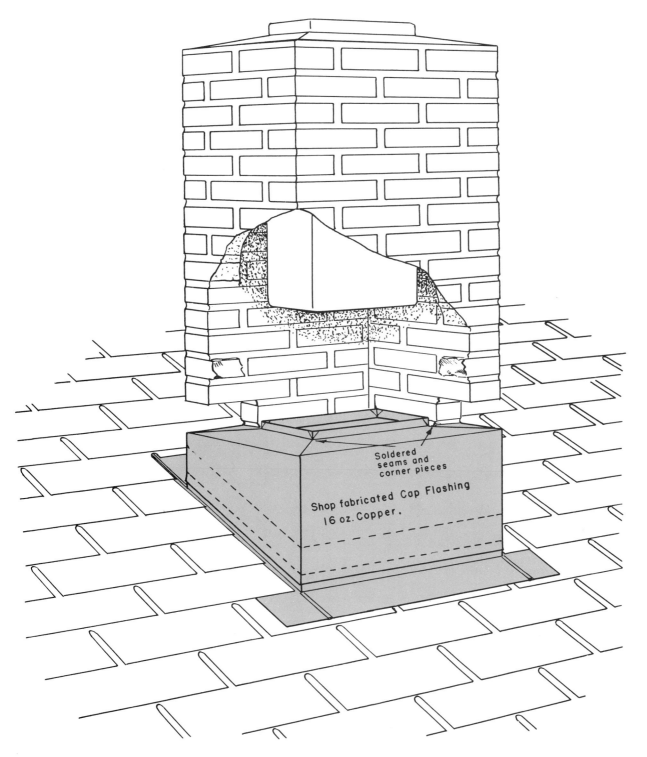

Soldered seams and corner pieces

Shop fabricated Cap Flashing 16 oz. Copper.

Fig. 8-6.

AnacondA SHEET COPPER

Suggested Specification. The chimney flashing is to be of 16-oz. cold rolled copper. There is to be a base flashing and a counter flashing, the latter extending through the masonry to the flue, with a 1″ flange or upstand at the flue. There is to be a ½″ hem at the bottom edge of the counter flashing for stiffness. All joints are to be without solder where possible, but where soldering is required the joint shall be scraped clean or blind-soldered. The base flashing shall consist of an apron with soldered corners and a hem at the bottom for concealed copper clips to hold the exposed flashing flange down to the roof. There are to be 7″ × 7″ flashing squares woven into the successive courses of shingles, with 3″ of copper extending vertically and 4″ onto the roof.

Suggested Specification. The chimney flashing is to be of 16-oz. cold rolled copper consisting of a base flashing and counter flashing. The base flashing is to be 7″ × 7″ flashing squares leafed in between courses of shingles. The head flashing and the apron are to be made up and soldered.

The counter flashing is to be of cold rolled temper and shall extend through the masonry, turning up 1″ at the flue. The exposed bottom edge is to have a hem for stiffness, and all of the bends are to be made on a bending brake. The work is to be blind-soldered wherever possible. Face soldering shall be washed and scraped clean.

Fig. 8-8.

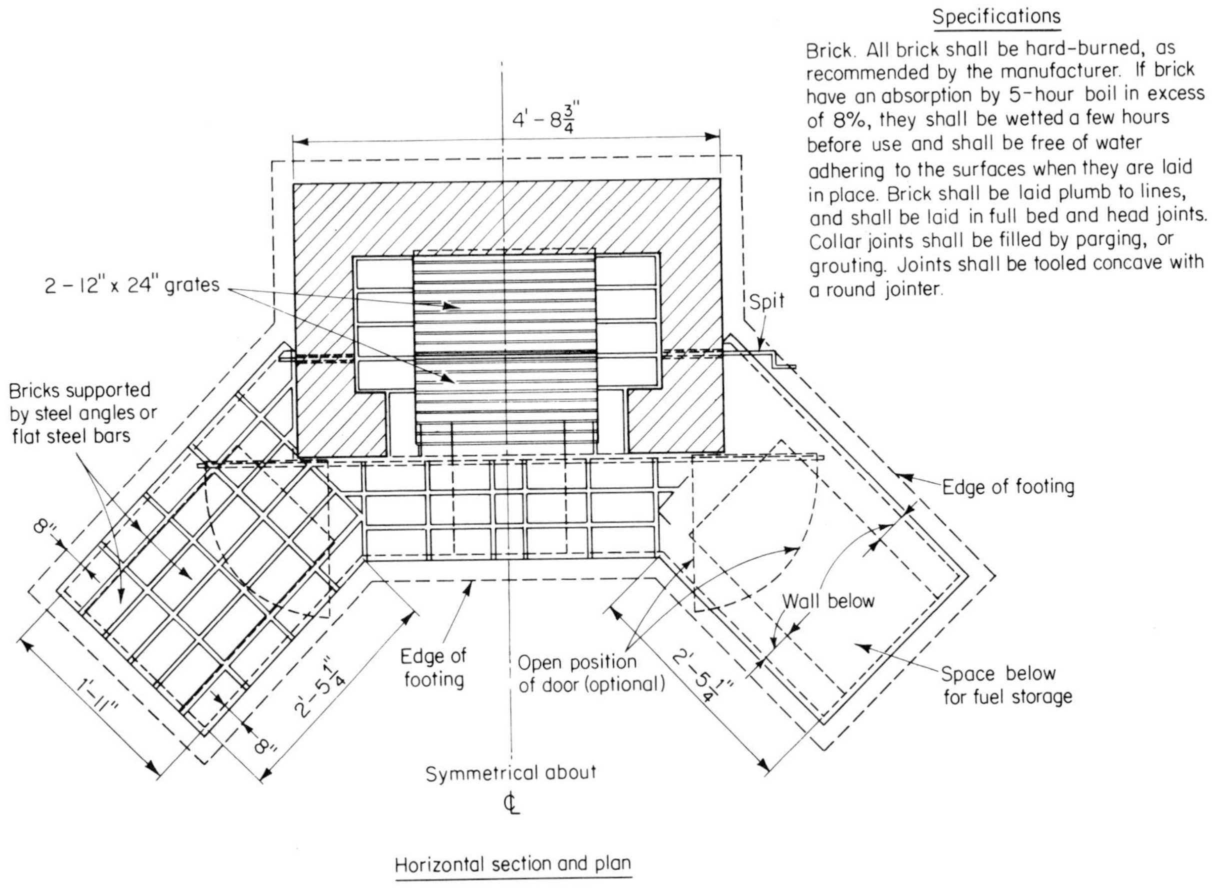
Specifications
Brick. All brick shall be hard-burned, as recommended by the manufacturer. If brick have an absorption by 5-hour boil in excess of 8%, they shall be wetted a few hours before use and shall be free of water adhering to the surfaces when they are laid in place. Brick shall be laid plumb to lines, and shall be laid in full bed and head joints. Collar joints shall be filled by parging, or grouting. Joints shall be tooled concave with a round jointer.
4'-8¾"
2 - 12" x 24" grates
Spit
Bricks supported by steel angles or flat steel bars
Edge of footing
8"
Wall below
1'-11"
2'-5¼"
Edge of footing
Open position of door (optional)
2'-5¼"
Space below for fuel storage
8"
Symmetrical about
℄
Horizontal section and plan

Suggested Specification. Chimney flashing shall be in two parts, a base counter flashing with a $4'' \times 4''$ roof flange and a 4" curb, and a hood or one-piece counter flashing with a hem at the bottom edge about 1" above the roof. The work shall be shapely and clean, and there shall be no solder on the face of the copper.

DESIGN FOR AN OUTDOOR FIREPLACE

Figs. 8.8, 8.9, and 8.10 comprise a set of dwgs for an outdoor fireplace. Before designing an outdoor fireplace, check your local fire laws.

If the dwgs and specifications shown on the dwgs are adhered to, they should provide a trouble-free, long-lasting fireplace. Notice the brick support noted on Fig. 8.8 and shown on Fig. 8.10. The brickwork on either side of the firebox brickwork is notated; if it was drawn in elevation, it would be distorted. It is important to determine what is better drawn and what is better notated. Observe the open brickwork near the top of the chimney. Dwg 8.9 shows the bricks laid on edge and reinforced with ½" bars 8½" o.c. both ways.

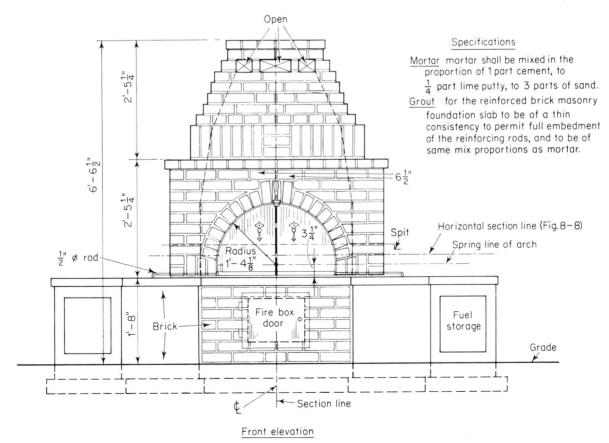

Fig. 8-9.

Specifications

Mortar mortar shall be mixed in the proportion of 1 part cement, to $\frac{1}{4}$ part lime putty, to 3 parts of sand.

Grout for the reinforced brick masonry foundation slab to be of a thin consistency to permit full embedment of the reinforcing rods, and to be of same mix proportions as mortar.

Front elevation

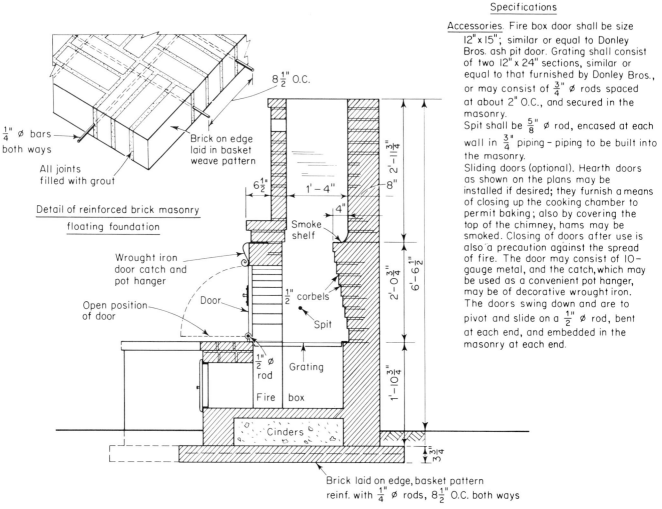

¼" ∅ bars both ways

All joints filled with grout

Brick on edge laid in basket weave pattern

Detail of reinforced brick masonry floating foundation

8½" O.C.

6½"   1'-4"

8"

4"

2'-1¾"

Smoke shelf

Wrought iron door catch and pot hanger

Open position of door

Door

½" corbels

Spit

2'-0¾"

6'-6½"

½" ∅ rod

Grating

Fire box

1'-10¾"

Cinders

3¾"

Brick laid on edge, basket pattern reinf. with ¼" ∅ rods, 8½" O.C. both ways

Fig. 8-10.

Cross section

Specifications

Accessories. Fire box door shall be size 12" x 15"; similar or equal to Donley Bros. ash pit door. Grating shall consist of two 12" x 24" sections, similar or equal to that furnished by Donley Bros., or may consist of ¾" ∅ rods spaced at about 2" O.C., and secured in the masonry.

Spit shall be ⅝" ∅ rod, encased at each wall in ¾" piping - piping to be built into the masonry.

Sliding doors (optional). Hearth doors as shown on the plans may be installed if desired; they furnish a means of closing up the cooking chamber to permit baking; also by covering the top of the chimney, hams may be smoked. Closing of doors after use is also a precaution against the spread of fire. The door may consist of 10-gauge metal, and the catch, which may be used as a convenient pot hanger, may be of decorative wrought iron. The doors swing down and are to pivot and slide on a ½" ∅ rod, bent at each end, and embedded in the masonry at each end.

TRASH BURNER

Fig. 8.11 is clear, concise, and easily understood by the mason. The whole plate is well balanced with care and completeness.

ASSIGNMENT:

Using the Table of Fireplace Dimensions on p. 172, draw to the scale of ½" to 1'-0" a domestic fireplace with a front horizontal opening of 48". Read this figure under letter "A" of the Table and located at "A" on Fig. 8.1.

TRASH BURNER

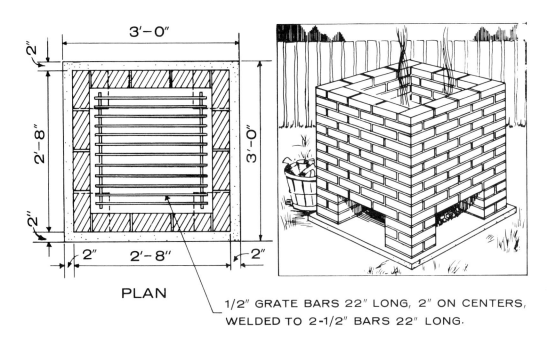

PLAN

1/2" GRATE BARS 22" LONG, 2" ON CENTERS, WELDED TO 2-1/2" BARS 22" LONG.

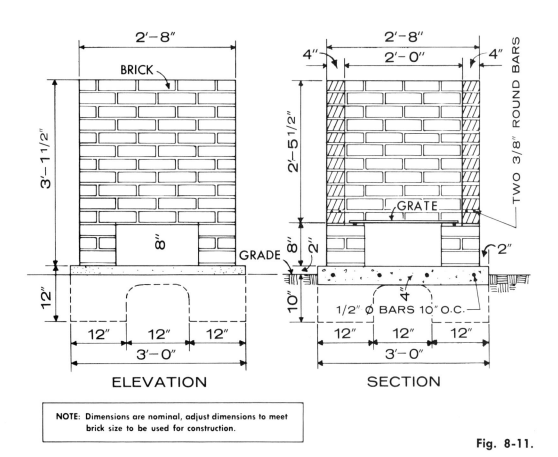

ELEVATION

SECTION

NOTE: Dimensions are nominal, adjust dimensions to meet brick size to be used for construction.

Fig. 8-11.

9 ARCHITECTURAL METAL, SHEET COPPER, FLASHING, AND METAL LATH

In this chapter we are going to examine metal details by four different manufacturers. These dwgs offer a rich experience in the excellence of presentation of structural details and must be carefully studied.

ARCHITECTURAL METALWORK

The following material is from Wooster Products, Inc., and is published with permission.

Fig. 9.1 shows sections of three different types, from many thresholds designed to meet different conditions for doors. These are excellent examples of simple detail dwgs prepared for immediate understanding by everyone from the architect to the tradesman applicator. Architectural dwgs would show them in large scale.

Fig. 9.2 shows two thresholds and a typical installation detail. These thresholds are designed to receive a hook strip at the bottom of the door.

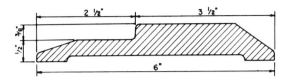

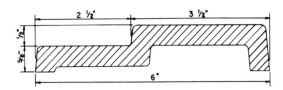

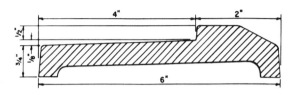

Fig. 9-1.   Three threshold sections.

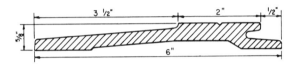

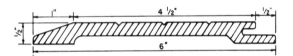

Fig. 9-2·   Thresholds with hook strips.

Alternatively these may be used to break the joint between two floors of slightly different elevations as may be encountered in alterations to buildings with existing floors.

STAIR TREADS

Fig. 9.3 shows the details for four different types of abrasive cast safety treads for application to steel pan stairs. They are produced in four different mediums; the type selected would be shown in the specifications. Note the four different fastening devices, which are important details.

Fig. 9.4 shows three sections and a plan for stair treads applied to concrete stairs. Two of the details show the treads for a flush-in concrete stair, and one shows the treatment for an existing concrete stair.

Fig. 9.5 shows a section of a truss rib tread for extra strength and rigidity. Examine the details for the fixings to meet different situations. Some of this type may be specified for heavy duty wear in warehouses and so on.

Fig. 9.6 shows an aluminum safety tread with masonry anchor for setting in wet concrete or terrazzo. The anchor is of aluminum extruded integrally the full length of the safety tread.

STEEL PAN
STAIR
APPLICATIONS

FERROGRIT — Abrasive Cast Iron
ALUMOGRIT — Abrasive Cast Aluminum
BRONZOGRIT — Abrasive Cast Bronze
NICKLOGRIT — Abrasive Cast Nickel Alloy

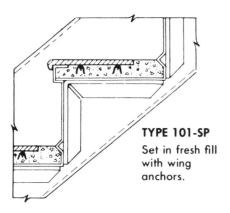

TYPE 101-SP
Set in fresh fill
with wing
anchors.

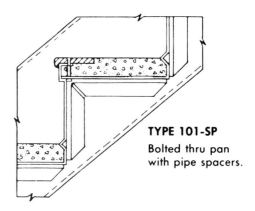

TYPE 101-SP
Bolted thru pan
with pipe spacers.

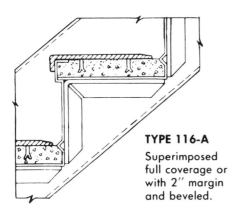

TYPE 116-A
Superimposed
full coverage or
with 2″ margin
and beveled.

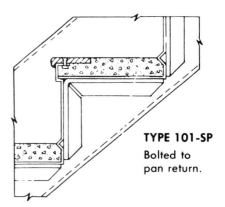

TYPE 101-SP
Bolted to
pan return.

Fig. 9-3.

CONCRETE STAIR APPLICATIONS

FERROGRIT — Abrasive Cast Iron
ALUMOGRIT — Abrasive Cast Aluminum
BRONZOGRIT — Abrasive Cast Bronze
NICKLOGRIT — Abrasive Cast Nickel Alloy

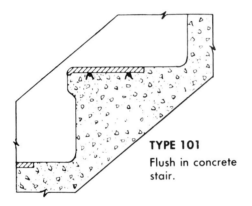

TYPE 101
Flush in concrete stair.

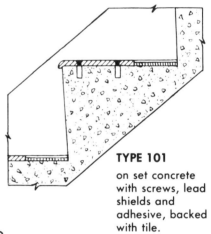

TYPE 101

on set concrete with screws, lead shields and adhesive, backed with tile.

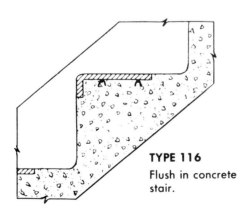

TYPE 116
Flush in concrete stair.

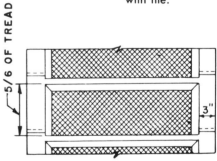

5/6 OF TREAD

3"

When safety treads are superimposed as shown above, allow 2" to 3" of margin at back and sides. Specify beveled sides and back.

Fig. 9-4.

TYPICAL INSTALLATIONS

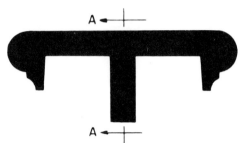

SECTION A-A

TRUSS RIBS: For extra strength and rigidity safety treads are cast with integral truss ribs when required.

Wooster abrasive cast structural treads and platforms are ideal for industrial plants and for ship ladders where a long wearing anti-slip tread is essential. Standard finish for Ferrogrit is black. Where a special color effect is desired the treads can be furnished unpainted for painting after installation. Other metals furnished with sand blasted finish.

Type 107 used structurally bolted to stringers.

Type 117-A ladder treads bolted directly to stringers.

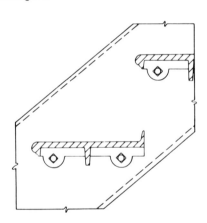

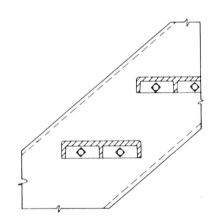

Type 105 used with flat plate risers fastened to nose and toeplate

Type 107-A fastened to carrier angles on stringers. Open risers.

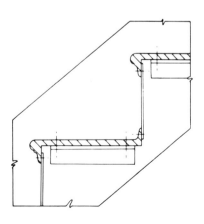

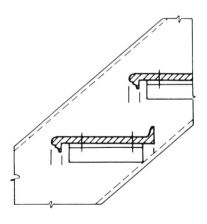

Fig. 9-5.

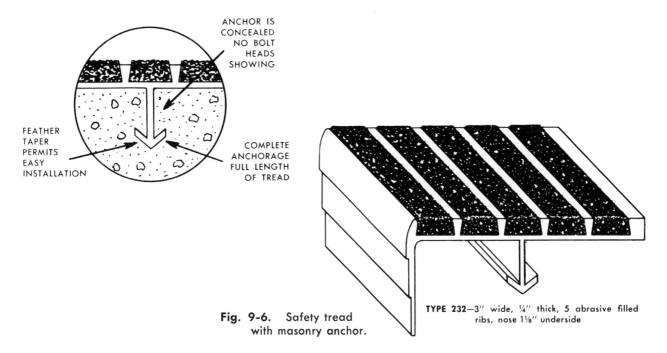

ANCHOR IS
CONCEALED
NO BOLT
HEADS
SHOWING

FEATHER
TAPER
PERMITS
EASY
INSTALLATION

COMPLETE
ANCHORAGE
FULL LENGTH
OF TREAD

Fig. 9-6. Safety tread
with masonry anchor.

TYPE 232—3″ wide, ¼″ thick, 5 abrasive filled
ribs, nose 1⅛″ underside

EXPANSION PLATES

Fig. 9.7 shows four abrasive cast expansion plates which are manufactured in four different mediums. All these details are very clearly defined, devoid of flourish or artistry, and are readily understood by all users.

MODERN SHEET COPPER PRACTICES

The following nine details are extracted from Publication C-1 of Modern Sheet Copper Practices issued by Anaconda American Brass Ltd. and are published with permission. Their foreword is as follows:

A guide for the correct uses of sheet copper

These drawings and specifications are intended as a guide to the Architect, to the Specification Writer, and to the Sheet Metalworker. They are not presumed to be a complete work in the application of sheet metal in building, but instead they represent a reissue of the best in construction detail. The drawings are original in type and modern in concept, and designed to be applied to present-day materials and methods.

The details and the specifications embody the advanced knowledge of sheet copper work, whereby it is established that all of the copper that is soldered or otherwise anchored shall be of cornice temper; also that the gage of the metal shall be heavy enough and in good proportion to the breadth and scale of the work; and finally that expansion joints and other provisions be made for freedom of movement wherever possible.

ABRASIVE CAST SPECIAL ITEMS

FERROGRIT • ALUMOGRIT • BRONZOGRIT • NICKLOGRIT

Wooster abrasive expansion plates are cast in durable, anti-slip abrasive metals, providing long-wearing plates for expansion joint assemblies. These plates are available in a variety of types as shown and are cast to order as detailed by the fabricator who furnishes the assembly.

ABRASIVE CAST EXPANSION PLATES

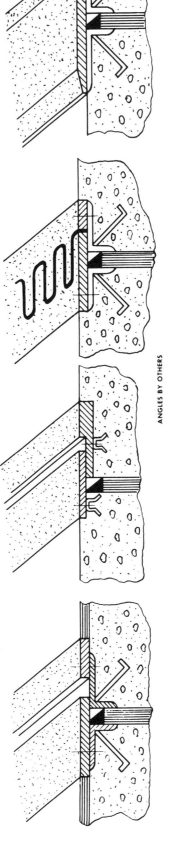

ANGLES BY OTHERS

TYPE NO. 100 EXPANSION PLATES: Two parallel plates, flat, installed flush with the finished floor. Widths as required. 4″ is minimum width for the widest plate, 1″ minimum for the second plate (1½″ or 2″ recommended). Individual lengths to 8′0″ for plates 3″ or more in width. 4′0″ maximum lengths for widths under 3″.

TYPE NO. 100-X EXPANSION PLATES: Two parallel, overlapping, plates installed flush with the finished floor. The first plate is flat, 3/8″ thick, the second plate is 3/4″ thick rebated to 3/8″ to receive the first plate. Width of each plate variable as required. Lengths same as for Type 100.

TYPE NO. 100 INTERLOCKING EXPANSION PLATES: Two interlocking plates ½″ thick with beveled fingers, one side regular and the other side opposite. Made in Alumogrit or Bronzogrit. The standard pattern provides plates that when joined are 7″ overall in width allowing ½″ expansion. The width can be adjusted to permit a maximum 1″ expansion. Standard length is 6′0″ or any multiples of 6′0″. Detailed drawing available on request.

TYPES NO. 110 AND NO. 114 EXPANSION PLATES: Type No. 110 has rounded edges. Type No. 114 has full one inch bevels. Both are singular types that set above the finished floor with beveled or rounded edges. Width is variable as required, 4″ minimum. Individual lengths to 8′6″.

Fig. 9-7.

SUGGESTED SPECIFICATION FOR FIG. 9.8

Standing Seam Copper Roofing may be applied by the Roll Method using strips of sheet copper of the proper width. These strips are to be joined together endwise by means of a ¾″ clinch lock joint, temporarily kept in alignment by indenting the metal at the folds of the lock with a center punch. The strips so assembled shall extend from ridge to eave or to the valley. The edges are to be turned up with roofing tongs as shown on the drawing, to form a double lock standing seam. The smaller upstanding edge of the formed strip is to be anchored to the roof deck at 12″ intervals with 1½″ × 3″ copper cleats. The finish at the ridge and at the eave and valley is to be as shown in detail.

The copper is to be 10-oz. Economy Copper Roofing applied in sheets 16″ × 72″ having a light cold rolled temper.

Alternate: The copper shall be of 16-oz. gauge in sheets 20″ × 96″.

SUGGESTED SPECIFICATION FOR FIG. 9.9

Endings for Insulated Built-up Roofs are to be made, as shown on the drawing, of 20-oz. cold rolled copper. The roof flange is to be built into the plies of roofing felt and fastened with nails or screws as shown, using ⅞″ No. 12 nails at 3″ spacing, or ¼″ screws at 6″ spacing. The end joints are to be lapped 3″ and soldered on the roof side, one of the roof fastenings being put through the lap. All bends are to be made with a bending brake, and particular care is to be exercised in making a neat and workmanlike finish at the exposed part of the edging. Unnecessary buckling and tool marks or other blemishes in the metal are not acceptable.

SUGGESTED SPECIFICATION FOR FIG. 9.10

Stone Coping "A": The copper which is to form a base flashing and a coping covering is to be of 24-oz. gauge cold rolled temper. It shall be made up of sections 8′-0″ long, and joints are to be either with a ¾″ soldered clinch lock seam or a 1½″ soldered lap seam, with ⅛″ copper rivets at 2″ spacings. In either case, the copper is to be cleaned, pretinned, and soldered with 50/50 lead-tin solder. The portion of copper that is built in to the plies of composition roofing is to have 1½″ diameter holes on 6″ centers to improve the bond with the membrane roofing. The outer edge of the coping covering is to be made secure by interlocking the covering with a continuous cleat of 20-oz. copper. In addition, the joint is to be made weathertight with an approved caulking compound.

Architectural Bronze Coping "B": The bronze coping will consist of ⅛″ thick architectural bronze, in accordance with the detail drawing. The sections of convenient length, 12′-0″ or more, shall be brazed together endwise with silver-alloy brazing solder, using a backer strip so that the finished work will show only a hairline joint. There are to be bronze holding clips

Standing seam roofing, roll method

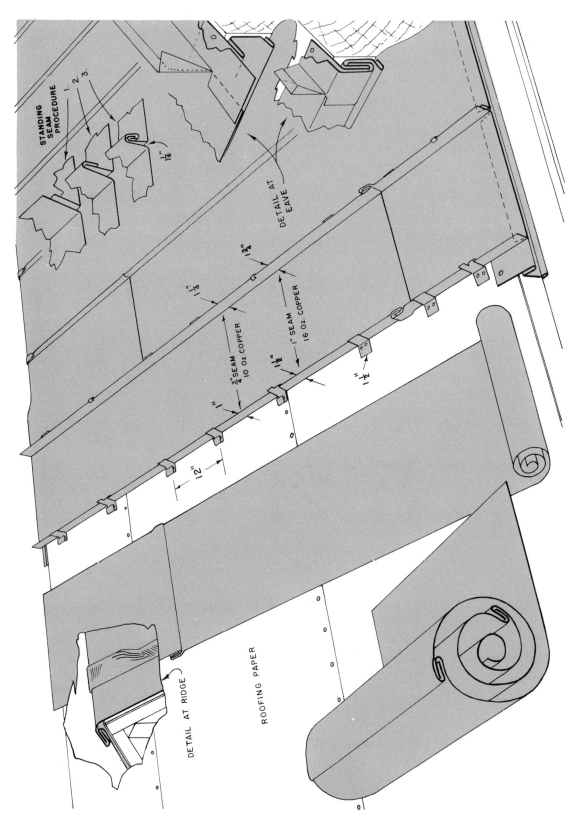

STANDING SEAM PROCEDURE

1. 2. 3.

$\frac{1}{16}$"

DETAIL AT EAVE

$1\frac{3}{4}$"

$1\frac{1}{4}$"

$\frac{3}{4}$" SEAM
10 OZ. COPPER

1" SEAM
16 OZ. COPPER

$1\frac{1}{2}$"

$\frac{3}{4}$"

1"

12"

ROOFING PAPER

DETAIL AT RIDGE

Fig. 9-8.

Edgings for insulated built-up roofs

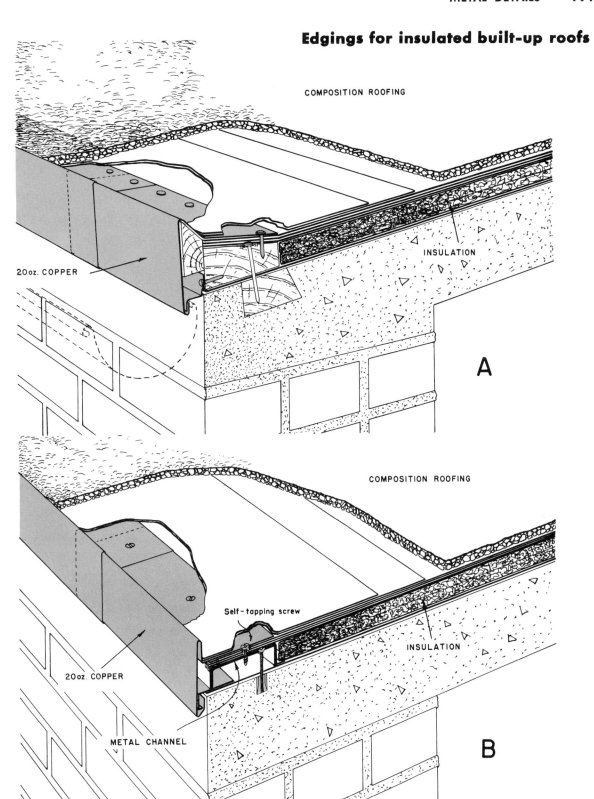

COMPOSITION ROOFING

20oz. COPPER

INSULATION

A

COMPOSITION ROOFING

Self-tapping screw

20oz. COPPER

INSULATION

METAL CHANNEL

B

Flashing at copings

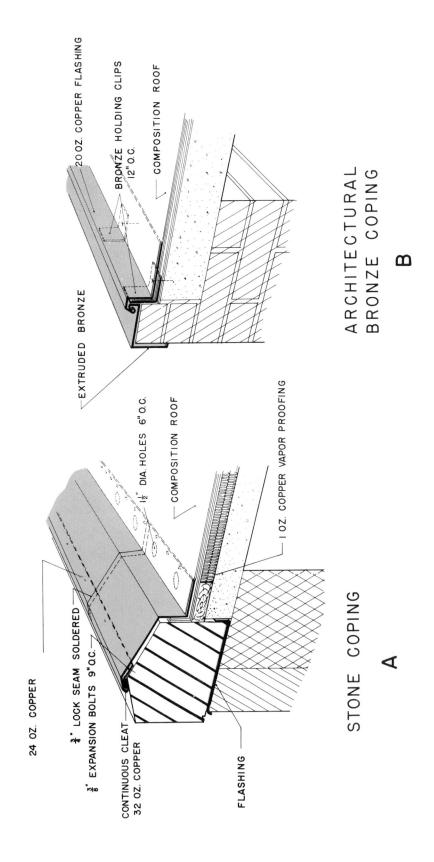

24 OZ. COPPER

20 OZ. COPPER FLASHING

BRONZE HOLDING CLIPS
12" O.C.

COMPOSITION ROOF

EXTRUDED BRONZE

$\frac{3}{4}$" LOCK SEAM SOLDERED

$\frac{3}{8}$" EXPANSION BOLTS 9" O.C.

CONTINUOUS CLEAT
32 OZ. COPPER

$1\frac{1}{2}$" DIA. HOLES 6" O.C.

COMPOSITION ROOF

1 OZ. COPPER VAPOR PROOFING

FLASHING

STONE COPING

A

ARCHITECTURAL
BRONZE COPING

B

ANACONDA SHEET COPPER

Fig. 9-10.

at spacings of not over 24″ brazed or riveted to the bronze coping, and anchored to the roof so as to get a positively true alignment and a permanent anchorage. This bronze coping is to be flashed with 20-oz. cold rolled copper, which is also to serve as a base flashing for the built-up composition roofing. The flashing is to interlock with the bronze at the outer edge, and the 4″ flange between the plies of roofing is to be fastened to the roof deck with copper nails or with screws at 3″ or 12″ spacings respectively.

SUGGESTED SPECIFICATION FOR FIG. 9.11

Built-in gutters are to be of cold rolled sheet copper of a gauge as called for on the drawings. The inner and outer edges of the gutter are to be free sliding, and there are to be expansion joints located midway between all downspouts. All fastenings are to be with clinch type copper cleats, either individual or continuous, made of 16-oz. copper. There are to be two copper nails in each individual cleat. Nails in continuous cleats shall be spaced 12″ apart. All cross joints are to be cleaned, pretinned, clinch locked, and soldered.

SUGGESTED SPECIFICATION FOR FIG. 9.12

Open valley

Valley linings are to be of 16-oz. copper in 8′-0″ lengths. The ends are to lap 6″ on slopes of 6″ per ft. or steeper. On lesser slopes the end joints are to be clinch locked and filled with white lead paste. The return bends for the clinch lock shall be 1½″ at the top edge and ¾″ at the bottom edge of the sheets of copper that make up the valley lining. The edges of the valley lining are to be turned back ¾″ to facilitate fastening with copper cleats, which are to occur at 12″ spacings. There shall be no nailing directly through the copper.

Closed valley

Flashing squares of 16-oz. copper 9″ square are to be inserted in each course of shingles at the valley. These are to be held in position by nailing at the top edge.

SUGGESTED SPECIFICATION FOR FIG. 9.13

Chimney Flashing shall be of 16-oz. cold rolled copper and shall be composed of a base flashing and counter flashing. The base flashing shall have a 4″ roof flange and a curb, or vertical flashing 8″ high. The counter flashing shall have a 4″ vertical face and shall extend into the chimney

Built-in gutters

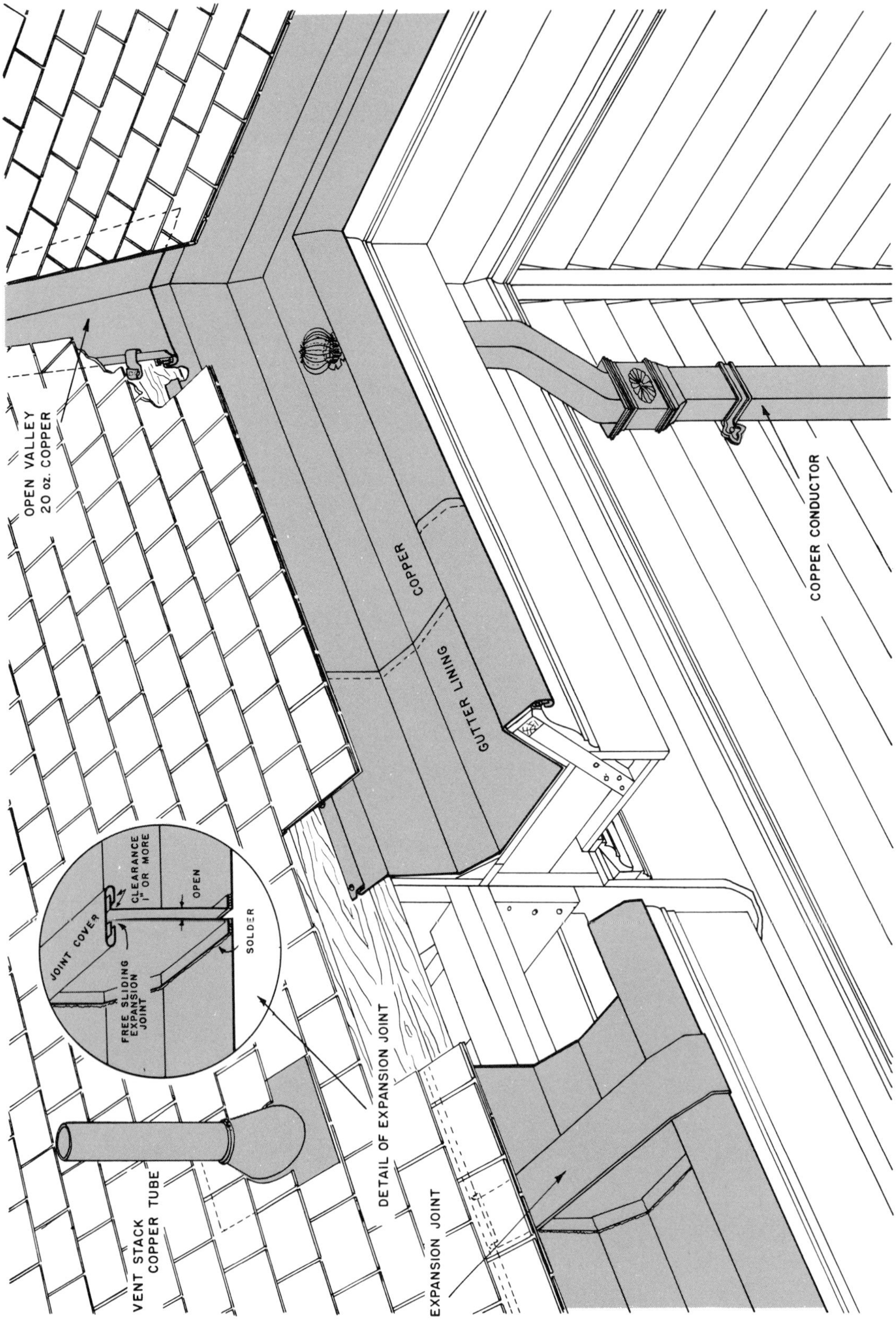

OPEN VALLEY
20 oz. COPPER

COPPER

GUTTER LINING

JOINT COVER

CLEARANCE 1" OR MORE

OPEN

FREE SLIDING
EXPANSION
JOINT

SOLDER

DETAIL OF EXPANSION JOINT

VENT STACK
COPPER TUBE

EXPANSION JOINT

COPPER CONDUCTOR

ANACONDA SHEET COPPER

Fig. 9-11.

ANACONDA SHEET COPPER

Valley flashings

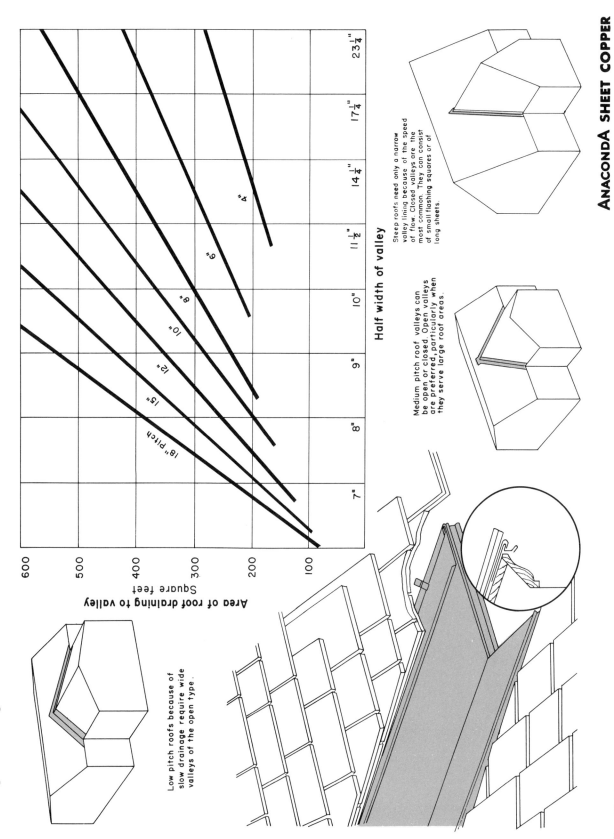

Area of roof draining to valley — Square feet

Half width of valley

Steep roofs need only a narrow valley lining because of the speed of flow. Closed valleys are the most common. They can consist of small flashing squares or of long sheets.

Medium pitch roof valleys can be open or closed. Open valleys are preferred, particularly when they serve large roof areas.

Low pitch roofs because of slow drainage require wide valleys of the open type.

Fig. 9-12.

Chimney flashing in flat roof

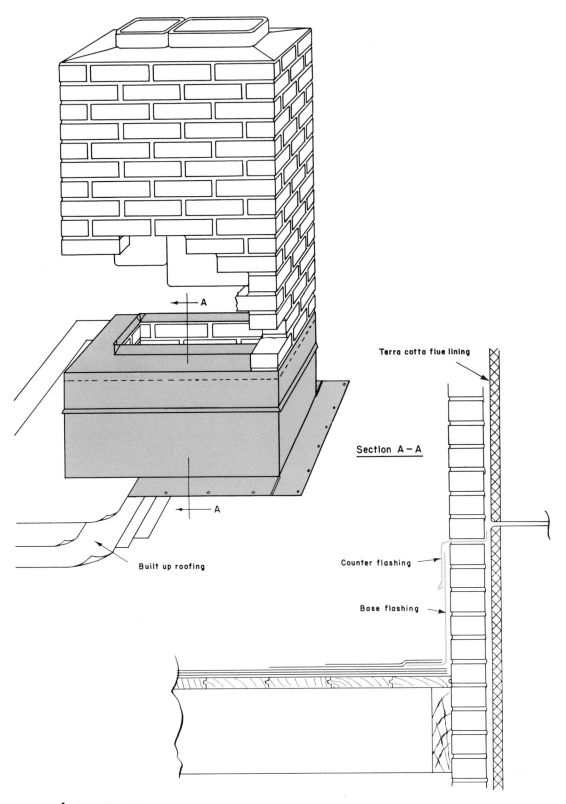

Built up roofing

Terra cotta flue lining

Section A – A

Counter flashing

Base flashing

ANACONDA SHEET COPPER

Fig. 9-13.

horizontally through the flue where it is to finish with a 1″ upstand. The exposed bottom edge of the counter flashing is to have a hem or cant for stiffness. All joints are to be blind soldered wherever possible and the work is to be left clean.

SUGGESTED SPECIFICATION FOR FIG. 9.14

The top member of the expansion joint flashing is to be cut open as shown, for a distance of at least 18″ from the point of intersection in each of the four directions. ¾″ × ½″ angles are to be soldered to the upstanding legs of the expansion fold to receive the freesliding cap with return bends at the edges for a clinch lock joint. The entire intersection of copper is to be made up on the bench with shop tools and the best facilities for soldering. The underside of the copper is to be tinned 1″ wide at the leading edges, and the whole assembly is set in place on the roof, then riveted and soldered. The soldering shall be neatly done and concealed wherever possible. All copper is to be of 20-oz. gauge and of cold rolled temper.

SUGGESTED SPECIFICATION FOR FIG. 9.15

The expansion joint covers at the floors and walls on the interior of the building are to be made up of extruded architectural bronze as shown in detail, with a minimum thickness of ⅛″. The material shall be of commercial grade and shall have a scratch-brush finish. All extruded bronze shall be cut to exact lengths, put together with clamps and assembled with a snug, driving fit. The joining shall be done principally with screws, but where added strength is required, the joints may be silver-alloy brazed. (Oxyacetylene welding may also be done, using filler-metal strips cut from the base metal, but the joints will never be completely free of porosity.)

The finish work shall be without marks or blemishes of any kind, and shall be cleaned and given a spray coat of best quality outdoor lacquer.

The expansion joint covers at the ceiling are to be made of a size and shape to conform to the bronze expansion joint covers at the walls against which they abut. The ceiling covers are to be of sheet metal, using No. 22 B&S gauge commercial bronze, quarter hard.

SUGGESTED SPECIFICATION FOR FIG. 9.16

The copings shall be covered with 20-oz. cold rolled copper formed as shown on the drawings. The pieces are to be brake formed in 8′-0″ lengths with clinch lock and blind soldered end joints, and expansion joints of 24′-0″ intervals. The copper coping is to have free sliding edges at both sides of the wall. This may be accomplished through the use of continuous copper cleats or by interlocking with other copper work. The cleats are to be securely fastened at 12″ spacings.

Flashing intersection of structural expansion joints

ANACONDA SHEET COPPER

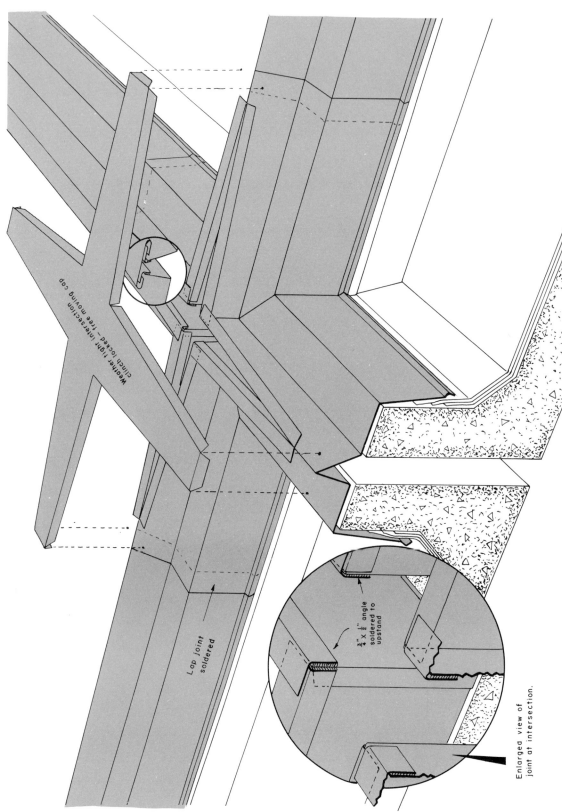

Weather tight intersection – clinch locked – free moving cap

Lap joint soldered

¾" X ½" angle soldered to upstand

Enlarged view of joint at intersection.

Fig. 9-14.

Expansion joint for floor and wall

ANACONDA EXTRUDED SHAPE

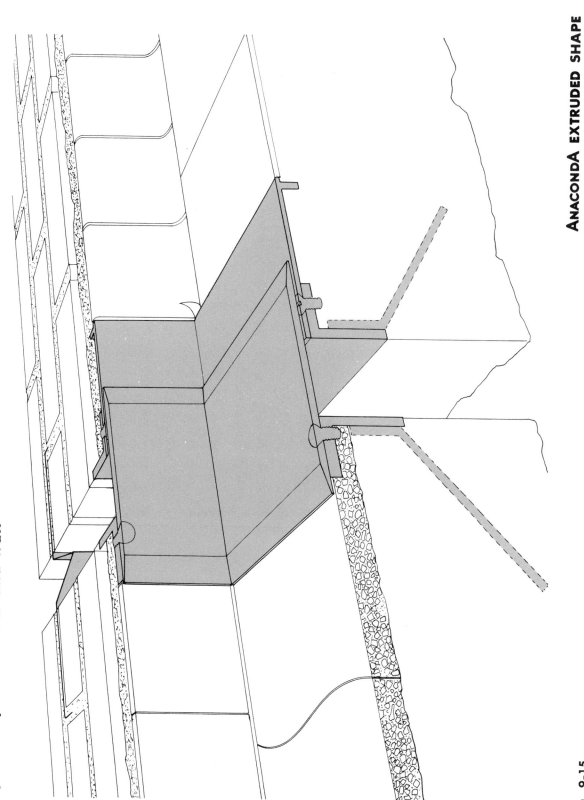

Fig. 9-15.

Coping covers and base flashing

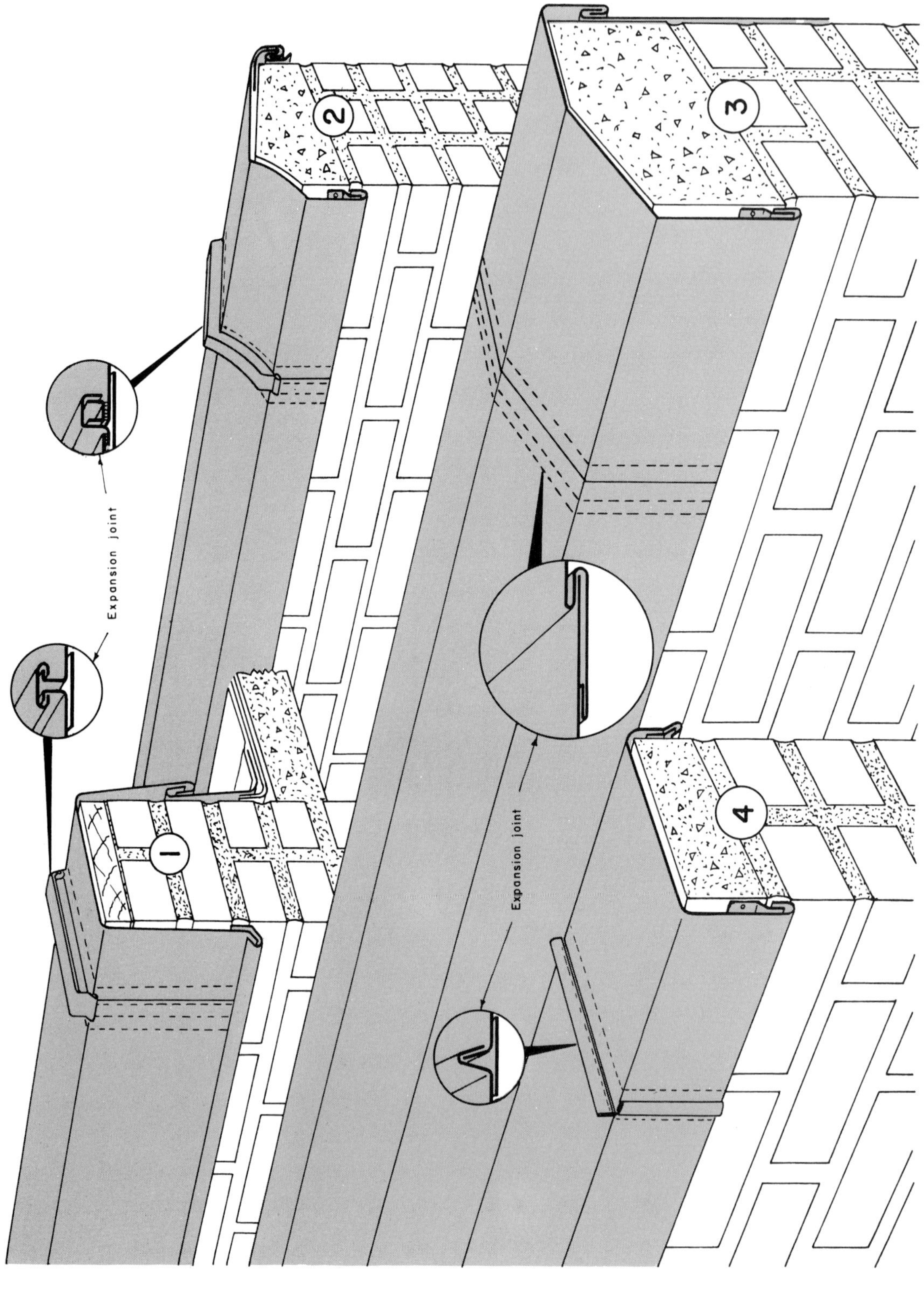

ANACONDA SHEET COPPER

Expansion joint

Expansion joint

Fig. 9-16.

FLASHING DETAILS

The following material is from Phoenix Building Products Inc. and is published by permission. The details show different treatments for different construction, and the following types of flashings are manufactured. See Fig. 9.17.

(a) Copper plus lead in weights of 2 and 3 oz. per sq. ft.

(b) Coated copper consisting of a core of electro-deposited copper weighing 2, 3, 5, or 7 oz. per sq. ft., heavily coated on both sides with special pliable bituminous mastic compound.

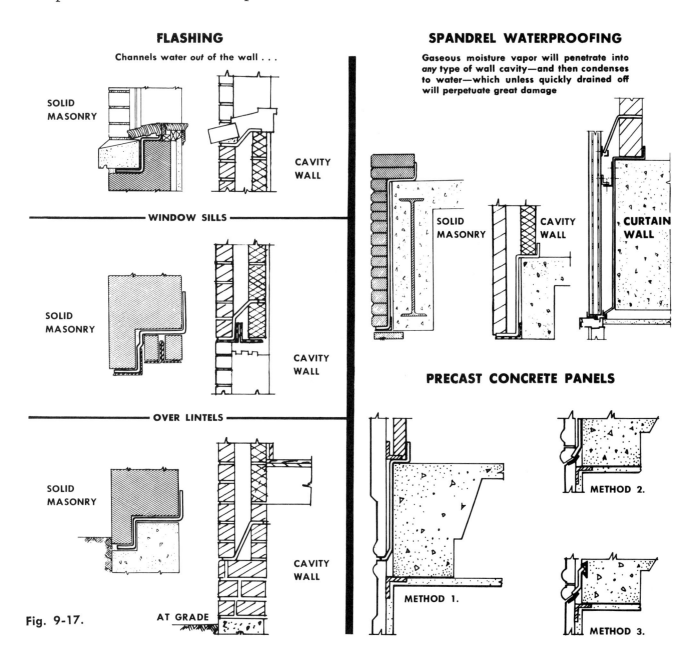

Fig. 9-17.

FLASHING

Channels water *out* of the wall . . .

SOLID MASONRY
CAVITY WALL

— WINDOW SILLS —

SOLID MASONRY
CAVITY WALL

— OVER LINTELS —

SOLID MASONRY
CAVITY WALL
AT GRADE

SPANDREL WATERPROOFING

Gaseous moisture vapor will penetrate into *any* type of wall cavity—and then condenses to water—which unless quickly drained off will perpetuate great damage

SOLID MASONRY
CAVITY WALL
CURTAIN WALL

PRECAST CONCRETE PANELS

METHOD 1.
METHOD 2.
METHOD 3.

(c) Copper flashing consisting of a sheet of 1, 2, or 3 oz. electro-deposited copper, bonded to a special waterproof backing.

(d) Flashing Reglets in galvanized steel, copper or aluminum.

(e) Plasta Seal, a superior Polyvinyl plastic membrane available in a wide range of gages and widths to meet varying specifications.

(f) Saturated Fabric, a strong elastic fabric of open mesh construction, obtainable in tar or asphalt saturation to meet specific requirements.

(g) Flashing Cloth, 4 oz. per sq. yd. of Osnaburg Cloth saturated and then coated on both sides with tough, high ductile asphalt to a total weight of at least 40 oz. per sq. yd.

METAL LATH

The following material is from the Pedlar People Ltd. and is published by permission.

Suspended metal lath ceilings

Fig. 9.18 shows details of a suspended metal lath ceiling. Carefully note the compression members and the specification to meet unusual conditions.

Fig. 9.19 shows details of studless metal lath partitions. Specifications are available giving minimum weights or sizes for metal lath, metal runners, legs of metal runners, base metal clips, tie wire, wood floor runners, and erection method for varying walls.

Metal lath hollow partitions with channel studs

Fig. 9.20 shows details of metal lath hollow partitions with channel studs. Specifications and fire ratings are available with these products. On all details one is impressed by the apparent simplicity of presentation with no wasted lines nor words.

Metal stud hollow partition details

Fig. 9.21 shows metal stud hollow partition details with dimensional limitations and also technical notes for comparatively large partitions.

Metal stud hollow partition attachment details

Fig. 9.22 shows eight attachment details for metal stud hollow partitions. These dwgs are not exhaustive.

SUSPENDED METAL LATH CEILINGS

- ● CHANNEL CLEARANCES
- ● COMPRESSION MEMBERS
- ● TIES AND SPLICES
- ● VENTILATION

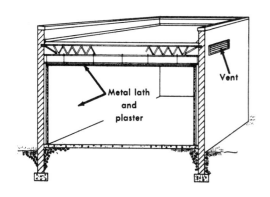

Where lath and plaster ceilings are located under roof construction, it is recommended that the space thus established be ventilated. Such ventilation shall be designed in accordance with accepted engineering practice.

VENTILATION

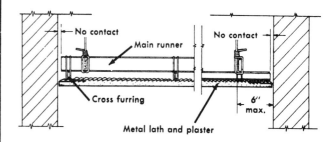

RUNNER AND FURRING CHANNEL CLEARANCES

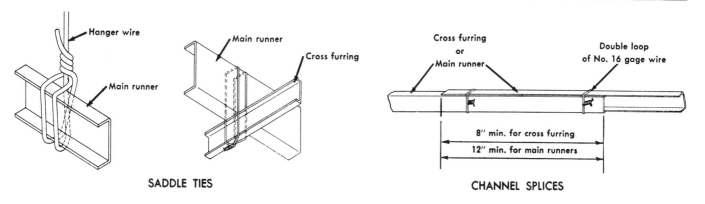

SADDLE TIES

CHANNEL SPLICES

8" min. for cross furring

12" min. for main runners

TIES AND SPLICES

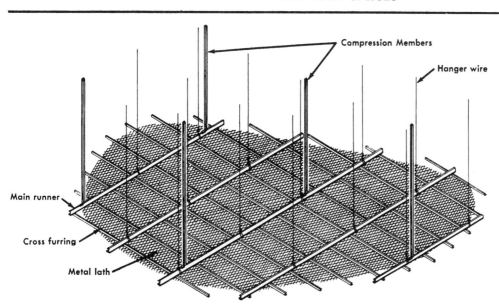

Hangers to resist compression—In regions subject to tornadoes or cyclones, where upward pressures are likely to be exerted or where suspended ceiling areas are exposed to high winds through outside openings during construction, hangers shall either be of a type to resist compression, or struts of ¾" channels or tees (of heavier size where hangers exceed 4' o.c.) may be used. These struts shall be used vertically between runner channels and the construction above, being spaced not to exceed 8' o.c. in both directions. They shall be in addition to the regular hangers.

COMPRESSION MEMBERS

Fig. 9-18.

203

STUDLESS METAL LATH PARTITIONS

STUDLESS 2" SOLID PARTITION DETAILS

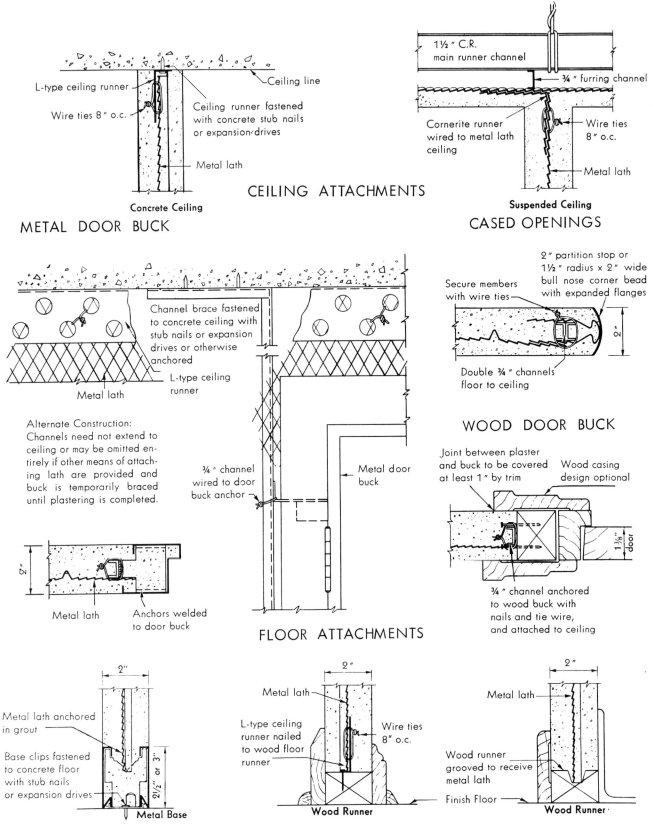

L-type ceiling runner

Wire ties 8" o.c.

Ceiling line

Ceiling runner fastened with concrete stub nails or expansion drives

Metal lath

Concrete Ceiling

METAL DOOR BUCK

1½" C.R. main runner channel

¾" furring channel

Cornerite runner wired to metal lath ceiling

Wire ties 8" o.c.

Metal lath

CEILING ATTACHMENTS

Suspended Ceiling

CASED OPENINGS

Channel brace fastened to concrete ceiling with stub nails or expansion drives or otherwise anchored

L-type ceiling runner

Metal lath

Alternate Construction: Channels need not extend to ceiling or may be omitted entirely if other means of attaching lath are provided and buck is temporarily braced until plastering is completed.

2"

Metal lath

Anchors welded to door buck

¾" channel wired to door buck anchor

Metal door buck

FLOOR ATTACHMENTS

2" partition stop or 1½" radius x 2" wide bull nose corner bead with expanded flanges

Secure members with wire ties

2"

Double ¾" channels floor to ceiling

WOOD DOOR BUCK

Joint between plaster and buck to be covered at least 1" by trim

Wood casing design optional

1⅜" door

¾" channel anchored to wood buck with nails and tie wire, and attached to ceiling

Metal lath anchored in grout

Base clips fastened to concrete floor with stub nails or expansion drives

2"

2½" or 3"

Metal Base

Metal lath

L-type ceiling runner nailed to wood floor runner

2"

Wire ties 8" o.c.

Wood Runner

Metal lath

2"

Wood runner grooved to receive metal lath

Finish Floor

Wood Runner

Fig. 9-19.

204

METAL LATH HOLLOW PARTITIONS WITH CHANNEL STUDS

DOOR BUCKS

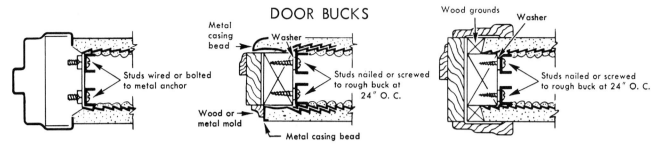

METAL DOOR BUCK — WOOD BUCK AND METAL CASING BEAD — WOOD BUCK AND CASING

CROSS TIES OR SPACES

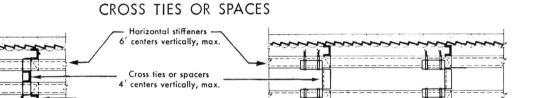

STUD ANCHORAGE

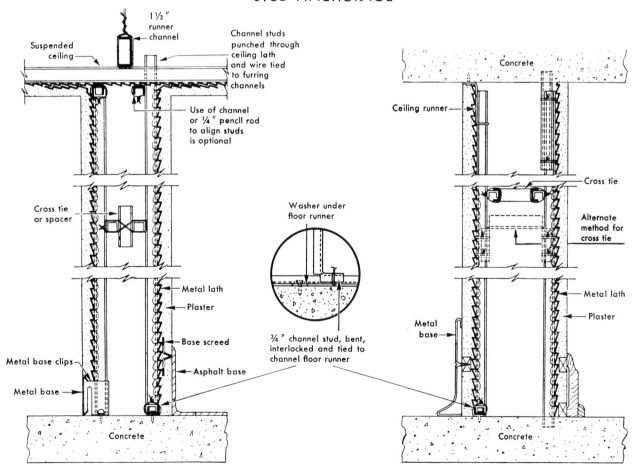

Fig. 9-20.

METAL STUD HOLLOW PARTITIONS
DETAILS
● DIMENSIONAL LIMITATIONS

● WALL ATTACHMENT DETAILS

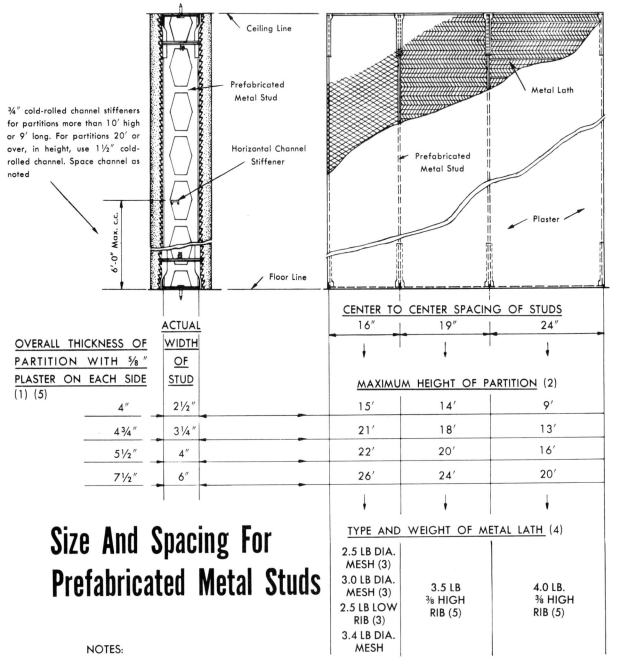

Ceiling Line

Prefabricated Metal Stud

¾" cold-rolled channel stiffeners for partitions more than 10' high or 9' long. For partitions 20' or over, in height, use 1½" cold-rolled channel. Space channel as noted

Horizontal Channel Stiffener

6'-0" Max. c.c.

Floor Line

Metal Lath

Prefabricated Metal Stud

Plaster

OVERALL THICKNESS OF PARTITION WITH ⅝" PLASTER ON EACH SIDE (1) (5)	ACTUAL WIDTH OF STUD	CENTER TO CENTER SPACING OF STUDS		
		16"	19"	24"
		MAXIMUM HEIGHT OF PARTITION (2)		
4"	2½"	15'	14'	9'
4¾"	3¼"	21'	18'	13'
5½"	4"	22'	20'	16'
7½"	6"	26'	24'	20'
		TYPE AND WEIGHT OF METAL LATH (4)		
		2.5 LB DIA. MESH (3) 3.0 LB DIA. MESH (3) 2.5 LB LOW RIB (3) 3.4 LB DIA. MESH	3.5 LB ⅜ HIGH RIB (5)	4.0 LB. ⅜ HIGH RIB (5)

Size And Spacing For Prefabricated Metal Studs

NOTES:

(1) Plaster thickness is measured from face of Metal Lath.

Plaster thickness is ¾" when measured from face of stud to face of finished surface.

(2) For lengths not exceeding 1½ times height. For lengths exceeding this, reduce height 20%.

(3) For prefabricated metal stud spacing not exceeding 12" center to center.

(4) Weights are exclusive of paper, fiber, or other backing.

(5) Rib metal lath with ribs against studs, increases partition thickness ½".

Fig. 9-21.

METAL STUD HOLLOW PARTITIONS

ATTACHMENT DETAILS FOR WALLS FACED WITH PLASTER AND CERAMIC TILE OR OTHER VENEERS

PLASTER CONSTRUCTION

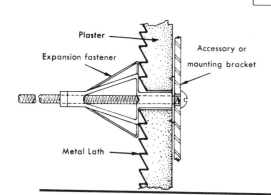

Plaster

Expansion fastener

Accessory or mounting bracket

Metal Lath

SUITABLE FOR
ATTACHMENT OF:

Closet Shelves
Wall Cabinets
Towel Bars
Soap Dishes
Paper Holders
Venetian Blinds
Wall Shelves
Tumbler Holders

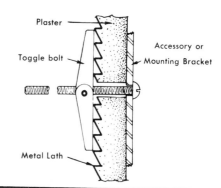

Plaster

Toggle bolt

Accessory or Mounting Bracket

Metal Lath

TILE OR VENEER CONSTRUCTION

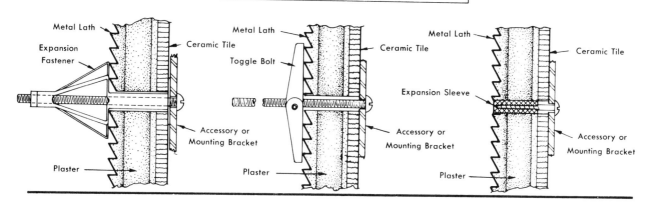

Metal Lath

Expansion Fastener

Ceramic Tile

Accessory or Mounting Bracket

Plaster

Metal Lath

Toggle Bolt

Ceramic Tile

Accessory or Mounting Bracket

Plaster

Metal Lath

Ceramic Tile

Expansion Sleeve

Accessory or Mounting Bracket

Plaster

PREFABRICATED METAL STUDS

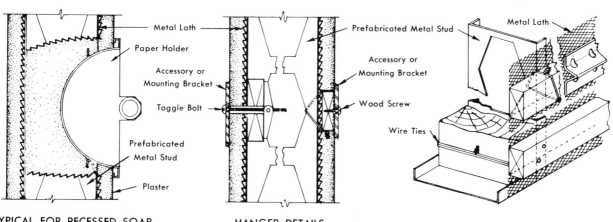

Metal Lath

Paper Holder

Accessory or Mounting Bracket

Prefabricated Metal Stud

Plaster

Prefabricated Metal Stud

Accessory or Mounting Bracket

Toggle Bolt

Wood Screw

Metal Lath

Wire Ties

TYPICAL FOR RECESSED SOAP DISH OR PAPER HOLDER

HANGER DETAILS
FOR HEAVY OBJECTS   FOR LIGHT OBJECTS

GROUNDS FOR BASE

Fig. 9-22.

10 A CHAPEL

In this chapter we are going to study many details of a children's chapel 28'-0" × 42'-0" which, with two classroom wings, was added to a church bldg complex. The material for this chapter was supplied through the courtesy of architect William M. Van Fleet, A.I.A., of California and is published with his permission.

The buildings were arranged to form an intimate open court with exposed aggregate paving surrounding a magnificent magnolia tree which is overlooked by a glass bay of the chapel and classroom windows, resulting in an area of contemplative calm. Fig. 10.1 shows the glazed north wall of the chapel, and Fig. 10.2 shows the stained glass window at the south.

Structurally the chapel is quite simple with four rein conc pier pads supporting two steel bents connected with an "I" beam which takes most of the shear in both directions. See Fig. 10.3. The perimeter foundations are rein conc, and the superstructure is wood framing.

PARTIAL PLOT PLAN

Fig. 10.4 shows a partial plot plan; locate the compass point, read up on the dwg, and note:

(a) the 9'-0" sidewalk plus 3'-0" to property line and 7'-6" to (dotted) bldg line. Remember that each year many bldgs are incorrectly located on incorrect bldg lots.

(b) 3 × 12 RWD (redwood). Wood supports (outriggers). See Fig. 10.12.

Fig. 10-1. North wall.

Fig. 10-2. South window.

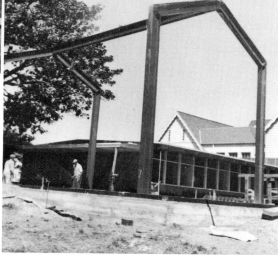

Fig. 10-3. General structure.

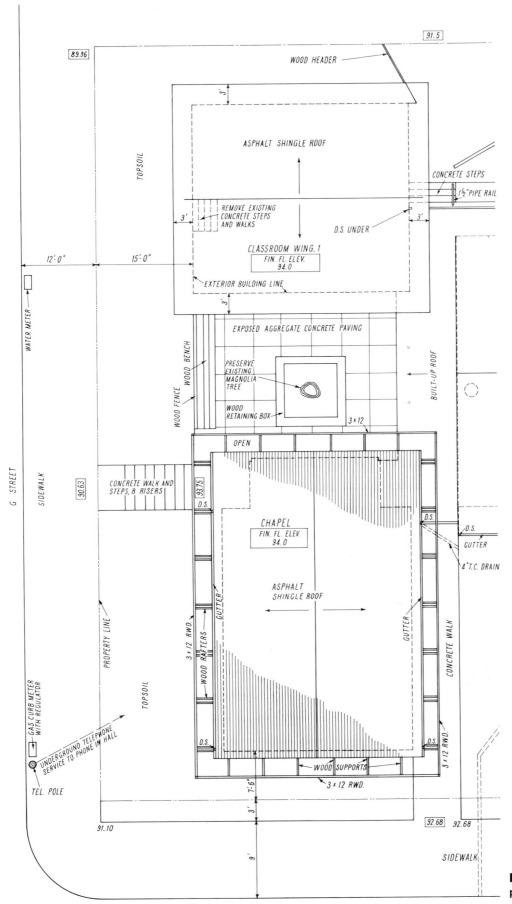

Fig. 10-4. Partial plot plan.

(c) eight riser conc steps, ele 90.63 to 93.75 and to 94.00 at the chapel floor.

(d) classroom wings 1 and 2 front onto the court and the old conc steps to be removed.

Where RWD is shown on the dwgs, it means "redwood," the name of a Californian tree (S. sempervirens) which grows to a height of more than 200 ft and up to 16 ft in diam. Another redwood specie growing in the same state is the sequoia (S. gigantea) and is the most massive tree on earth. One living tree is 272.4 ft in height, 27½ ft in diam, and over 4,000 years of age. Some redwood (which could have been part of a 2,000-year-old tree before the Founder of the church was born) is incorporated in this quiet chapel.

It is very sobering for engineers, architects, and everyone else to think of these things. We must design and build so that future generations will say, "Thank you."

PARTIAL ROOF PLAN

Fig. 10.5 shows a partial roof plan to be studied with sect details at Fig. 10.7 *Note:*

(a) *sect 1 & 2 for classroom ridge and wall-plate supporting 4 × 8 rafters.*

(b) *sect 3 shows 4'-0" horiz returning outrigger to N & S roof barge bds. The btm right dwg shows 2 × 6 T & G sheathing and 16" returning open eave seen at Figs. 10.7 & 10.12.*

(c) *sect 4 for a typical roof eave detail.*

(d) *the pipe cols supporting 4 × 6 beam for flat roof between the chapel and classroom Wing 1.*

Remember that it is a very different thing to study existing dwgs than to design and detail new concepts. Keep this in mind, please!

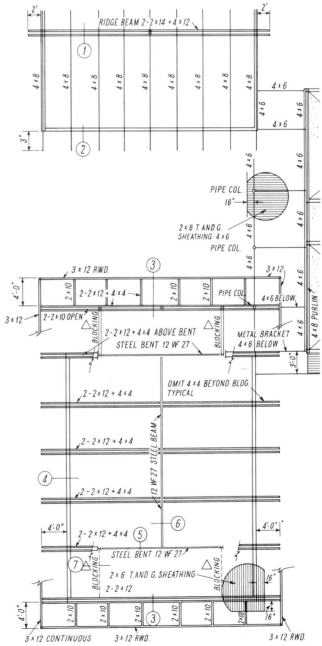

Fig. 10-5. Partial roof plan.

ROOF SECTION DETAILS

Fig. 10.6 shows detail Nos 1, 2, 3, and 4. *Note:*

(a) *sect 1,* detail of a 4 × 4 *classroom post* supporting a built-up ridge beam with a 4 × 12 core and two 2 × 14s. All wood beams, girders, and purlins are specified as select structural grade S4S, specie D.F. (surfaced four sides, Douglas Fir).

(b) *sect 2* shows a 4 × 4 post (*N & S classroom walls*) supporting double plates and 4 × 8 D.F. rafters with RWD T & G roofing. All posts and rafters are placed 4'-0" oc.

(c) *sect 3* shows 2 × 6 stud with double plates supporting a typical built-up chapel beam rafter of two 2 × 12s with a center core of 4 × 4. The outriggers to the barge bds of the NS chapel walls are reduced to 2 × 10 to match the beam rafter feet of the EW walls. See Fig. 10.2.

(d) *sect 4* shows a 2 × 6 stud wall (16" oc) with a 4 × 6 post under each beam rafter supporting 2 × 6 top plates and solid 4 × 12 blocking. Note the 4 × 4 shown by dotted lines under the T & G and the 4 × 4 center core of the typical chapel beam. The beam rafters are reduced to 2 × 10s at the eaves with a fascia bd of 3 × 12 RWD.

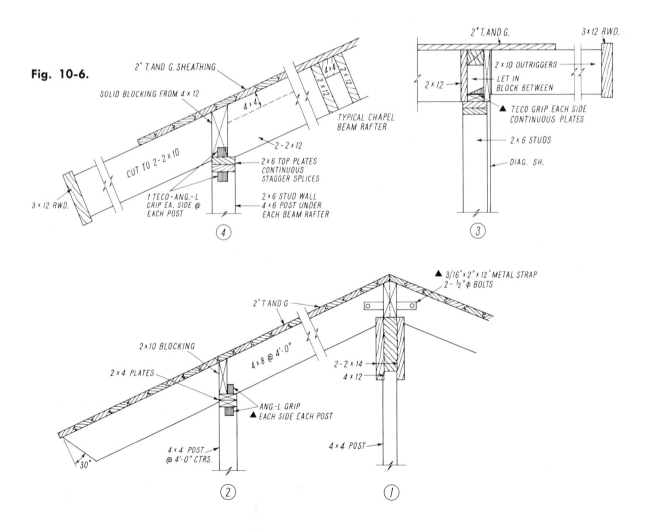

Fig. 10-6.

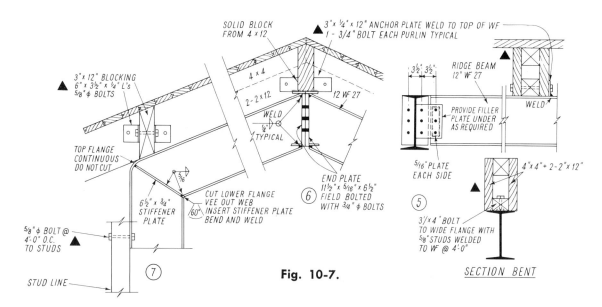

Fig. 10-7.

Fig. 10.7 shows details 5, 6, and 7. *Note:*
(a) *sect 5* shows the bolted connection details of the 12 ᵂ 27 ridge beam to the steel bent. See Fig. 10.3.
(b) *sect 6* shows the weld and bolt details of the bents with the chapel rafter beam and solid 4 × 12 block over.
(c) *sect 7* shows an interesting detail for the fabrication of the angle of the bent. Study the flanges; the top is cont and the lower is cut away for bending and is rein with a welded stiffener plate.

FOUNDATION PLAN

Fig. 10.8 shows the chapel foundation plan to be studied with the details at Fig. 10.9. *Note:*
(a) *sects 5, 6 and 7* for warm air duct system and HRs (heat registers). Count the different sizes of ducts!
(b) *sect 8* shows the outline of pier pads and the plan of the 'H' cols.
(c) *sect 9* indicates the outside fdn detail.
(d) read the dwg notations. The floor registers are balanced at 75 C.F.M. (cubic feet per minute).

FOUNDATION PLAN DETAILS

Fig. 10.9 shows four foundation plan details. *Note:*
(a) *sect 5* shows a typical exterior fdn wall of the chapel. *Read the dwg from the btm up and list all the information you can derive from it!*
(b) *sect 6*, duct imbedded in concrete. This is important.

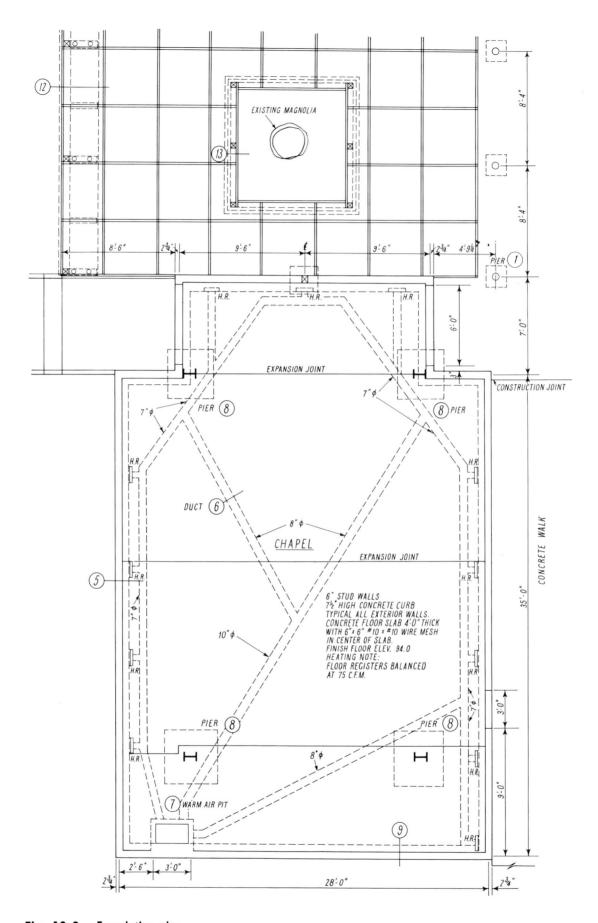

Fig. 10-8. Foundation plan.

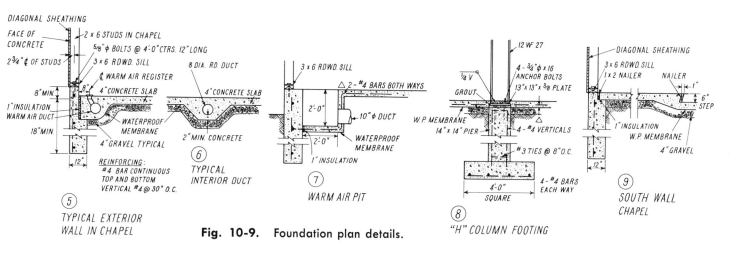

Fig. 10-9. Foundation plan details.

(c) *sect 7* shows the warm air pit over which the gas heating unit is installed. Pay careful attention to the waterproof membrane and the insulation. It is very important that there be no heat loss at the pit.

(d) *sect 8* shows the "H" col ftg which conducts most of the superimposed load of the structure to the earth. Study the rein conc, the grouted and bolted steel plate, the W.P. (waterproof) membrane, and the conc floor of the chapel.

(e) *sect 9* shows the S fdn wall of the chapel with conc floor of chancel 0'-6" higher than the main chapel floor. See Fig. 10.10.

FLOOR PLAN

Fig. 10.10 shows dim. flr. plan. *Note:*

(a) plan of chancel, gas heater for warm air ducts, cabinet, S.S. (stainless steel) sink, cabinet, and conc step up from the main flr to the chancel. See Fig. 10.9.

(b) electric wiring and outlets.

(c) HR (heat registers). Count them and compare with Fig. 10.9.

(d) W wall dim. with modular 7'-0" spaces.

(e) 4 × 6 post behind the central mullion of N wall.

(f) an extract from the window schedules is as follows:
W3 1⅜" × 9" × 5'-6" oak, 2" top and side rails, 2½" btm. Open at btm.
W4 1⅜" × 16⅞" × 6'-4" oak as above.
D1 refers to the Door Schedule as follows:
D1 Pair 1¾" × 6'-0" × 7'-0" solid core.

(g) the metal threshold under the door.

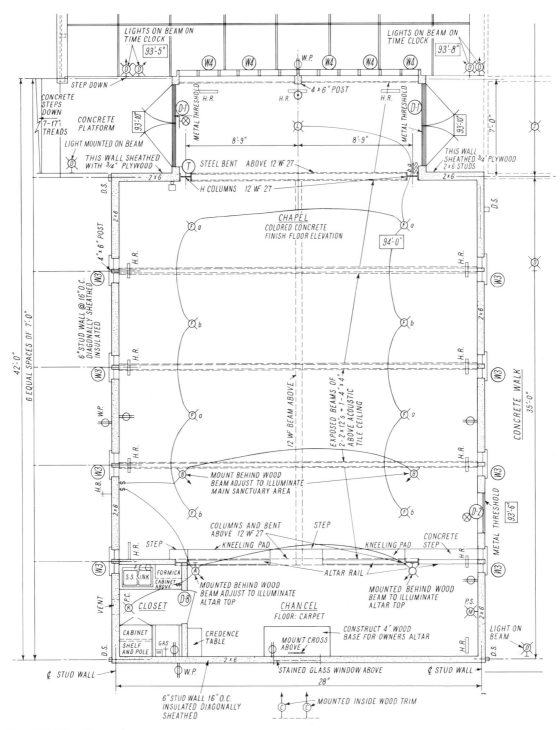

Fig. 10-10. Floor plan.

EXTERIOR ELEVATIONS NORTH AND SOUTH WALLS

Fig. 10.11 shows the N and S exterior wall elevations. The relative elev are shown at Fig. 10.19. *Note:*

(a) the flat roof between the chapel and classroom Wing 1 supported with pipe cols (see Figs. 10.1 & 10.5).

(b) the hinged sashes and fixed $\frac{3}{16}$" glass.

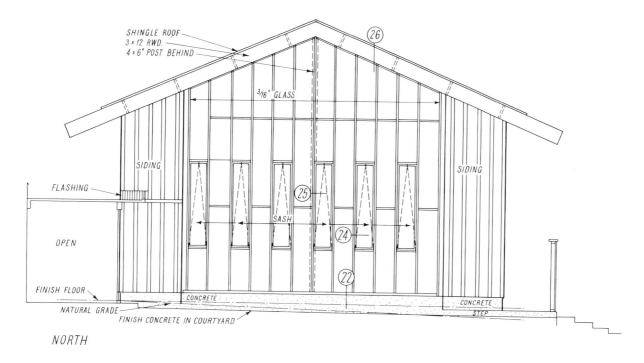

SHINGLE ROOF
3 × 12 RWD.
4 × 6" POST BEHIND

26

³⁄₁₆" GLASS

SIDING

25

SIDING

FLASHING

SASH

24

22

OPEN

FINISH FLOOR

CONCRETE

NATURAL GRADE

CONCRETE
STEP

FINISH CONCRETE IN COURTYARD

NORTH

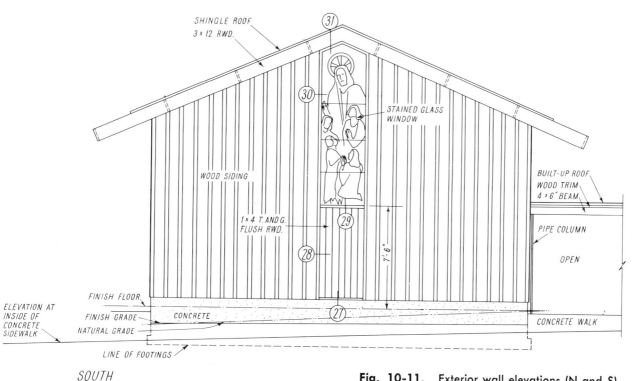

SHINGLE ROOF
3 × 12 RWD.

31

30

STAINED GLASS
WINDOW

WOOD SIDING

BUILT-UP ROOF
WOOD TRIM
4 × 6" BEAM

PIPE COLUMN

OPEN

1 × 4 T. AND G.
FLUSH RWD.

29

28

7'-6"

FINISH FLOOR

ELEVATION AT
INSIDE OF
CONCRETE
SIDEWALK

FINISH GRADE

CONCRETE

27

NATURAL GRADE

CONCRETE WALK

LINE OF FOOTINGS

SOUTH

Fig. 10-11. Exterior wall elevations (N and S).

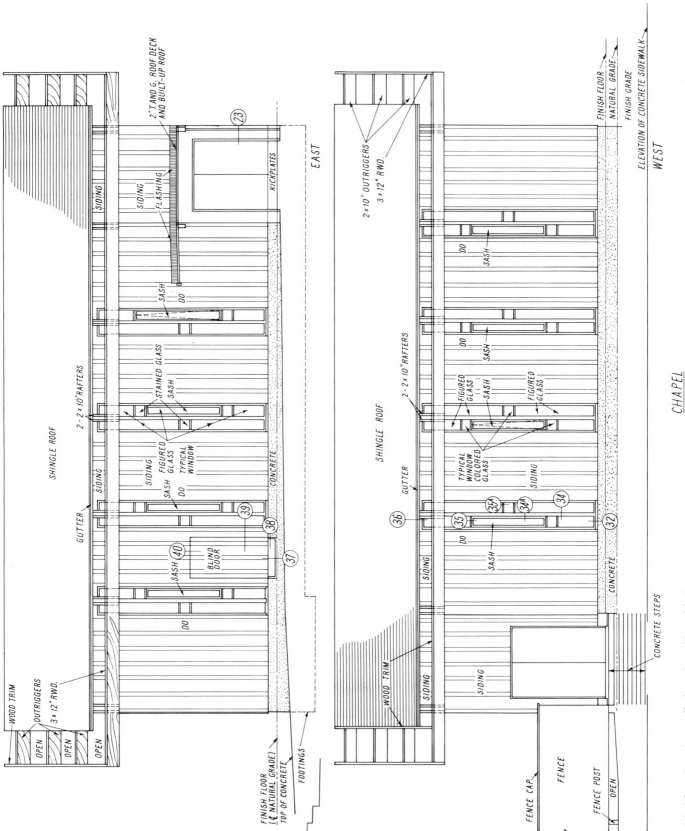

Fig. 10-12. Exterior wall elevations (E and W).

(c) the shingle roof (N wall), 3 × 12 RWD fascia, and the 4 × 6 post (shown with dotted lines) behind the mullion seen at Fig. 10.10.

(d) sect details 22, 23, 24, 25, and 26 shown at Fig. 10.14. Sect. 23 is taken from the east elev at Fig. 10.12.

(e) the S wall details 27, 28, 29, 30, and 31 are shown at Fig. 10.15.

EXTERIOR ELEVATIONS EAST AND WEST WALLS

Fig. 10.12 shows the EW exterior wall elev. The relative interior elev are shown at Fig. 10.20. *Note:*

(a) the stepped ftg and natural grade at the E wall.

(b) the kick plate of the dbl door.

(c) window sashes, stained and figured glass.

(d) the returned open eave of roof to gable verges and the stopped ridge beam.

(e) sect details 37, 38, 39, and 40 at Fig. 10.16.

(f) natural and finish grade and conc steps at W wall.

(g) sect details 32, 34, 34A, 35A, 35, and 36 are shown at Fig. 10.17.

SECTION THRU CHAPEL

Fig. 10.13 shows sect thru chapel. *Note:*

(a) the elev of flr to top of plate line and "I" beam.

(b) the sandwich flr of gravel, grout, W.P. and conc.

(c) the clg finish and shingle roofing ending at the open eaves with a G.I. (galvanized) gutter which is a small but very necessary detail.

It is most important to remember that adequate detailing attracts fair and competitive bids.

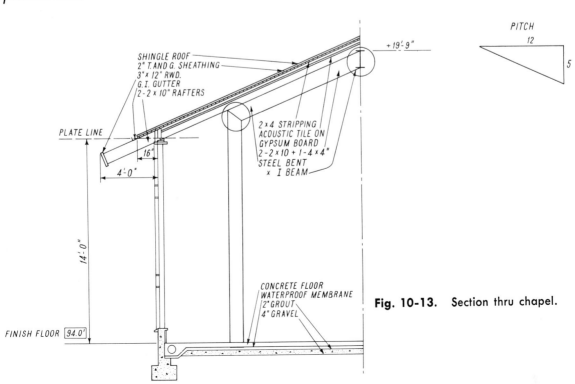

Fig. 10-13. Section thru chapel.

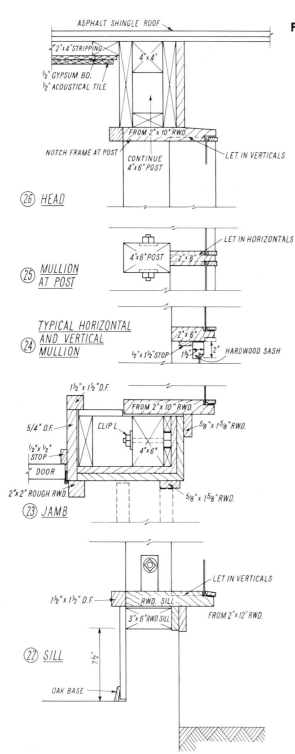

Fig. 10-14.   Section details North wall.

SECTION DETAILS: NORTH WALL

Fig. 10.14 shows sect details 22, 23, 24, 25, and 26 to be studied with Fig. 10.11. *Note:*

(a) *sect 22* shows a typical sill with RWD framing; carpentry detail; D.F. (Douglas Fir) trim to interior sill and oak base below.

(b) *sect 23* shows the corner return of the E (door jamb) to the N wall (see Fig. 10.12). The door is hinged to open outwards to conform to the Fire Ordinance for public bldgs. Where ⅝″ is shown it means 1¼″ which is a mill term. The bolt secures the metal clip angle (clip "L") tie down, to anchor the 4 × 6 post to the fdn.

(c) *sect 24* shows a typical horiz bar, and the mullion is of similar detail; one side is shown to receive fixed glass and the other a sash.

(d) *sect 25* shows the head of the mullion with built-up beam over. The N wall is framed with 4″ × 6″ members secured at the top, btm, and sides to which the window framing is toe nailed.

Fig. 10-15. Section details South wall.

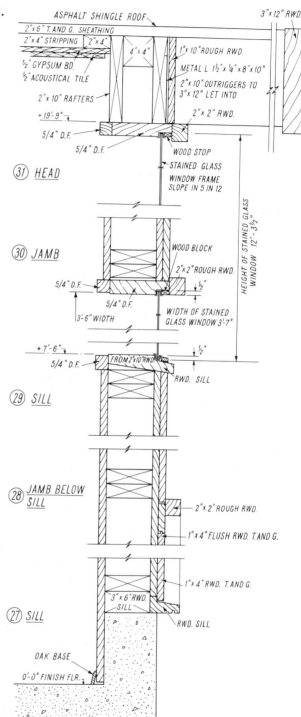

SECTION DETAILS: SOUTH WALL

Fig. 10.15 shows the S wall details. Study these with Fig. 10.11 and understand their interrelation. *Note:*

(a) *sect 27* shows the S wall sill. Compare this with the sill shown at *sect 22*, Fig. 10.14.

(b) *sect 28* shows the horiz sect below the window sill. Notice the 1″ × 4″ flush RWD T & G and the typical 2 × 2 rough RWD cover mould outside.

(c) *sect 29* shows a vertical sill sect under the stained glass window.

(d) *sect 30* shows a horiz jamb sect at the stained glass window and note the dim.

(e) *sect 31* shows the head over the window with roof framing, roofing and interior clg details.

Make a scale model of this area of the window framing.

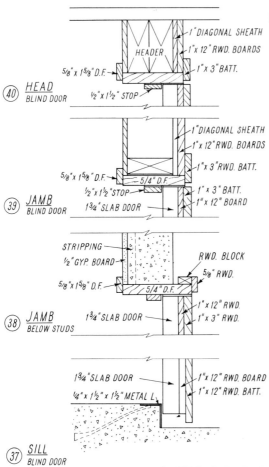

Fig. 10-16. Section details East wall.

SECTION DETAILS: EAST WALL

Fig. 10.16 shows sect details 37, 38, 39, and 40 of blind door to be studied with Fig. 10.12. (The blind door is provided as an emergency exit but is not a design element.) *Note:*

(a) *sect 37* shows a vert sect of sill and blind door with metal "L" anchored to the conc with door detail and RWD bd and batt (batten) outside finish.

(b) *sect 38* shows horiz detail of sill and door.

(c) *sect 39* shows horiz detail of jamb.

(d) *sect 40* shows vert detail of head.
List all the information given on these four details.

SECTION DETAILS: WEST WALL

Fig. 10.17 shows sect details 32, 34, 34A, 35, 35A, and 36. Very carefully examine Fig. 10.12 and establish in your mind the exact details we are studying. *Note:*

(a) *sect 32* shows sill at conc ftg with fixed glass detail.

(b) *sect 33 & 34A* show horiz sect at the jamb for fixed glass or sash as shown with dotted lines.

(c) *sect 34 & 34A* show horiz at mullion (with 4×6 core) post for fixed glass or sash.

(d) *sect 35A* shows vert member for fixed colored glass. This window is shown to the right of the sash at Fig. 10.12.

(e) *sect 35* shows vert detail for fixed glass and vent angle of window.

(f) *sect 36* shows the head of the framing and finishing for the glazed portions of the wall with roof details over.

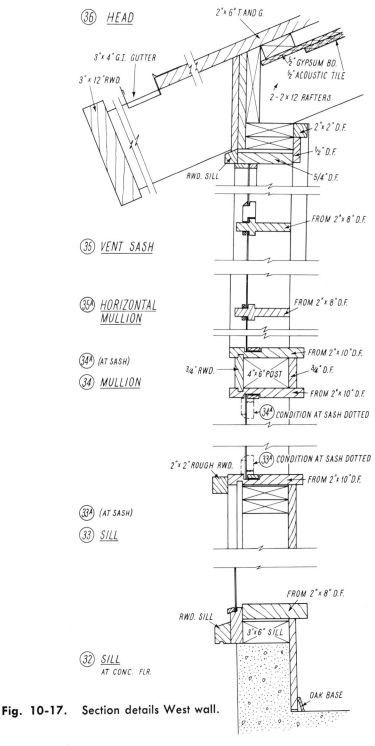

Fig. 10-17. Section details West wall.

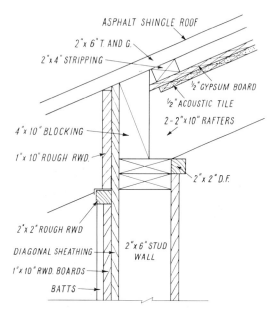

ASPHALT SHINGLE ROOF

2"x 6" T. AND G.

2"x 4" STRIPPING

½" GYPSUM BOARD

½" ACOUSTIC TILE

2 - 2"x 10" RAFTERS

4"x 10" BLOCKING

1"x 10" ROUGH RWD.

2"x 2" D.F.

2"x 2" ROUGH RWD

DIAGONAL SHEATHING

1"x 10" RWD. BOARDS

BATTS

2"x 6" STUD WALL

Fig. 10-18.   Typical wall section.

TYPICAL WALL SECTION

Fig. 10.18 shows a typical wall section. *Note:*
(a) 2 × 6 stud wall with diag sheathing; 1 × 10 RWD bd with batts to cover the joints.
(b) all the exterior wall siding is of RWD including the 1 × 10 closure between the rafter feet.

INTERIOR ELEVATIONS: NORTH AND SOUTH WALLS

Fig. 10.19 shows the interior elev of the N and S walls. *Note:*
(a) part of the N wall window is obscured by the steel bents (see Fig. 10.3).
(b) alternate sashes are btm hinged.
(c) the exposed chapel beam.
(d) the steel bents and the "I" beam are completely exposed (they are finished painted grey). The cold air return is an important detail easily forgotten. Even though it had been missed on the detailing the contractor would have to cut it in, and his annoyance might be reflected in his future consideration of your request bids to him.

INTERIOR ELEVATIONS: EAST AND WEST WALLS

Fig. 10.20 shows the interior elev of the E and W walls, which should be studied with the floor plan at Fig. 10.20. *Note:*
(a) the step up to the chapel at E wall.

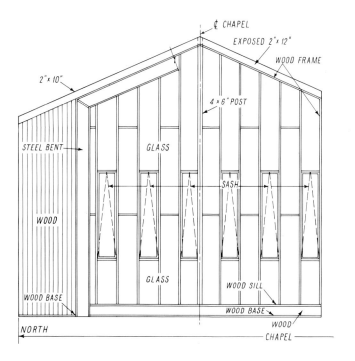

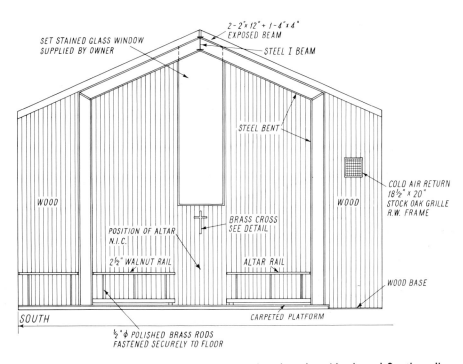

Fig. 10-19. Interior elevations North and South walls.

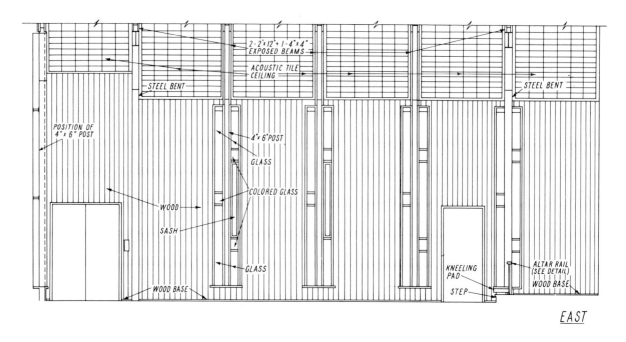

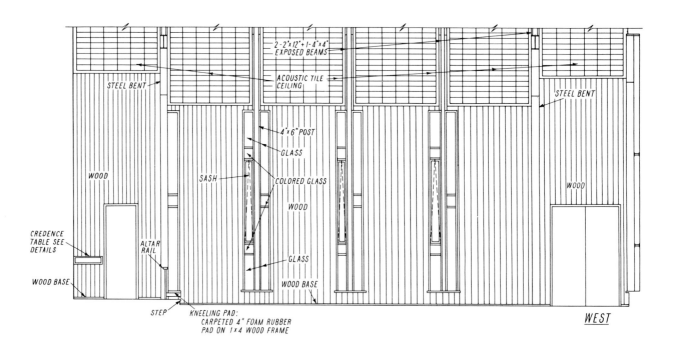

Fig. 10-20.   Interior elevations East and West walls.

Fig. 10-21. Chapel interior.

(b) the dbl doors and the blind door D2 seen on plan.
(c) the dbl door at W wall and the single door near the credence table in the chancel.

Carefully examine the interior finish, the glazing, and the chancel furnishing. You should now have a feeling of being within this chapel.

WITHIN THE CHAPEL

Fig. 10.21 shows the furnishings within the chapel with its soft natural lighting from stained, figured, and plain glazing.

ASSIGNMENTS:

1. Make a freehand (outside) perspective view of the chapel from the northwest.
2. Using any building mediums of your choice, design and prepare working drawings for a place of divine worship in your own area.

11 HEAVY TIMBER CONSTRUCTION

In this chapter we are going to examine a portion of the "Theme Building" framed with glue-laminated (glu-lam) beams for the World Exhibition at Montreal. In the part of the pavilion that we are to study there are 32 different types of beams ranging in size from 4⅜″ wide, 24″ deep, and 6.7230′ in length, to 38″ wide, 60″ deep, and 70.8750′ in length.

The total height of the beam roof framing is 104′-9¼″, and the width of the bldg from col to col is 183′-0″. We must keep in mind that the dwgs in this chapter are from only one part of the structure.

The dwgs were released from the Crown Corporation by Mr. R. Desmarais, the site architect, at the suggestion of Mr. A. Erickson of Erickson/Massey, the architects of the bldg, and are published by permission.

PLAN OF ROOF SUPPORTS

Fig. 11.1 shows a plan of dodecagonal cols supporting glu-lam roof beams for "Man in the Community Pavilion," which is part of the "Theme Building." Carefully note the coordinates, all dim., top of col elev, col #'s and sect ref 1/3.5.

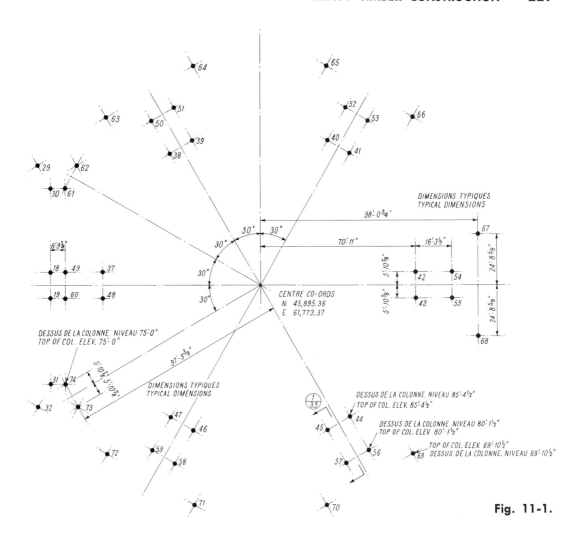

Fig. 11-1.

SECTION THROUGH ROOF

Fig. 11.2 shows sect 1/3.5 roof members with each beam identified with a letter and figure combination. Study the beam schedule at p. 236 and identify the fabrication method for each beam.

PLAN OF ROOF

Fig. 11.3 shows part of the roof beams. Note the legend, the live load design, and the col #'s corresponding to the previous dwg. *In its symbolic and symmetrical design this bldg represents the philosophy of our technological age.*

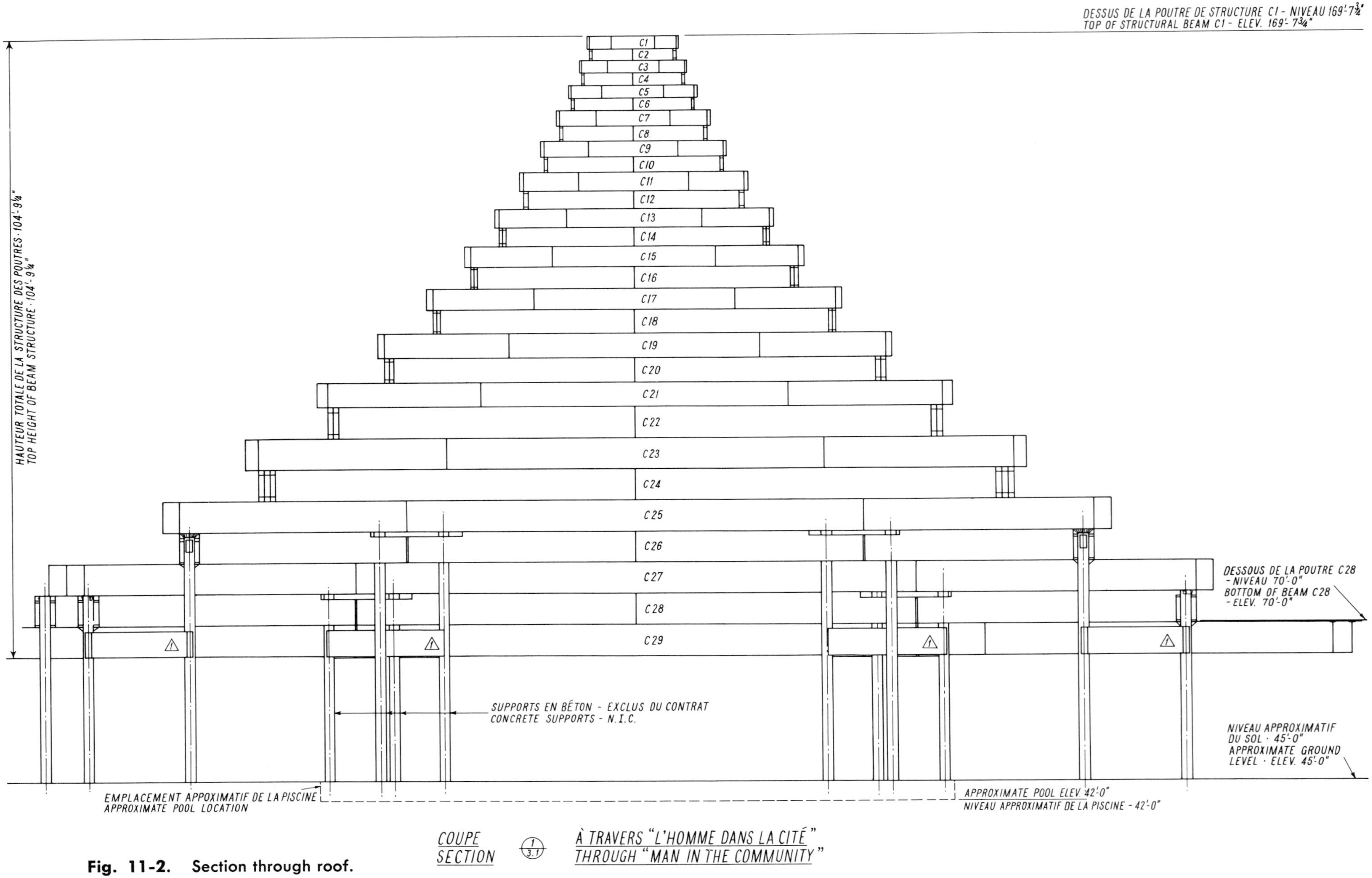

Fig. 11-2. Section through roof.

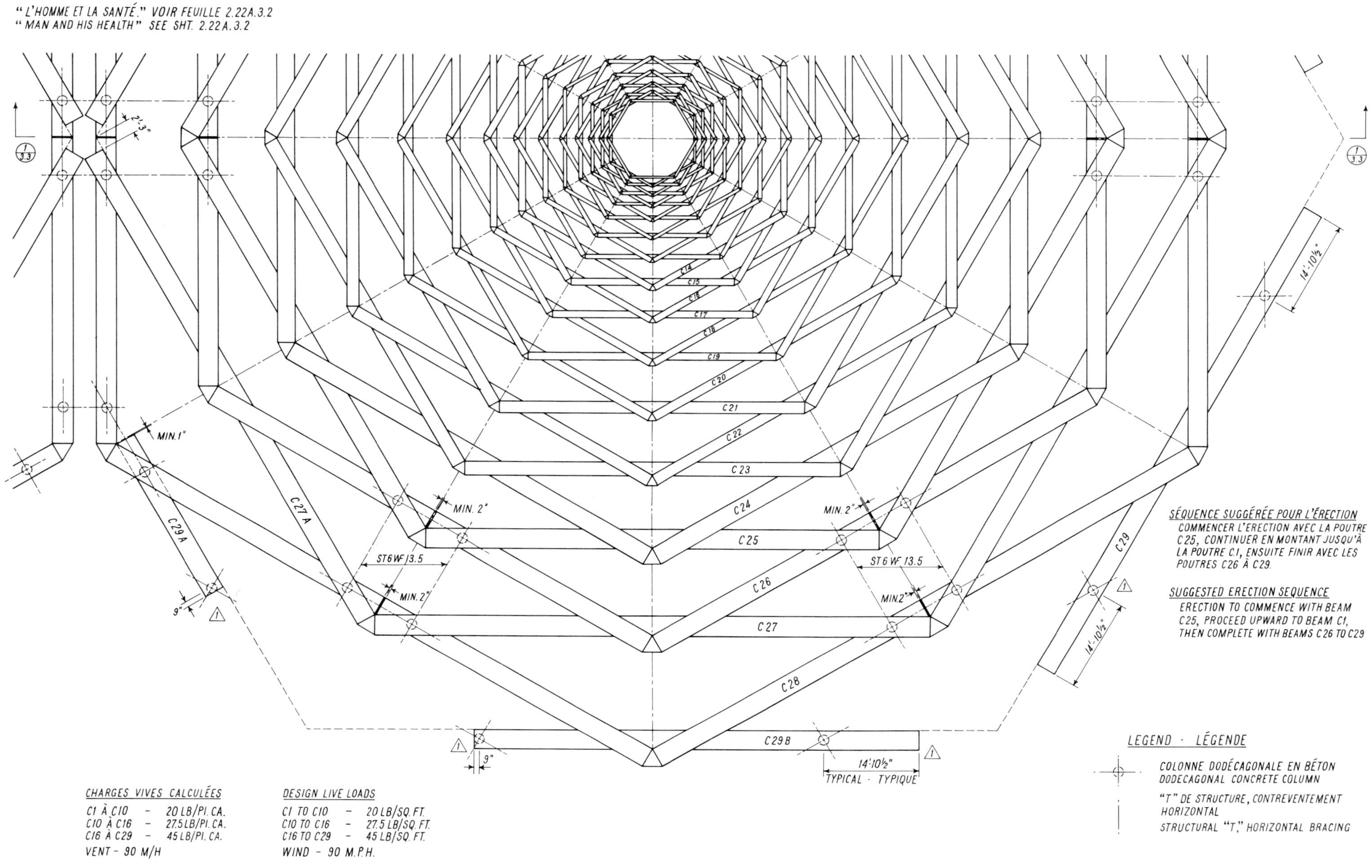

"L'HOMME ET LA SANTÉ." VOIR FEUILLE 2.22A.3.2
"MAN AND HIS HEALTH" SEE SHT. 2.22A.3.2
1/3.3
2'-3"
MIN. 1"
C29A
9"
C27A
MIN. 2"
ST6WF 13.5
C14
C15
C16
C17
C18
C19
C20
C21
C22
C23
C24
C25
C26
C27
C28
C29
C29B
14'-10½"
TYPICAL · TYPIQUE
SÉQUENCE SUGGÉRÉE POUR L'ÉRECTION
COMMENCER L'ERECTION AVEC LA POUTRE C25, CONTINUER EN MONTANT JUSQU'À LA POUTRE C.1, ENSUITE FINIR AVEC LES POUTRES C26 À C29.
SUGGESTED ERECTION SEQUENCE
ERECTION TO COMMENCE WITH BEAM C25, PROCEED UPWARD TO BEAM C1, THEN COMPLETE WITH BEAMS C26 TO C29
LEGEND · LÉGENDE
COLONNE DODÉCAGONALE EN BÉTON
DODECAGONAL CONCRETE COLUMN
"T" DE STRUCTURE, CONTREVENTEMENT HORIZONTAL
STRUCTURAL "T," HORIZONTAL BRACING
CHARGES VIVES CALCULÉES
C1 À C10 - 20 LB/PI. CA.
C10 À C16 - 27.5 LB/PI. CA.
C16 À C29 - 45 LB/PI. CA.
VENT - 90 M/H
DESIGN LIVE LOADS
C1 TO C10 - 20 LB/SQ. FT.
C10 TO C16 - 27.5 LB/SQ. FT.
C16 TO C29 - 45 LB/SQ. FT.
WIND - 90 M.P.H.

Fig. 11-3. Part of roof plan.

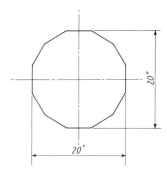

PLAN - COLONNE DODÉCAGONALE EN BÉTON
PLAN - DODECAGONAL CONCRETE COLUMN

Fig. 11-4.

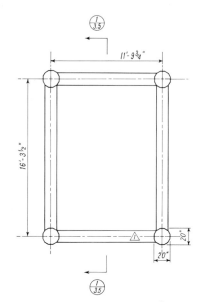

PLAN DU CONTREVENTEMENT AUX COLONNES - "L'HOMME DANS LA CITÉ"
PLAN OF BRACING AT COLUMNS - "MAN IN THE COMMUNITY"   **Fig. 11-5.**

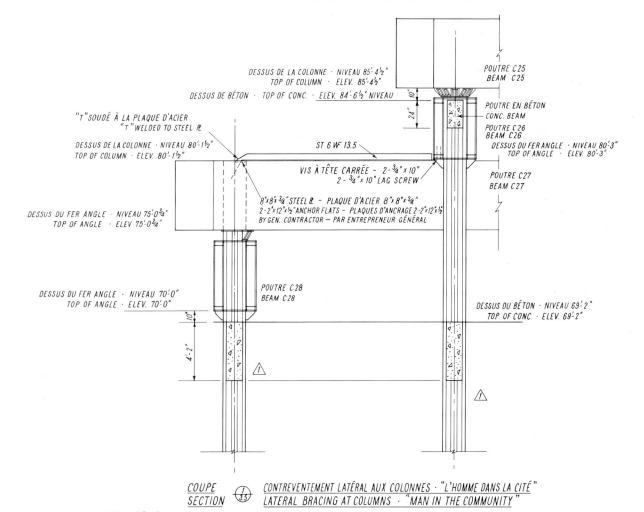

COUPE   _CONTREVENTEMENT LATÉRAL AUX COLONNES · "L'HOMME DANS LA CITÉ"_
SECTION   _LATERAL BRACING AT COLUMNS · "MAN IN THE COMMUNITY"_

Fig. 11-6.   _REMARQUE · FERS ANGLES ANCRÉS DANS LES COLONNES EN BÉTON PAR L'ENTREPRENEUR GÉNÉRAL_
NOTE · STEEL ANGLES ANCHORED IN CONC. COLUMNS BY GEN. CONCTRACTOR

PLAN OF DODECAGONAL COLUMNS AND BRACING

Fig. 11.4 shows a plan of a col. Fig. 11.5 shows a plan of the bracing for groups of four such cols, and Fig. 11.6 shows the lateral bracing at sect 1/3.5.

PROGRESS PHOTOGRAPH

Fig. 11.7 shows the positioning of one of the larger beams onto the concrete braced cols. The largest beam in the structure is 38″ wide, 60″ deep, and 70.8750′ in length.

Fig. 11-7.

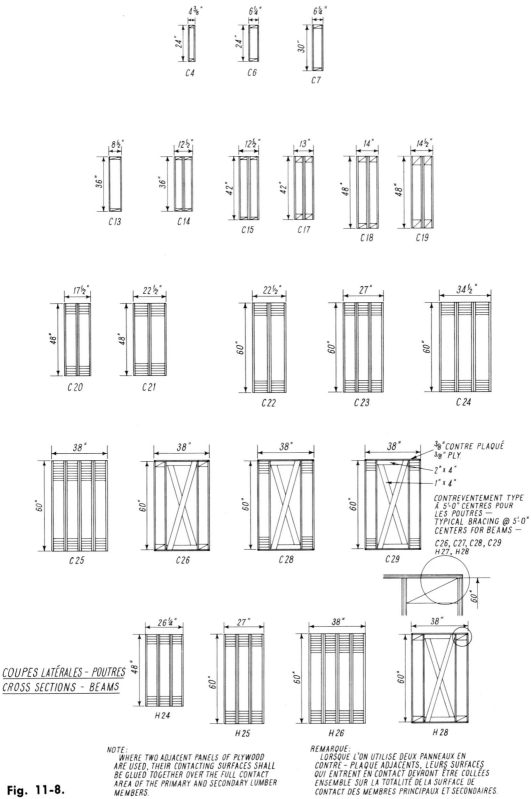

COUPES LATÉRALES - POUTRES
CROSS SECTIONS - BEAMS

Fig. 11-8.

NOTE:
   WHERE TWO ADJACENT PANELS OF PLYWOOD
   ARE USED, THEIR CONTACTING SURFACES SHALL
   BE GLUED TOGETHER OVER THE FULL CONTACT
   AREA OF THE PRIMARY AND SECONDARY LUMBER
   MEMBERS.

REMARQUE:
   LORSQUE L'ON UTILISE DEUX PANNEAUX EN
   CONTRE - PLAQUÉ ADJACENTS, LEURS SURFACES
   QUI ENTRENT EN CONTACT DEVRONT ÊTRE COLLÉES
   ENSEMBLE SUR LA TOTALITÉ DE LA SURFACE DE
   CONTACT DES MEMBRES PRINCIPAUX ET SECONDAIRES.

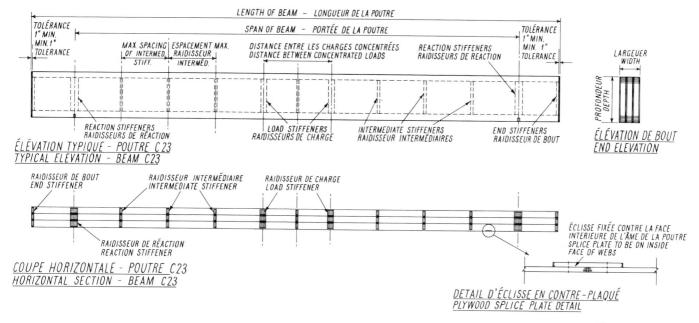

Fig. 11-9.

BEAM CROSS SECTIONS

Fig. 11.8 shows the cross sect of each beam which is engineered for a specific function. This is indeed (together with the beam schedule) a study in the engineering principles of glu-lam construction.

BEAM DETAILS

Fig. 11.9 shows a typical elevation, horizontal sect, and detail of a plywood splice plate for Beam C23. Read the following beam schedule for dimensions and other relative data. Note very carefully the load stiffeners and reaction stiffeners.

BEAM SCHEDULE

The following beam schedule is of the utmost importance. It is from such documents that estimating quantities and the actual fabrication method for the beams is derived.

CAMBER OF TRUSSES AND BEAMS: STANDARD DETAILING SYMBOLS

The source of the following material is the Canadian Institute of Timber Construction. It is taken from the Timber Construction Manual and is published with permission.

BEAM SCHEDULE – DÉTAILS DES POUTRES

"Man in the community" – "L'homme dans la cité"

Beam mark / Marque de la poutre	Number of beam / Nombre de poutres	Depth of beam / Profondeur	Width of beam / Largeur	Length of beam / Longueur	Span of beam / Portée	Dist between concentrated loads / Dist entre les charges concentrées	Flanges Material / Semelles Matériel	Flanges No.	Flanges Dimensions	Webs No. / Âmes No.	Webs Thickness / Épaisseur	Stiffener Size / Grandeur	Load / Charge	Reaction / Réaction	Intermediate / Intermédiaire	interm'd max spacing / Espacement interm'd max	End / Bout	Splice plate Thick / Épaisseur	Splice plate Width / Largeur	Notes / Remarques
C1	1	24"	4⅜"	6.7230'	5.3623'	—	ÉPINETTE – QUALITÉ DE STRUCTURE / SPRUCE – STRUCTURAL GRADE	2	2x4"	2	⅜"	2x4"	2x2	2x2	—	—	1	⅜"	6"	POUR ÉLÉVATION · VOIR FEUILLE No. 2.22A.2.1 / FOR ELEVATION – SEE SHEET No. 2.22A.2.1
C2	1	24"	4⅜"	7.3420'	5.9813'	1.3606'		2	2x4"	2	⅜"	2x4"	2	2	1	30"	1	⅜"	6"	
C3	1	24"	4⅜"	8.0568'	6.6962'	1.3606'		2	2x4"	2	⅜"	2x4"	2	2	1	30"	1	⅜"	6"	
C4	1	24"	4⅜"	8.8823'	7.2091'	1.3606'		2	2x4"	2	⅜"	2x6"	2	2	1	30"	1	⅜"	6"	
C5	1	24"	6¼"	9.6550'	7.7112'	1.6313'		2	2x6"	2	⅜"	2x6"	2	2	1	30"	1	⅜"	6"	
C6	1	24"	6¼"	10.5472'	8.6034'	1.9438'		2	2x6"	2	⅜"	2x6"	2	2	1	30"	1	⅜"	6"	
C7	1	30"	6¼"	11.5774'	9.6337'	1.9438'		2	2x6"	2	⅜"	2x6"	2	2	1	24"	1	⅜"	6"	
C8	1	30"	6¼"	12.7671'	10.8233'	1.9438'		2	2x6"	2	⅜"	2x6"	2	2	1	24"	1	⅜"	6"	
C9	1	30"	6¼"	14.1407'	12.1969'	1.9438'		2	2x6"	2	⅜"	2x6"	2	2	1	24"	1	⅜"	6"	
C10	1	30"	6¼"	15.7269'	13.3498'	1.9438'		2	2x6"	2	⅜"	2x8"	2	2	1	24"	1	⅜"	6"	POUR RAIDISSEURS DE CENTRE VOIR COUPE / FOR CENTRE STIFFENERS SEE SECTION
C11	1	36"	8¼"	17.3660'	14.8002'	2.2324'		2	2x8"	2	⅜"	2x8"	2	2	1	24"	1	⅜"	6"	
C12	1	36"	8¼"	19.2587'	16.6512'	2.5658'	SAPIN DOUGLAS – QUALITÉ DE CONSTRUCTION / DOUGLAS FIR – CONST GRADE	2	2x8"	2	½"	2x8"	2	2	1	36"	2	½"	8"	
C13	1	36"	8½"	21.4201'	18.1099'	2.6019'		2	2x8"	2	⅜"	2x6"	2	2	1	24"	2	⅜"	6"	
C14	1	36"	8½"	23.5310'	19.6434'	3.2209'		2	2x6"	2	⅜"	2x6"	2	2	1	24"	2	⅜"	6"	
C15	2	42"	12½"	25.9684'	22.0809'	3.8875'		4	2x6"	2	⅜"	2x6"	2	3	1	24"	2	⅜"	6"	
C16	2	42"	12½"	28.7829'	24.8121'	3.8875'		4	2x6"	2	⅜"	2x6"	3	3	1	36"	2	½"	8"	
C17	2	42"	13"	31.9848'	27.7750'	3.9597'	GLULAM – 18C	4	4x6"	2	½"	4x6"	3	3	2	36"	2	¾"	14"	
C18	2	48"	14"	35.5857'	31.1483'	4.1874'		4	4x6"	2	¾"	2x6"	3	4	2	66"	2	¾"	14"	VOIR COUPE / SEE SECTION
C19	2	48"	14½"	39.6955'	34.6860'	4.4262'		4	6x6"	2	⅞"	2x6"	4	5	2	66"	2	⅞"	14"	VOIR COUPE / SEE SECTION
C20	2	48"	17½"	44.1525'	37.8766'	4.9426'		4	7x6½"	2	⅞"	1⅝x7x4	4	5	2	66"	2	⅞"	14"	VOIR COUPE / SEE SECTION
C21	2	48"	22½"	48.8179'	41.8202'	6.1642'		4	9x8⅛"	2	1⅛"	1⅝x9"	4	6	2	66"	2	1⅛"	22"	VOIR COUPE / SEE SECTION
C22	2	48"	22½"	54.2049'	46.4573'	6.9976'		4	9x8⅛"	2	1⅛"	1⅝x9"	5	6	2	74"	2	1⅛"	22"	VOIR COUPE / SEE SECTION
C23	3	60"	27"	59.9924'	50.3453'	7.6471'		6	9x8⅛"	6	1"	1⅝x8x7	5	6	2	74"	2	1"	16"	VOIR COUPE / SEE SECTION
C24	3	60"	34½"	65.9535'	54.6405'	9.4796'		6	9x8⅛"	6	1¼"	1⅝x9"	5	6	2	74"	2	1¼"	22"	VOIR COUPE / SEE SECTION
C25	4	60"	38"	72.5000'	60.6818'	11.2348'		7+13 TOP/DESSUS; 7+8% BOT/DESSOUS	8	1¼"	1⅝x9"	6	VOIR REMARQUES / SEE NOTES	2	74"	2	1¼"	22"	VOIR ÉLÉVATION · RAIDISSEUR DE RÉACTION – POUTRE C25 / SEE ELEVATION · REACTION STIFFENER – BEAM C25
C26	2x2	60"	38"	40.0296'	28.2114'	—	ÉPINETTE S. / SPRUCE	4	4x8"	4	½"	4x8"	2*	2*	2	36"	2	½"	6"	
C27	2x2	60"	38"	88.7879'	76.9697'	11.8182'	GLULAM	4	7x8⅛"	4	¾"	1⅝x7"	—	5	2	66"	2	¾"	14"	
C28	2x2	60"	38"	49.4334'	34.6152'	—	ÉPINETTE S. / SPRUCE	4	4x8"	4	½"	4x8"	4*	4*	2	36"	2	½"	6"	
C29	2	60"	38"	85.0000'	55.2500'	11.8182'	GLULAM	4	7x8⅛"	4	¾"	1⅝x7"	3*	6	2	66"	2	¾"	14"	
C27A	2	60"	38"	86.5379'	76.9697'	11.8182'	GLULAM	4	7x8⅛"	4	¾"	1⅝x8"	2*	5	2	66"	2	¾"	14"	
C29A	2	60"	38"	28.3763'	21.7172'	—	ÉPINETTE / SPRUCE	4	4x8"	4	½"	2x8"	—	—	2	36"	2	½"	6"	
C29B	2x2	60"	38"	70.8750'	55.2500'	11.8182'	GLULAM	4	7x6½"	4	¾"	1⅝x6½"	3*	6	2	36"	2	¾"	14"	

"L'homme et la santé" – "Man and his health"

Beam mark	Number	Depth	Width	Length	Span	Dist between conc. loads	Material	Flanges No.	Flanges Dimensions	Webs No.	Thickness	Stiffener Size	Load	Reaction	Intermediate	spacing	End	Splice Thick	Splice Width	Remarques
H22	2	48"	21½"	52.5471'	45.6938'	—	GLULAM	4	9¾x5"	4	½"	2x10"	—	2	2	36"	2	½"	8"	DELETE · SUPPRIMEZ
H23	2	48"	22½"	58.5110'	50.8885'	6.8309'	GLULAM	4	9¾x5"	4	¾"	2x10"	2	3	3	66"	2	¾"	12"	DELETE · SUPPRIMEZ
H24	3	48"	26½"	65.0368'	56.7480'	7.5385'	GLULAM	6	7x6½"	6	⅞"	1⅝x7"	3	3	3	66"	2	⅞"	14"	
H25	3	60"	27"	72.5000'	62.2695'	8.2721'	GLULAM	6	7x8⅛"	6	1"	1⅝x7"	3	5	3	74"	2	1"	16"	
H26	4	60"	38"	80.0592'	68.2411'	9.9848'	GLULAM	4	7+13 TOP/DESSUS; 7+8% BOT/DESSOUS	8	1¼"	1⅝x7"	4	5	4	74"	2	1¼"	22"	
H27	2x2	60"	38"	44.3939'	32.5757'	—	ÉPINETTE / SPRUCE	4	4x8"	4	½"	2x8"	—	4	3	36"	2	½"	8"	
H28	2x2	60"	38"	49.4334'	37.1672'	—	ÉPINETTE / SPRUCE	4	4x8"	4	½"	2x8"	—	3	3	36"	2	½"	8"	
H27A	2x2	60"	38"	47.1834'	37.6152'	—	ÉPINETTE / SPRUCE	4	7x6½"	4	¾"	2x8"	3*	6	2	36"	2	½"	14"	

NOTES:
1. WEBS SHALL BE P.M.B.C. EXTERIOR DOUGLAS FIR UNSANDED SHEATHING
2. ALL STIFFENERS SHALL BE SPRUCE, STRUCTURAL GRADE
3. ALL TIMBER FLANGES ARE GIVEN IN NOMINAL DIMENSIONS
   - 2x4 → 1⅝x3⅝   · 4x6 → 3⅝x5½
   - 2x6 → 1⅝x5½   · 4x8 → 3⅝x7½
   - 2x8 → 1⅝x7½   · 6x6 → 5½x5½
4. ALL STIFFENERS ARE GIVEN IN NOMINAL DIMENSIONS EXCEPT IN BEAMS WHERE GLULAM FLANGE IS USED
5. AVOID SCARF JOINT IN TIMBER BETWEEN ⅓L AND ⅔L

REMARQUES:
1. LES ÂMES SERONT FAITES AVEC DES PANNEAUX DE CONTRE PLAQUÉ P.M.B.C. EXTÉRIEUR, SADIN DOUGLAS NON SABLÉ
2. TOUS LES RAIDISSEURS SERONT EN ÉPINETTE, QUALITÉ DE STRUCTURE
3. TOUTES LES SEMELLES DES POUTRES SONT DONNÉES EN DIMENSIONS NOMINALES
4. TOUS LES RAIDISSEURS SONT DONNÉS EN DIMENSION NOMINALES EXCEPTÉ POUR LES POUTRES DONT LES SEMELLES SONT EN GLULAM
5. ÉVITER LES ASSEMBLAGES À MIS BOIS ENTRE ⅓ ET ⅔ DE LA LONGUEUR

TOUS LES POUTRES ET LA FAÎTE SERONT TRAITÉES ANTIFUGES · VOIR DEVIS / ALL BEAMS AND ARCHITECTURAL CAP TO BE FIREPROOFED · SEE SPECS.

EXTERIOR FACE ONLY TO BE FIREPROOFED / PARTIE EXTÉRIEURE SEULEMENT SERONT TRAITÉES ANTIFUGES

BOWSTRING ROOF TRUSSES

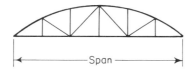

Segmental Overlapping Sawn Timber Chords

Camber in bottom chord only, equal to 3/8 inch per 10 feet of span.

Continuous Glulam Top Chord

Camber in bottom chord only, equal to 3/4 inch per 10 feet of span.

TRIANGULAR ROOF TRUSSES

Where feasible, camber both top and bottom chords.

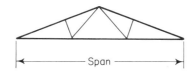

Sawn Timber or Rod and Sawn Timber

Camber in top chords equal to 3/4 inch per 10 feet of span; camber in bottom chord equal to 1/2 inch per 10 feet of span.

Glulam Timber or Rod and Glulam Timber

Camber in top chords equal to 1/4 inch per 10 feet of span; camber in bottom chord equal to 3/8 inch per 10 feet of span.

HOWE AND PRATT ROOF TRUSSES

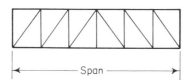

Sawn Timber or Rod and Sawn Timber

Camber in top and bottom chords equal to ½ inch per 10 feet of span.

Glulam Timber or Rod and Glulam Timber

Camber in top and bottom chords equal to 3/8 inch per 10 feet of span.

SIMPLE GLULAM AND OTHER BUILT-UP BEAMS

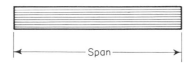

Camber equal to deflection due to twice the dead load.

Alternatively, camber of 3/8 inch per 10 feet of span will suit many conditions of loading

TWO- SPAN AND OTHER CONTINUOUS GLULAM BEANS

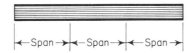

Camber built into these structures should account for the loading combinations on the various spans.

With roof spans, the centre-span camber should be greater than the adjacent-span camber to prevent excessive overloading due to unforeseen live loads as, for example, rain water accumulation.

CANTILEVERED GLULAM BEAMS

Inadequate camber in cantilevered beams should be avoided for pleasing appearance.

The advice of the fabricator should be sought for camber requirements in these structures.

Fig. 11-10. Camber of trusses and beams.

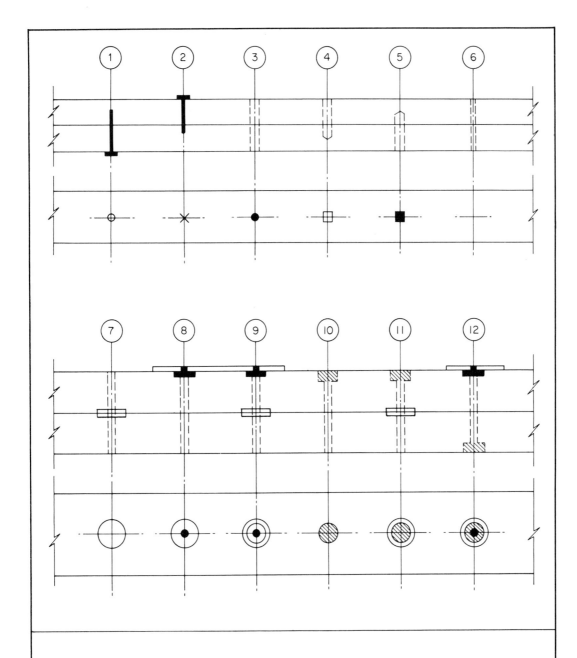

EXPLANATION OF SYMBOLS

For all symbols, indicate sizes and quantities required on drawings.

1. Nail or spike, near side.
2. Nail or spike, far side.
3. Machine bolt.
4. Lag Screw, far side.
5. Lag Screw, near side.
6. Drift bolt.
7. One or more split rings and bolt.
8. One or more shear plates and bolt.
9. Split rings and shear plates on same bolt.

10. Counterbore for bolt.
11. Split rings and counterbore.
12. Shear plates and counterbore.

Note: Where mixed sizes occur or the above symbols do not provide a clear explanation of the connection, a detail showing the hardware arrangement should be drawn.

Fig. 11-11. Standard detailing symbols.

ABBREVIATIONS

Economy	. . . . . . F.B.	Ogee (cast) washer	. . O.G.	Drill	. . . . **D**
Machine bolt	. . . . M.B.	Malleable washer	. . M.I.W.	Chamfer	. . . . Chfr.
Lag screw	. . . . . . L.S.	Countersink	. . . . . . C' sink	Lamination	. . . . . Lam.
Carriage bolt	. . . . C.B.	Counterbore	. . . . . C' bore	Wood screw	. . . . . . W.S.
Drift	. . . . Dr.	Turnbuckle	. . . . . T.B.	Near side	. . . . N.S.
Tie rod	. . . . T.R.	Dap	. . . . Dap	Far Side	. . . . F.S.
Split ring	. . . . S.R.	Plate	. . . . PL. or **℉**	Nail or spike	. . . . . . Nl.
Shear plate	. . . . . SH.PL.	Angle	. . . . L, L^S	Mark (ed)	. . . . . . M**K**

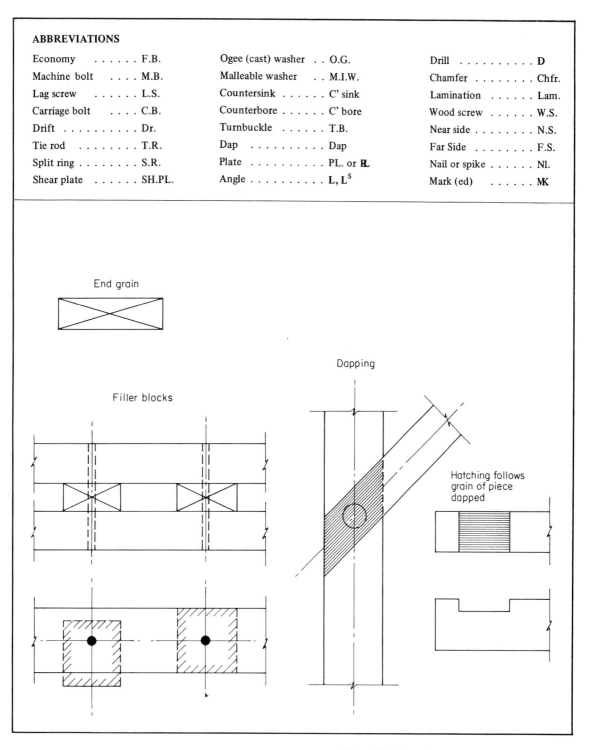

End grain

Filler blocks

Dapping

Hatching follows grain of piece dapped

Fig. 11-12.   Standard detailing symbols.

HEAVY TIMBER CONSTRUCTION DETAILS

The following material is from the Canadian Wood Development Council and is published by permission. The self-explanatory detail dwgs must be given careful study so that a ready understanding of the engineering principles and devices for heavy timber members will be known. It is very important to keep your filing system and library up to date, not only in adding new material but in discarding superseded matter. *You should always be able to find required information quickly; research is time consuming.*

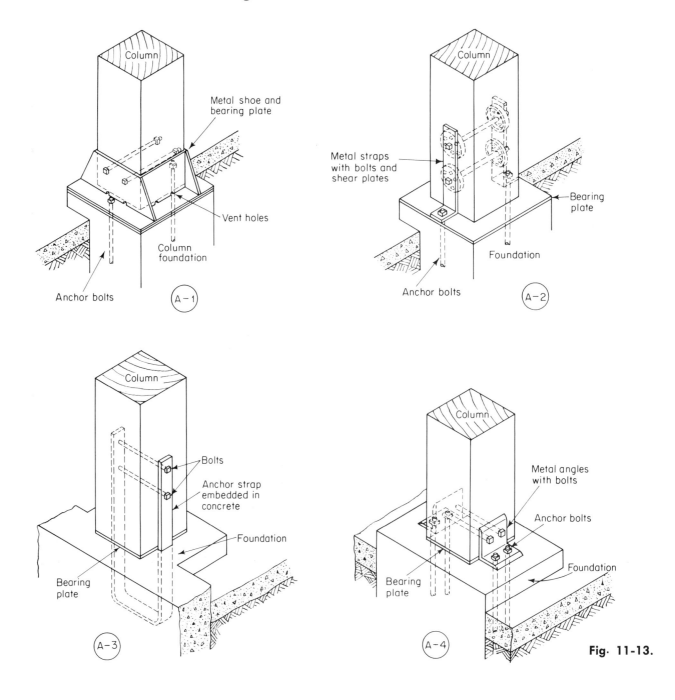

Fig. 11-13.

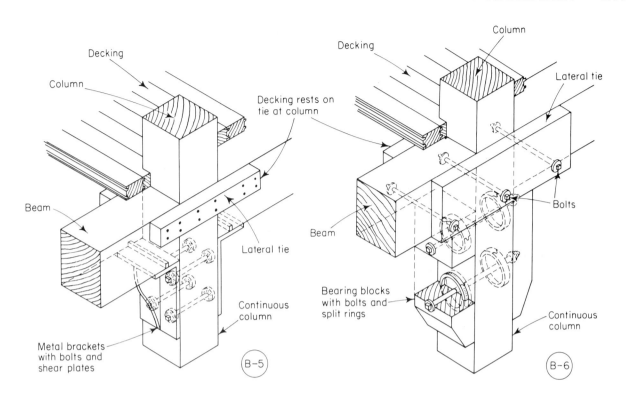

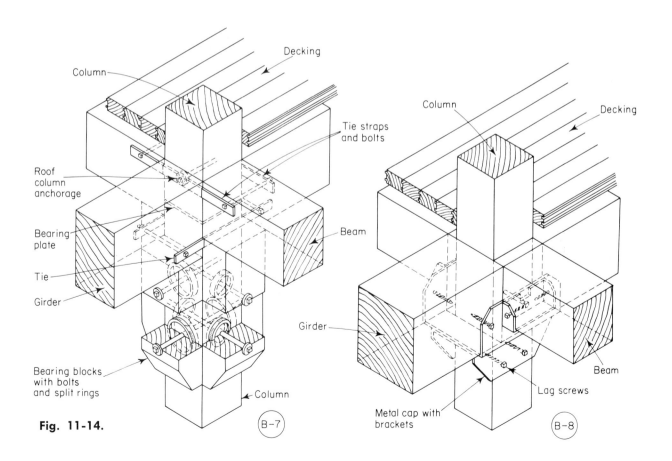

Fig. 11-14.

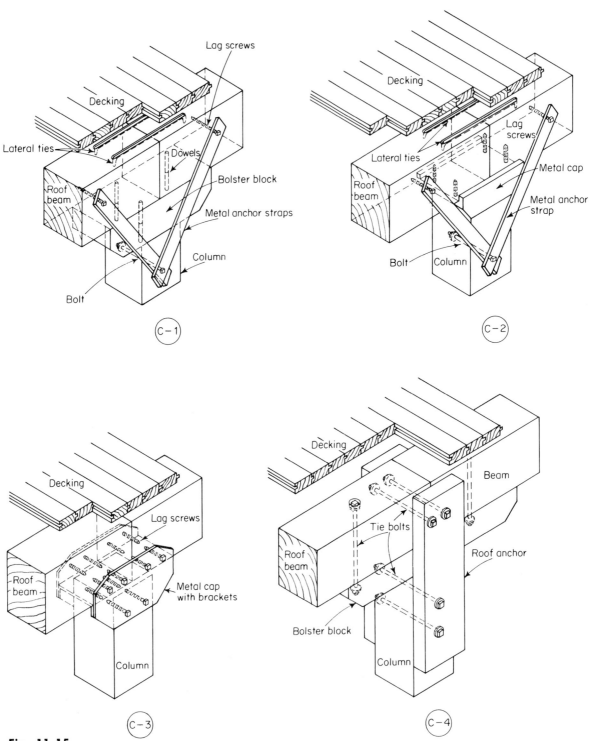

Fig. 11-15.

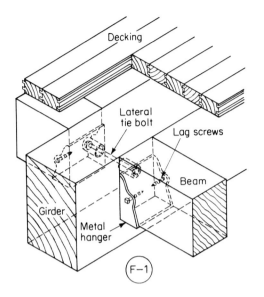

F-1

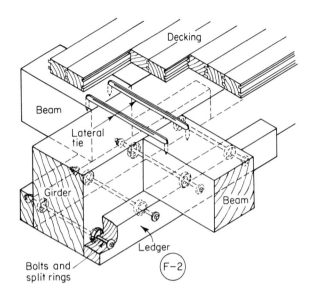

F-2

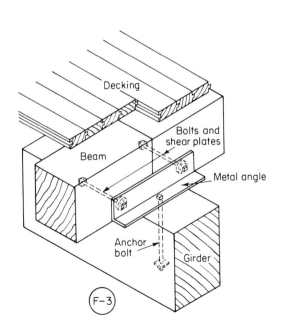

F-3

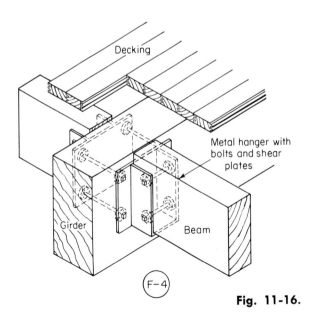

F-4

Fig. 11-16.

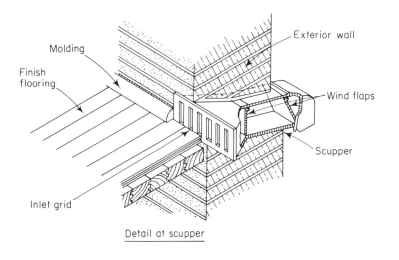

Molding

Finish flooring

Exterior wall

Wind flaps

Scupper

Inlet grid

Detail at scupper

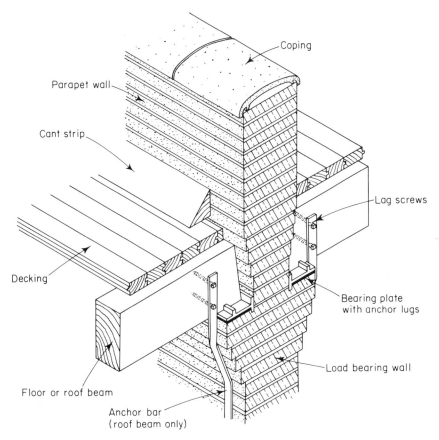

Coping

Parapet wall

Cant strip

Lag screws

Decking

Bearing plate with anchor lugs

Floor or roof beam

Load bearing wall

Anchor bar (roof beam only)

Typical framing at fire or party wall

Fig. 11-17.

ASSIGNMENT:

1. Research heavy timber construction for your filing system. Write for material to as many sources as you can locate in your technical library and phone book.
2. Make a plan, front and side elevation of Figs. 11.14 B-7; 11.16 F-2, and 11.17 (Typical Framing at Party Wall).

A CITY 12
PARKING
GARAGE

In this chapter we are going to examine parts of the drawings for a rectangular 115'-0" × 226'-0" three-tier prestressed concrete garage with 40'-6" clear span beams erected at Olympia, the capital city of the State of Washington. The drawings and many valuable suggestions for this chapter were supplied through the courtesy of Mr. Warren A. Brown, Supervisor, and Mr. Wallace L. Bailey, Assistant Supervisor of the Division of Engineering and Architecture for the State of Washington.

This garage was cleverly devised to take every advantage of the topographical features of the land and enabled the architects and engineers to provide a garage with three separate direct drive-in entrances from three separate road levels. There are no ramps between floors, but there are two sets of stairways.

Examine the perspective single line drawing of the garage at Fig. 12.1.

The drawing schedule is as follows:

ARCHITECTURAL SHEETS

A1 Plot plan & index
A2 First-floor plan & window schedules
A3 Second-floor plan

PARKING GARAGE BUILDING NO. 1

STATE OF WASHINGTON
OLYMPIA

STATE CAPITOL GROUP
WASHINGTON

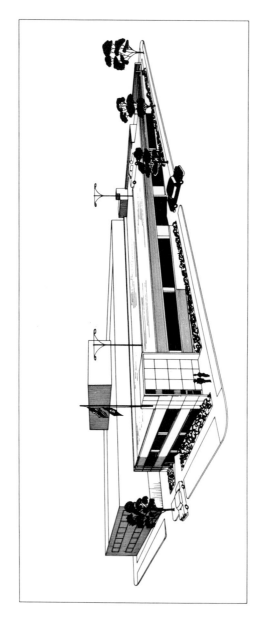

PLANS AND SPECIFICATIONS BY
DEPT. OF GEN. ADMINISTRATION
THE DIVISION OF ENGINEERING

STATE CAPITOL COMMITTEE

GOVERNOR ALBERT D. ROSELLINI
HON. CLIFF YELLE, STATE AUDITOR
HON. BERT COLE, LAND COMMISSIONER

Fig. 12-1.

A4 Roof deck plan
A5 Stair tower details
A6 Stair tower details
A7 Elevations

STRUCTURAL

S1 Footing plan & sections
S2 Second-floor framing plan
S3 Roof framing plan & column plan
S4 Sections
S5 Section

MECHANICAL

ME1 First-floor mechanical & electrical
ME2 Second-floor mechanical & electrical
ME3 Roof deck mechanical & electrical
ME4 Ventilation & plumbing

ARCHITECTURAL DRAWINGS

Sheet A1 shows:

The existing grade, sewer, water main, existing trees, two survey pins marking the NW and SW corners of the building, and notes stating where two B.M.'s are to be found. Bench marks are levels marked on city monuments, stone steps, underpinning of some buildings, and so on. They are used as reference to form a basis for elevations in the area. Those in cities are listed in the City Engineer's Department. Some are marked thus T , the center of the bar being the level given.

ASSIGNMENTS:

1. Make a single line plan of the garage that we are going to study and show the plot plan elevations. Toward the right-hand side of a piece of 8½″ × 11″ paper draw a rectangle 4½″ × 2½″. Dimension the short walls (north and south) 115′-0″ and the long walls 226′-0″. These are the outside dim of the garage. At the SW corner of the plan mark the highest given plot elev, 84′-0″. *At the center* of the west wall mark an elev, 76′-0″ and at NE corner mark an elev 69′-0″. *These three different levels are the approx points of ingress and egress for cars. They are on three different road levels and serve three different floor levels without any internal ramps in the building itself.* Examine your elev marked plan and think about the grade of the land. Below the plan draw a horiz line the

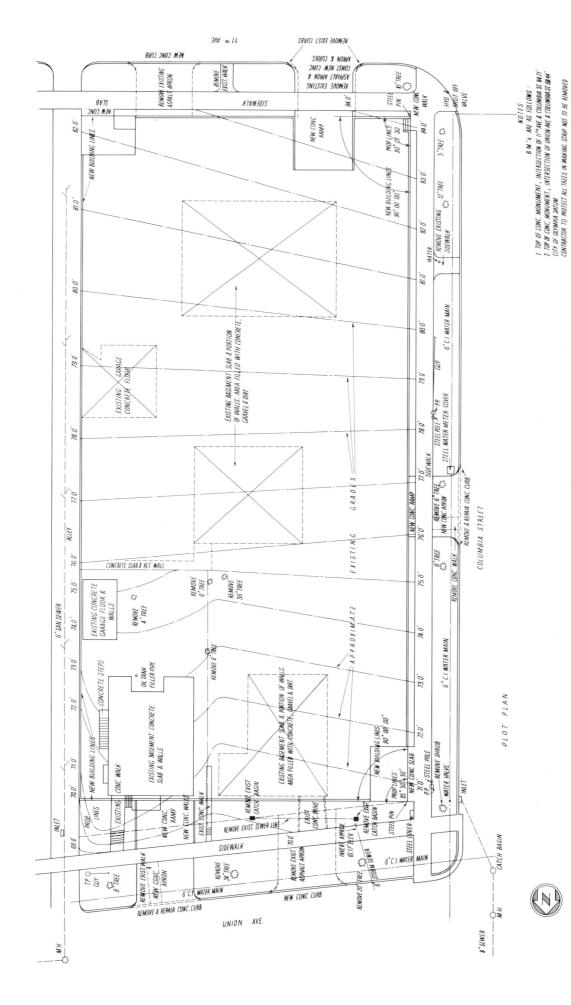

Fig. 12-2. Plot plan.

same length as the longest wall. In the center of the line mark the 76'-0"
level, at the north end mark the 69'-0" level, and at the south end mark the
84'-0" level. Draw (without a scale) a profile of the grade of the land.
Visualize the land and all land for which you are going to make drawings.
*Remember that without visualization there would be no architectural draw-
ings. Practice it! It is part of your future profession.*

2. To the left of your plan, draw a perpendicular line about 0'-9" long.
Establish a point about the center of the line as being 76'-6" *second floor
and street level*. Use a scale of ⅜" to 1'-0". Above the 76'-0" level, scale
off a point for the 84'-0" plot elev. Below the 76'-0" level scale off a point
for the 69'-0" plot elev. The difference between the heights of the finished
car parking floors is to be 10'-0" (±). Again using the 76'-6" elev as a
center, scale off 10'-0" up for the top (third floor) parking level. Using the
76'-6" elev as a center, scale off 10'-0" down for the btm (first floor) level.
What is the scaled perpendicular depth (±) of the *ramp down* from the
69'-0" plot elev to the first floor parking level? What is the scaled perpendicular height (±) of the *ramp* required from the 84'-0" plot elev to the
third (top) floor level? Check your scaled measurements arithmetically.
Turn to Fig. 12.11 and examine the north elev. This drawing gives the exact
elev required for the three floors.

3. Go to the City Engineer's Department and make a list of city bench
marks. See one for a bridge, one for a public building, and one for a
monument.

4. Go to the city library and find the address of the U. S. Coast and
Geodetic Survey. Ask for information regarding their work and the different types of marking devices they have for levels.

Sheet A2 shows:

The first-floor plan and twenty-one main columns, seven on the west
wall, seven on the east wall, and seven octagonal columns down the center
of the garage supporting 40'-6" clear spans on either side. These are all
prestressed concrete columns as shown on the following drawings. One of
the central octagonal columns (or trees) is shown in the process of erection
at Fig. 12.3.

Fig. 12-3. Central column.

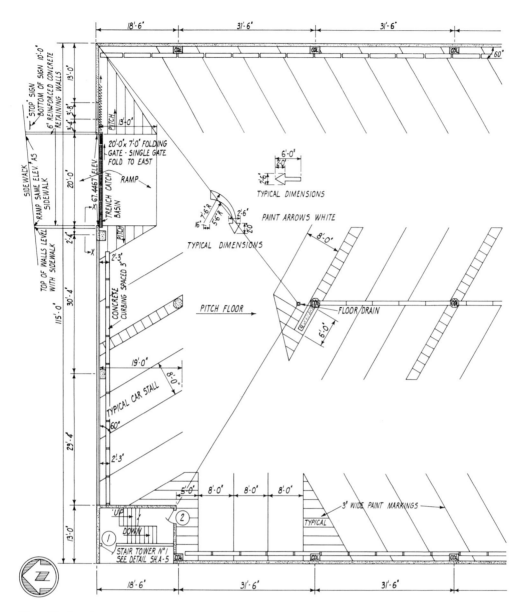

Fig. 12-4. First-floor plan.

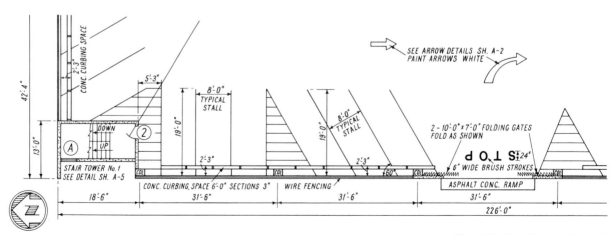

Fig. 12-5. Second-floor plan.

A plan of part of the northern portion of the bldg is shown at Fig. 12.4, and the north elev taken from Sheet A7 should be read at the same time (see Fig. 12.11). It may be seen that a direct car drive is afforded at the lowest level from the adjacent road. This is the lowest tier, and there is a slight *down ramp* to the parking area, but there is no floor-to-floor ramp in the building. *Note very carefully that the elevation of the first floor is 66.3635'.*

Sheet A3 shows:

The second-floor plan with a direct car drive into the garage from the west side road. See Fig. 12.5 for the second-floor plan at the west entrance and see Fig. 12.14 for a portion of the west elevation showing the central drive-in direct from the street. *Note very carefully that the elevation of the second floor as shown on the elevation drawing is 76.530'.* What is the exact difference in elevation between the first and second floors?

Sheet A4 shows:

The third-floor open roof plan with a slight *up ramp* for the drive-in entrance onto the garage direct from the south side road. Note very carefully that the third level of the garage is not only a floor but is also the roof of the building on which cars are parked. See Fig. 12.6 for part of the open roof plan and see Fig. 12.12 for the south elevation. *Note very*

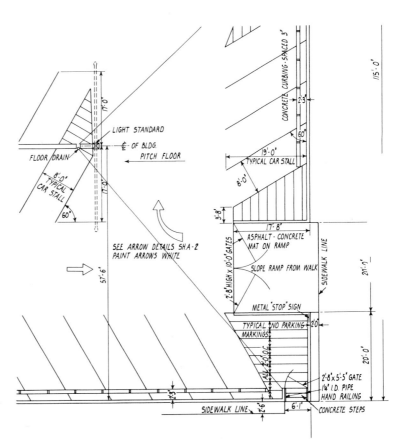

Fig. 12-6.   Roof deck plan.

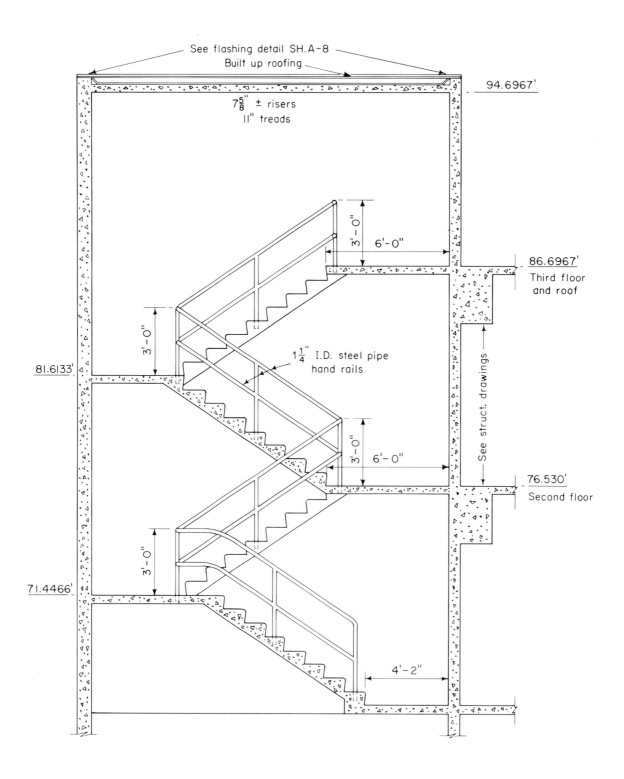

Fig. 12-7.   Section through stair tower.

carefully that the elevation of the third (open roof) level is 86.6967' as shown on the elevation drawing. What is the exact difference in elevations between the second- and third-floor levels?

Sheet A5 shows:

No. 1 stair tower plan, elevation, and details. Study Fig. 12.7, which shows a section through the stair tower at Z—Z, and Fig. 12.8, which shows a plan of the stairs for the first floor.

Pay careful attention to the electric circuit shown in the concrete wall. The circuit with the section mark J for junction box extends to the second and third floors. The panel is shown as being on the second floor. You must realize the importance of every detail in the structure. Assuming that it had been forgotten to detail the conduit to be placed in the concrete wall, one of two things would happen. Either the conduit would have to be placed on the face of the concrete, which would be unsightly, or it would have to be chased (cut) into the concrete and patched over, which would also be unsightly. Such additional work would probably be charged by the contractor as an extra. Extras are chargeable items for any legitimate alterations made to the structure with the consent of the architect and engineers and acceptable by the owner. Extras sometimes amount to a very large sum of money and may have to be settled in a court of law.

Fig. 12-8. Plan of stairs—first floor.

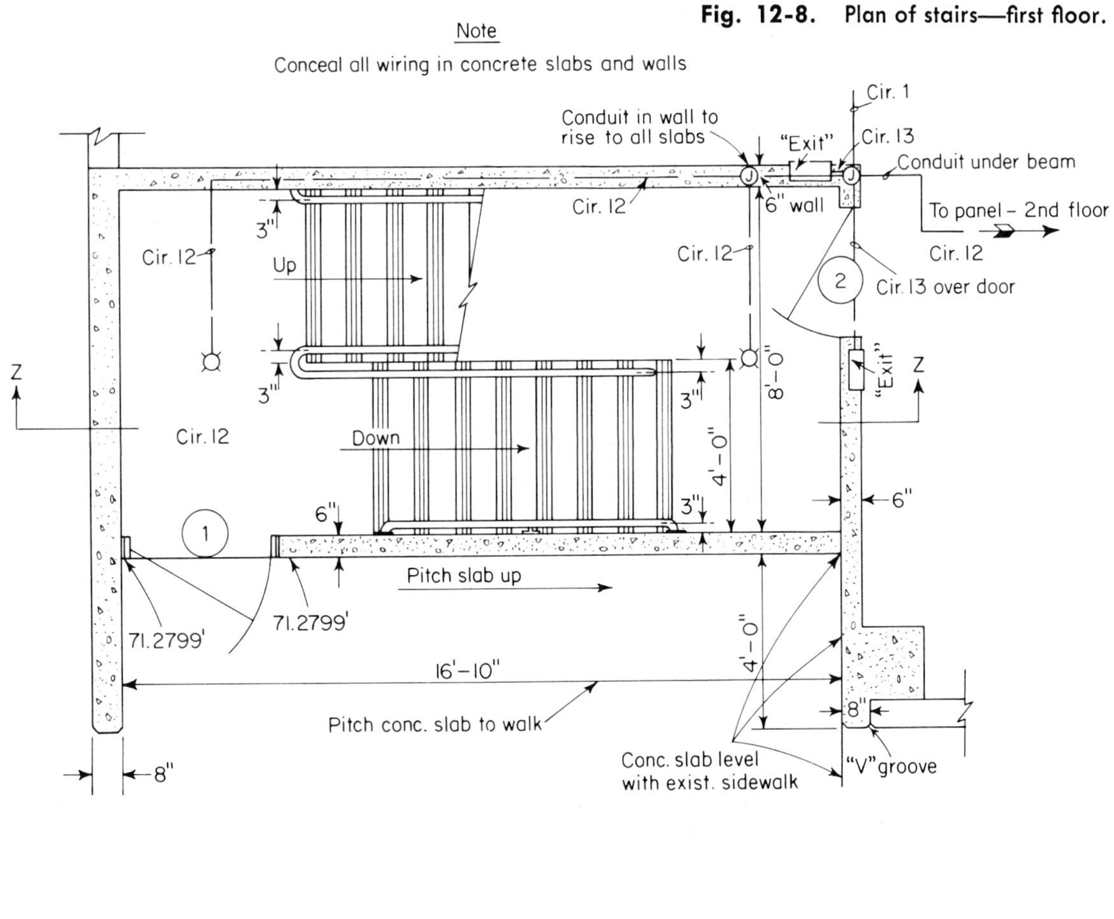

Note
Conceal all wiring in concrete slabs and walls

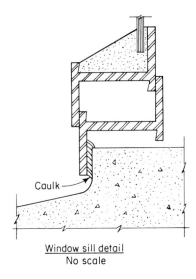

Caulk

Window sill detail
No scale

Fig. 12-9.

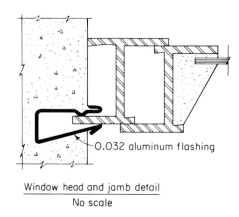

0.032 aluminum flashing

Window head and jamb detail
No scale

Fig. 12-10.

ASSIGNMENTS:

1. Reproduce Figs. 12.7 and 12.8, to the scale of ½″ to 1′-0″ and complete the plans of the stairs for the second and third floors; the doors for the other floors are in the same relative position as for the first floor.

2. On what drawing would you expect to see the reinforcing for the stairs?

3. Who is responsible for determining the reinforcing for these stairs?

Sheet A6 shows:

No. 2 stair tower plan, elevation, and details. These are somewhat similar to those on the preceding drawing. Some detail drawings may be made without any definite scale. At Fig. 12.9 and Fig. 12.10 are shown two examples. They are both details for the same window and show at a glance the type of fastening device to be used and the closure details of the window. This type of drawing is very good practice.

ASSIGNMENT:

Carefully examine the window of the room that you are in, make a detail drawing (without definite scale) of the fastening devices probably used in securing the window to the wall, and also show the closure details of the window to the jamb and to the sill.

Sheet A7 shows:

The north, south, east, and west elevations of the garage. It is from these elevations together with the plans that a first appreciation of the size, shape, and general architectural features of a building are known. But it is from the sections, floor plans or horizontal sections and structural details that the composition of the building is known.

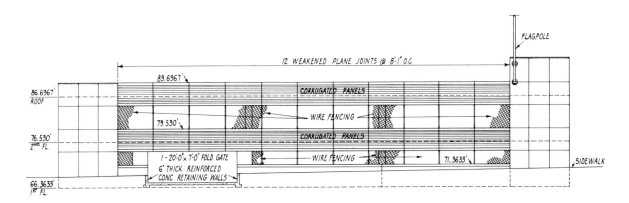

Fig. 12-11. North elevation.

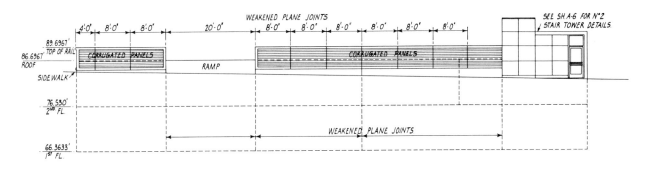

Fig. 12-12. South elevation.

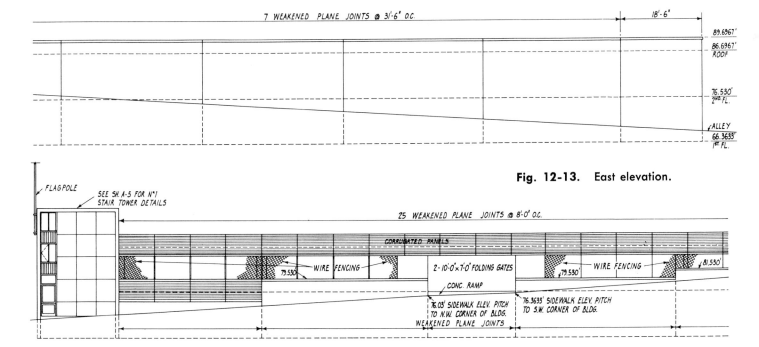

Fig. 12-13. East elevation.

Fig. 12-14. West elevation.

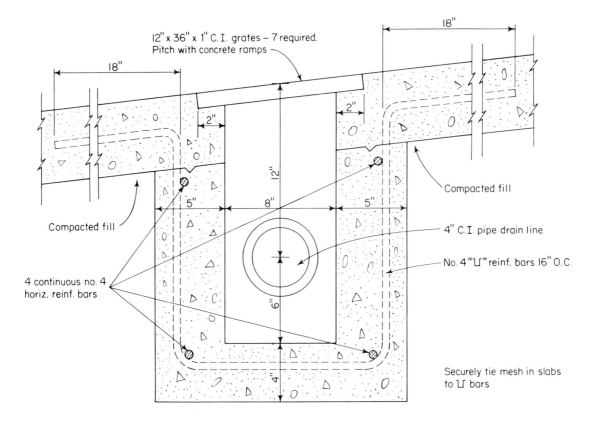

18"

12" x 36" x 1" C.I. grates – 7 required.
Pitch with concrete ramps

18"

2"

2"

Compacted fill

12"

5"

8"

5"

4" C.I. pipe drain line

Compacted fill

No. 4 "⊔" reinf. bars 16" O.C.

4 continuous no. 4
horiz. reinf. bars

6"

4"

Securely tie mesh in slabs
to ⊔ bars

Fig. 12-15. Typical section through a catch basin.

Fig. 12-16. Floor-to-wall flashing detail.

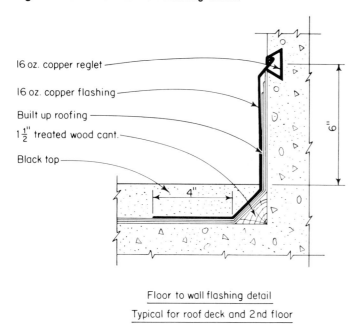

16 oz. copper reglet

16 oz. copper flashing

Built up roofing

1½" treated wood cant.

Black top

6"

4"

Floor to wall flashing detail

Typical for roof deck and 2nd floor

Sheet A8 shows:

Various details. At Fig. 12.15 is shown a typical section through a catch basin. Observe at the top of the detail a notation that the cast iron grates are to be set to the pitch of the car ramp. See Fig. 12.4 for the northern end floor plan. At the entrance is shown a catch basin for the rainwater from the ramp.

At Fig. 12.16 is shown a floor-to-wall detail. This is an excellent drawing, quite definite and self-explanatory.

STRUCTURAL DRAWINGS

Sheet S1 shows:

A footing plan and some details. At Fig. 12.17 is shown a northern portion of the plan. Locate section marks 1/1 and 2/1 and examine the structural details for them. At Fig. 12.18 is shown a typical structural detail for an outside column footing. Note the size of the footing. At Fig. 12.19 is shown a typical structural detail for a center column footing. Notice how much larger the center footing is than the outside ones. This is an engineering necessity. The garage is conceived so that all the weight falls towards the center of the building. The details are adequate and without ambiguity.

ASSIGNMENT:

List all the details shown by the drawing and lettering on Fig. 12.17.

Sheet S2 shows:

The second-floor framing plan. Look closely at Fig. 12.20, which is a picture taken during the actual erection of the garage. It shows an outside column, a center column, and a main beam (B-1).

Sheet S3 shows:

The roof framing plan, beam and column schedules. At Fig. 12.21 is shown a portion of the northern framing plan for the roof. Locate section marks C-1, C-2, and C-3. The letter "C" means column. Note that fourteen columns (C-1) are required, seven on each long wall. There are seven center columns, but only two C-3's, both of which are shown at the north wall. See the column schedule on page 259.

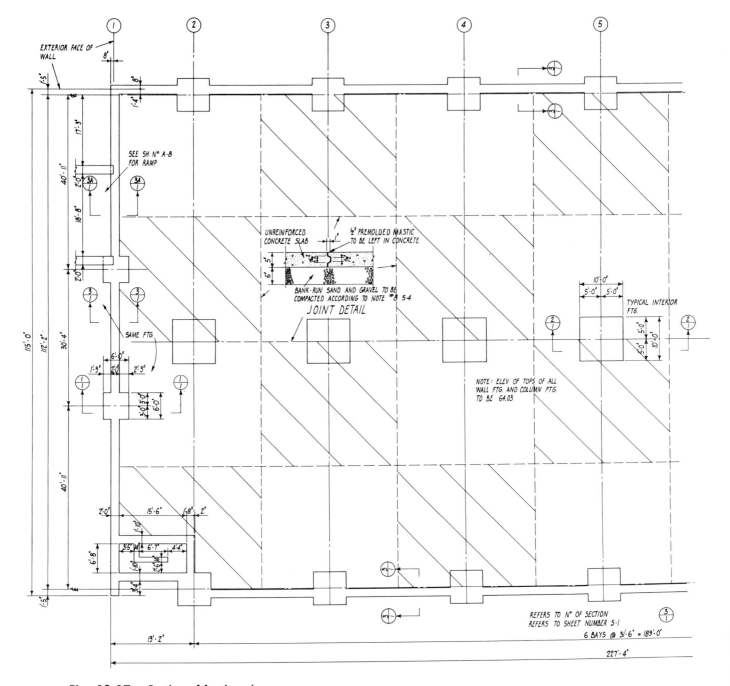

Fig. 12-17. Portion of footing plan.

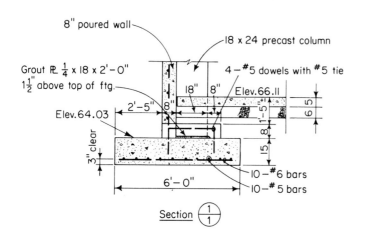

Section $\frac{1}{1}$

Fig. 12-18. Typical structural detail for an outside column footing.

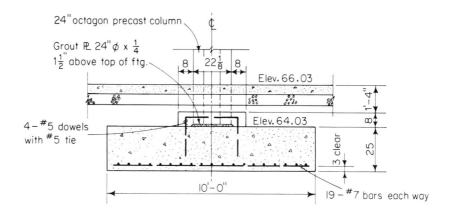

24" octagon precast column

Grout ℞ 24" ⌀ x ¼
1½" above top of ftg.

Elev. 66.03

4 – #5 dowels
with #5 tie

Elev. 64.03

8
22⅛
8

1'-4"

8"

3 clear

25

10'-0"

19 – #7 bars each way

Fig. 12-19. Typical structural detail for a center column footing.

Fig. 12-20. Outside column, center column, and main beam.

COLUMN SCHEDULE

Mark	No. req'd	Size	Reinforcing steel		Remarks
			Vertical	Ties	
C-1	14	Various	Various	#4 at 12	See Section 5/4
C-2	7	Various	Various	Spiral ½ ⌀ at 2¼	See Section 5/4
C-3	2	18" × 24"	4 #7	#3 at 18	12 × 24 tip & Roof

Locate on the plan at Fig. 12.21 the section marks B-1, B-2, and B-3, and examine the following beam schedule. B-1 is the largest beam in the building—a 42" × 30" "T" beam, 40'-6" long. The B-2 beams fit into the webs of the B-1 beams, and the latter support the concrete roof slabs. The

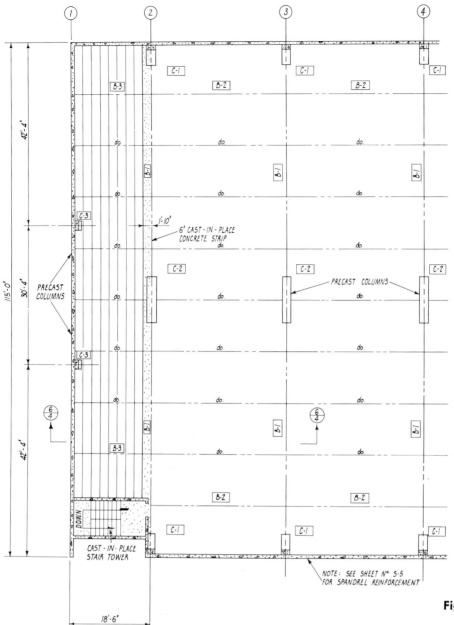

Fig. 12-21. Roof framing plan.

B-3 beam is similar but smaller than the B-2. It also fits into the B-1 web at one end and is supported at the other end by the north wall with its two columns. See the following beam schedule.

			BEAM SCHEDULE		
			Pre-tensioning		
			Total final force	Maximum eccentricity	Tendon
Mark	No. req'd	Beam size			
B-1	14	42″ × 30″ 'T'	167,000 lbs	4.55 for stem	$16^{11}/_{32}$ ⌀ Pre-tension
			216,000 lbs	varies	$16^{3}/_{8}$ Post-tension
B-2	108	6 × 18 RB	160,000	3″	$16^{5}/_{16}$ ⌀ Pre-tension
B-3	32	6 × 12 RB	60,000	2½″	$16^{5}/_{16}$ ⌀ Pre-tension

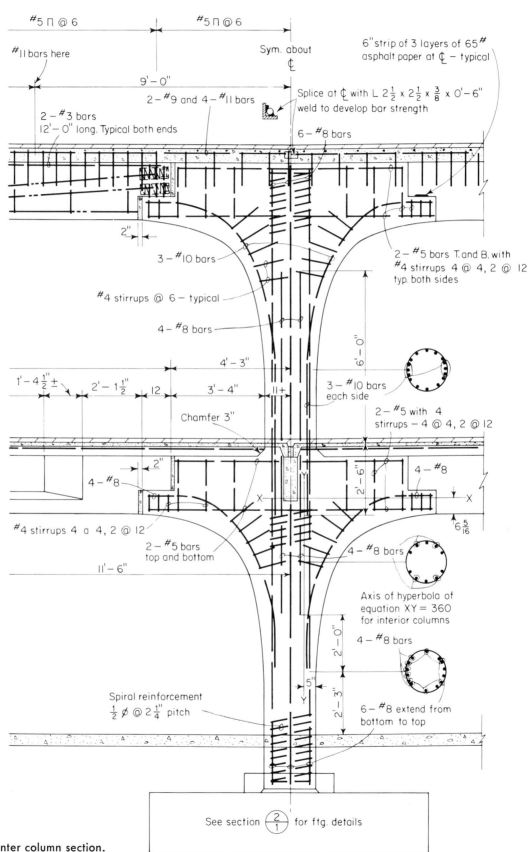

Fig. 12-22. Center column section.

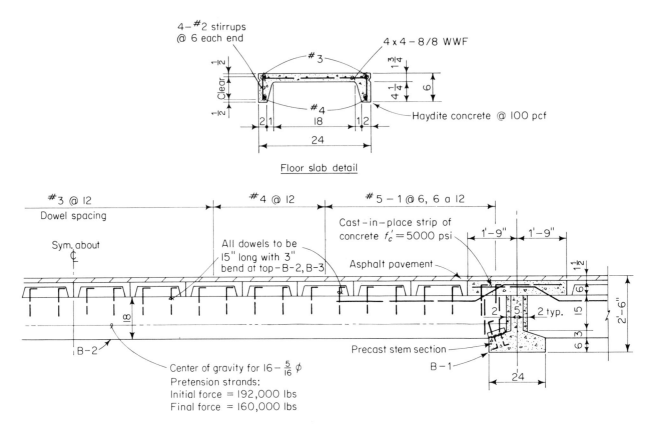

Fig. 12-23. End section.

Sheet S4 shows:

Sections of columns and beams. The center column with its massive reinforcing is shown at Fig. 12.22, which must be closely studied for structural details. At Fig. 12.23 is shown an end section of B-1 with B-2 fitting into its web and supporting the concrete floor slabs, which are shown in end section.

ASSIGNMENT:

Go to any concrete multistory parking garage in your area and make a (no scale) detail drawing of one of the center columns showing all the structural members that are framed into it.

A TECHNICAL SCHOOL SHOP BUILDING 13

The following drawings are published with the permission of the Honourable F. C. Colborne, Minister of Public Works, Government of the Province of Alberta, Canada, and were prepared under the direction of H. A. Henderson, B. Arch., M.R.A.I.C., Chief Architect.

In this chapter we are going to examine parts of some of the dwgs for a prestressed concrete framed, masonry curtained wall shop building. Our study will cover part of the southeast and eastern portion of the structure. It is 300'-0" long and 120'-0" wide. The main body of the building is designed for the shops and is 300'-0" long and 80'-0" wide; the other 40'-0" of width is taken up by a main hall, classrooms, offices, and washrooms. We will concern ourselves with the main framing of the building for the welding shop areas and include some detail drawings of other features. The south (front) and the east elevations are shown in Fig. 13.1.

The footings for the building are concrete piles supporting a continuous concrete placed reinforced ground beam and prestressed columns. The columns support a continuous concrete beam, which in turn supports the roof beams. There are 38 prestressed concrete "T" beams for the roof. They are all 80'-0" long, and 32" deep; thirty of these beams measure 8'-0" across the top. The roofing is placed directly on top of the roof beams.

Many of the following Architectural and Structural dwgs will be referred to throughout this chapter.

Fig. 13-1. South and East elevations.

ARCHITECTURAL DRAWINGS

Note that all these dwgs are in the 100 series

STRUCTURAL DRAWINGS

The mechanical dwgs are in the 300 series, and the electrical dwgs are in the 400 series. Remember the series in which dwgs appear; this helps to identify the section marks on each sheet.

ARCHITECTURAL DRAWINGS

Drawing No. 2—main floor

Let us examine an eastern portion of the floor plan. See Fig. 13.2. The large letters at the right and the figures at the top are grid symbols referring to columns. Carefully locate columns F and G, and see Fig. 13.18.

The numbers in the centers of the shops, rooms, and halls are room numbers which refer to Room schedules on Sheets 110 and 111 (see index) where is stated the type of finish for walls, floors, ceilings and so on for each room. As an example, the floors and general finish of a hall would be different from that of a shop, classroom, or washroom.

The doors are all section marked, such as CC/2. They also refer to another dwg where the door schedule is shown. Find this dwg number on the index. Locate on this portion of the plan all the other doors and list them.

The section mark C/6 refers to section dwg "C" on Sheet 6 (see index). Locate other section marks referring to the section dwgs and see Fig. 13.6.

Section mark U/102 refers to dwg "U" on Sheet 102. Apart from the pre-stressed concrete columns, the plan also shows masonry curtain walls. The contractor would be reading the specifications at the same time and would find that all these masonry walls are to be built with stack bond and also that the finished texture of the blocks varies throughout the building, some blocks having different textures on either side. On the left of room No. 109 (hall) are student lockers. Rooms Nos. 106, 107, and 108 are not included in this exercise.

Drawing No. 3—mezzanine floor

The portion of the mezzanine floor shown at Fig. 13.3 is located immediately above the floor shown in Fig. 13.2. *Locate:*
(a) The room numbers (note that the second floor rooms are in the number 200 series).
(b) the door section marks.
(c) the window section marks (see index).

One of your very exacting tasks on the preparation of dwgs is indexing and section marking the sheets. You are most earnestly advised to try to clear your mind of your intimate knowledge of your own dwgs and to put yourself in the position of others reading them for the first time. Bear in mind that contractors are known to make additions to their bids where dwgs are not well detailed, indexed, and section marked. It is very important, and it requires a discipline on your part to give fingertip references and section marks throughout all your work.

How is the mezzanine floor supported? See Fig. 13.7.

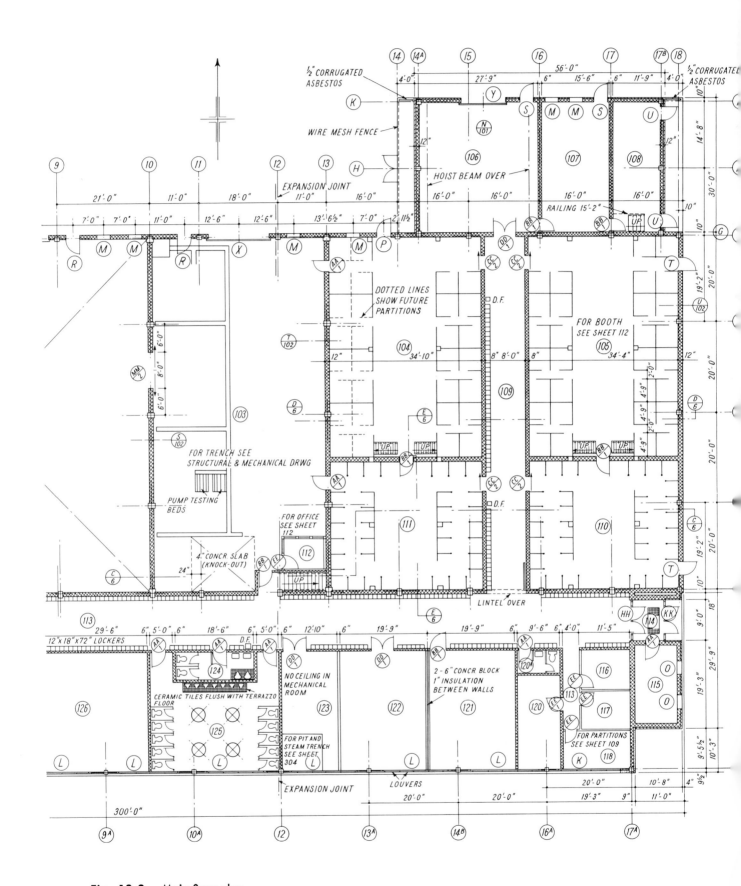

Fig. 13-2. Main floor plan.

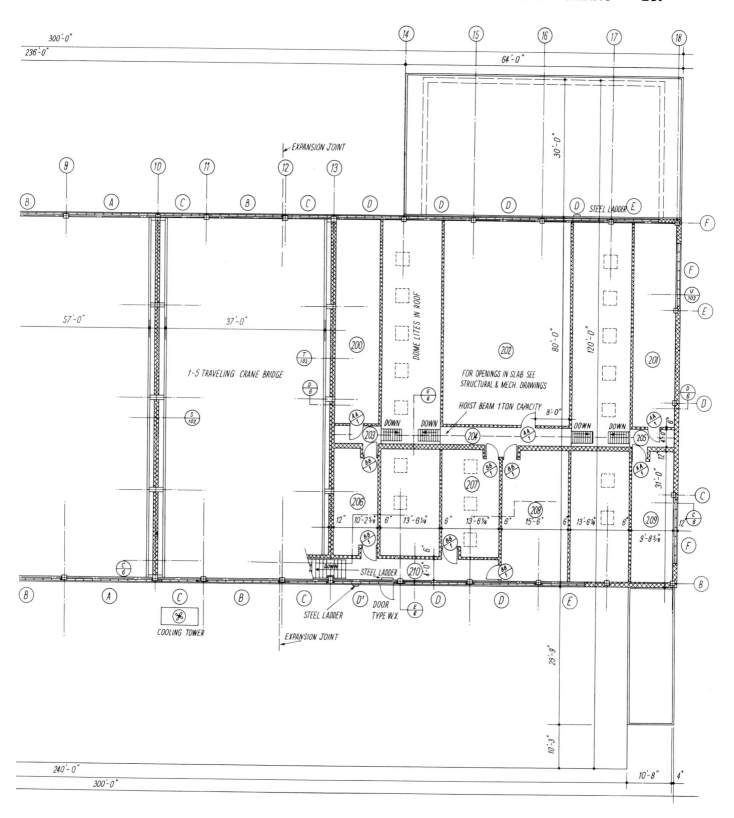

Fig. 13-3. Mezzanine floor plan.

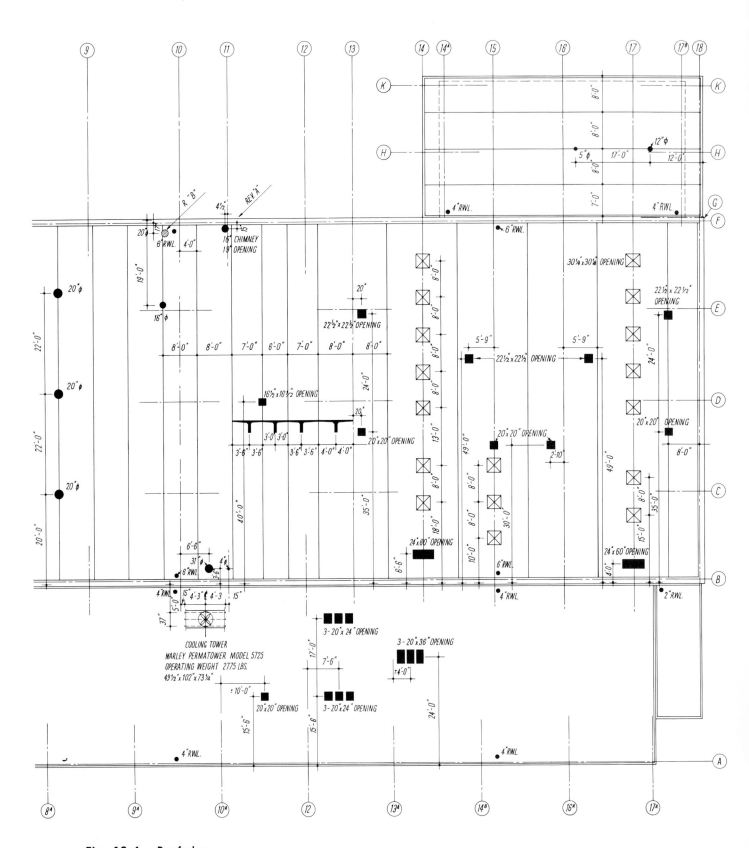

Fig. 13-4. Roof plan.

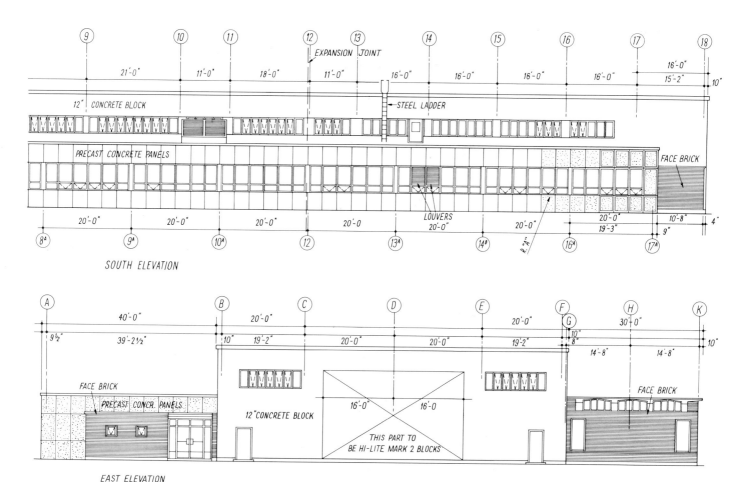

SOUTH ELEVATION

EAST ELEVATION

Fig. 13-5. Elevations.

Drawing No. 4—roof plan

The portion of the roof plan shown at Fig. 13.4 covers the other two floors we have examined. The large letters and figures indicate the grid lines. Note carefully F and G.

It can be seen that the Plexiglass Dome Lites are all arranged to cut into the flanges of adjoining roof beams (see Fig. 13.10). I asked the engineer on this job what his tolerances were for the framework of this building and he replied, "One eighth of an inch in level, perpendicular, and diagonals." *Your dimensioning of dwgs must be exact.* With the exception of seven, all the main roof "T" beams are 8'-0" in width.

Drawing No. 5—elevations

At Fig. 13.5 is shown part of the south and all of the east elevations. Note the column letters and figures and locate columns F and G. There are lots of wide open spaces on these elevations, which make for easy reading. There is only one note on the original dwg; this states that all concrete blocks are to be laid in stack bond. What is a stack bond?

An important paragraph in the specifications states that face brick shall match that on existing buildings in this project.

Drawing No. 6—sections C/6, D/6, E/6

At Fig. 13.6 is shown Section E/6. Locate on Fig. 13.2 this section mark and also grid letters B, C, and D. Observe both the 12″ and the 6″ concrete block walls. For the texture finish, one would have to read the specifications; it would also be shown on the Room Schedules for finish.

Above the door is shown a suspended ceiling of acoustic tile on an aluminum grid. Locate this ceiling on the mezzanine plan. Remember that we are only going over dwgs originated by others; can we originate our own dwgs? Practice the visualization of details of construction for the room you are in.

Make a detail dwg 3″ to 1′-0″ of the fastening devices of the door frame for the main entrance of the building you are now occupying.

Drawing No. 102

There are six wall sections shown on the original sheets; two complementary sections are shown at Fig. 13.7. Locate on Fig. 13.3 the two wall sects. T/102 and U/102. The letter in each case indicates the sequential alphabetical arrangement of the sections on Sheet 102 (see index). These dwgs are clear, well done, and require a minimum of lettering. Note the predetermined 100′-0″ datum line finish of the main floor and the relative heights of the other floor and the roof. These sects also show excellent end sects of the roof beams.

Fig. 13-6. Section E/6.

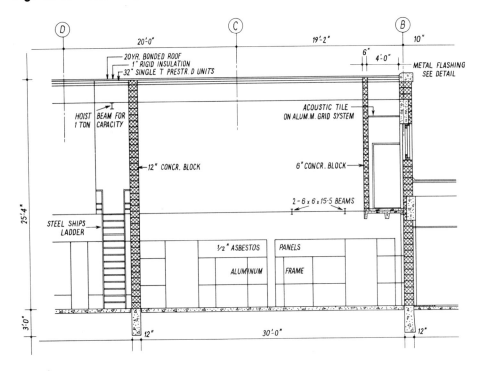

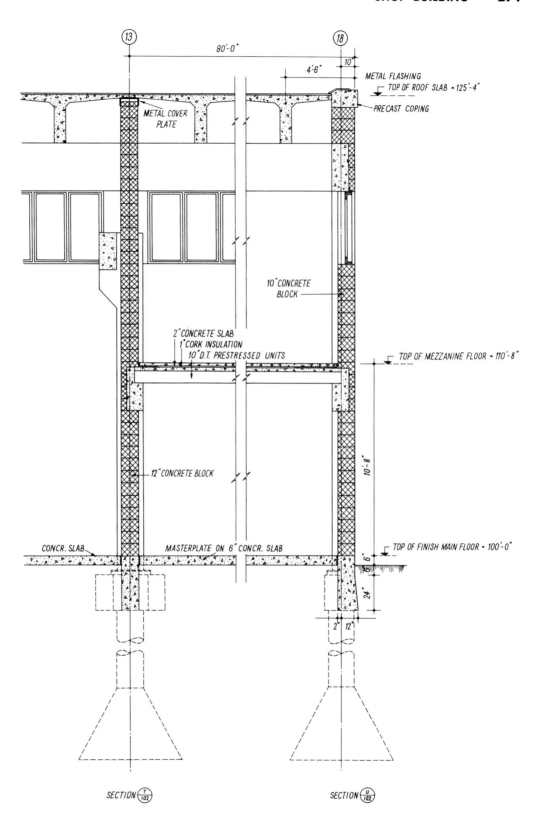

Fig. 13-7. Wall sections.

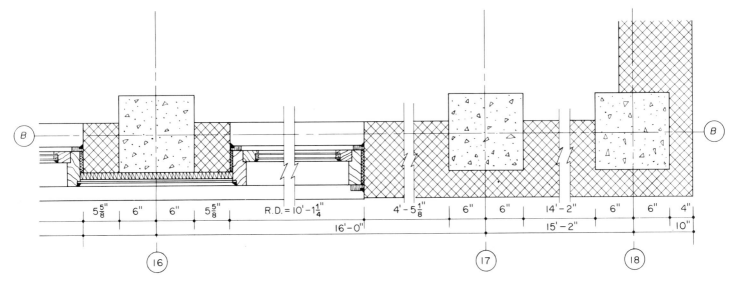

Fig. 13-8.   Column section.

Drawing No. 104

There are a number of window detail and col sect on the original dwgs. Locate grid lines B-17 and B-18 on Fig. 13.2 and examine the col sect at Fig. 13.8. Remember to look again at the mezzanine floor plan, Fig. 13.3.

Drawing No. 108

The original sheet shows five isometric dwgs of columns. Fig. 13.9 shows an isometric dwg of the beam connection for columns 4, 7, 10, and 13 on grid B. These columns are not shown on the plans of this text exercise but are included because they are more complex than those for the east end of the building. This type of dwg is easily understood and is excellent drawing practice.

In large cities the delivery of large prestressed members of buildings requires a police escort. There is only one place to put such members upon delivery, and that is to incorporate them immediately into the building structure.

For practice, make a perspective freehand sketch of that portion of the south (front) of the building (shown at Fig. 13.1) and the east elevation.

Drawing No. 112—dome skylight

At Fig. 13.10 is shown a part section detail of a double dome skylight. The original is drawn to the scale of 3″ to 1′-0″ and clearly shows the method of securing and rendering watertight the dome to the roof. The specs state that these skylights are to be installed to the manufacturer's specifications. This is quite usual for special pieces of manufactured units.

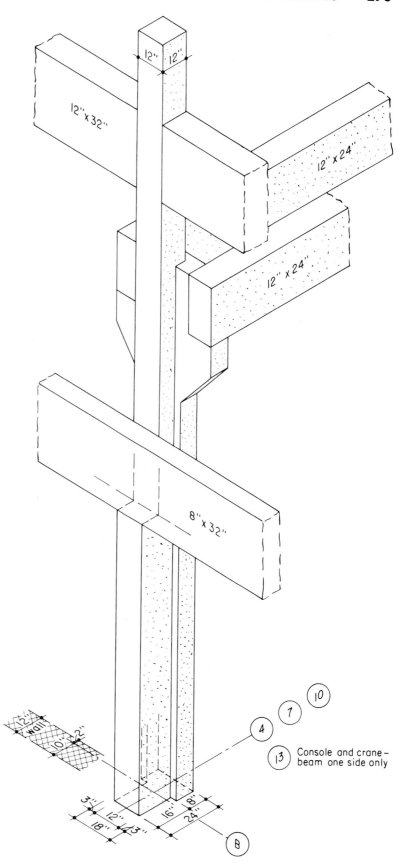

Fig. 13-9.   Beam-column connections.

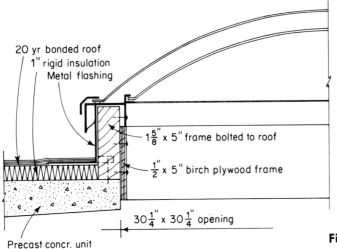

20 yr bonded roof
1" rigid insulation
Metal flashing

$1\frac{5}{8}$" x 5" frame bolted to roof

$\frac{1}{2}$" x 5" birch plywood frame

$30\frac{1}{4}$" x $30\frac{1}{4}$" opening

Precast concr. unit

Fig. 13-10. Dome skylight.

It is very important when specifying such items to be sure that the contractor will have them on hand at the right time, for installation or the building construction may be delayed.

The only way to keep abreast with new pieces of manufactured units for buildings is to read professional publications and manufacturers' brochures and the filing of such literature in the A.I.A. (American Institute of Architects) data filing system. See Chapter 2.

Student locker

A section of a student locker is shown at Fig. 13.11. *The original is drawn to full size details.* Study the dwg from the bottom up: (a) concrete base with wood furring strip to receive the locker screwed thru the bottom. (b) Terrazzo base 0'-6". (c) The locker. (d) Angle irons ¾". (e) Plaster on metal lath, supported at the bottom and top with a metal stop for the plaster. (f) Acoustic tiles on a metal grid system (for the ceiling) suspended on #8-G.A. wire hangers (number eight gage galvanized wire hangers).

STRUCTURAL DRAWINGS

Drawing No. 201—pile layout

Fig. 13.12 shows the plan layout of piles for that portion of the plan shown at Fig. 13.2. Both these dwgs should be read together. The legend for this sheet is as follows:

Legend

●   Q=24" Pile

•   P=16" Pile

•   R=18" Pile

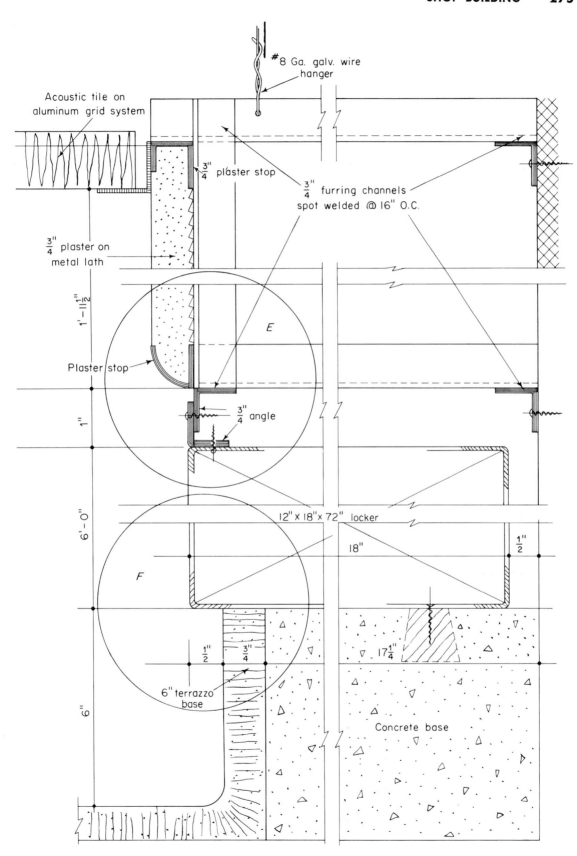

#8 Ga. galv. wire hanger

Acoustic tile on aluminum grid system

$\frac{3}{4}$ plaster stop

$\frac{3}{4}$ furring channels spot welded @ 16" O.C.

$\frac{3}{4}$ plaster on metal lath

$1'-11\frac{1}{2}"$

E

Plaster stop

1"

$\frac{3}{4}$ angle

6'-0"

12" x 18" x 72" locker

18"

$\frac{1}{2}"$

F

$17\frac{1}{4}"$

$\frac{1}{2}"$ $\frac{3}{4}"$

6"

6" terrazzo base

Concrete base

Fig. 13-11. Student locker section.

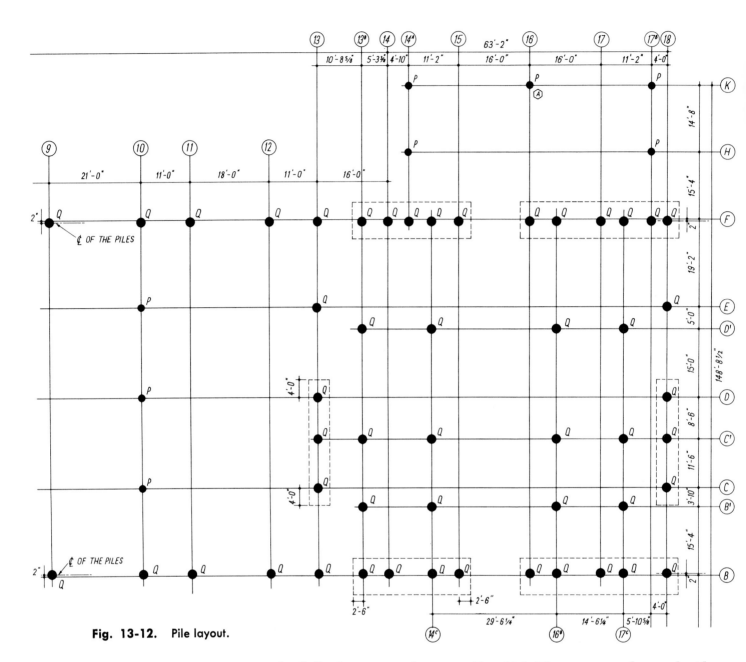

Fig. 13-12. Pile layout.

The "R" piles are not shown on Fig. 13.2. They support the south side single-story section of the building for classrooms and other facilities. Note carefully it is stated on the original sheet that:

On line "F" the ₵ of the piles is 2″ southward.

On line "B" the ₵ of the piles is 2″ northward.

Drawing No. 202—plan of grade beams

Fig. 13.13 shows similar grid line references as for other plan dwgs. The dwg should be read with Fig 13.2 and with the preceding dwg. A control joint detail, and a typical deepening in the slab on grade detail are shown at Fig. 13.14.

Locate the control joints shown on this dwg. What is a control joint?

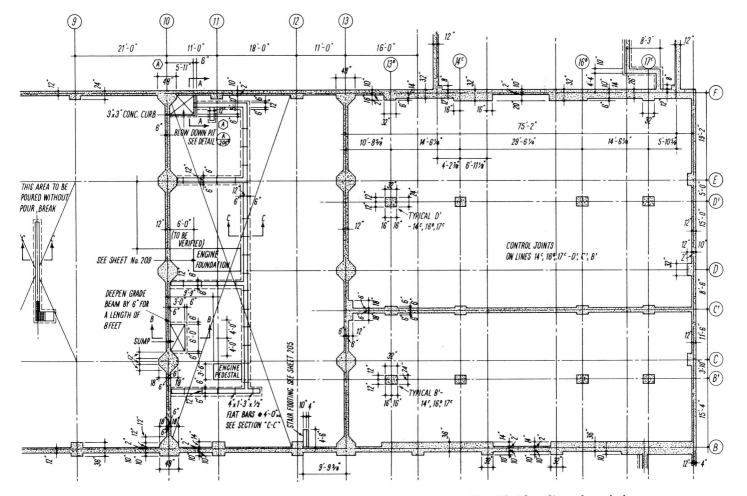

Fig. 13-13. Plan of grade beams.

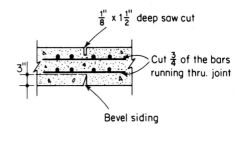

$\frac{1}{8}'' \times 1\frac{1}{2}''$ deep saw cut

Cut $\frac{3}{4}$ of the bars running thru. joint

Bevel siding

Detail of control joint

Not to scale

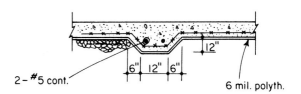

2 – #5 cont.

12"

6" 12" 6"

6 mil. polyth.

Typical deepening in slab on grade for all 6" block partitions

Fig. 13-14. Details.

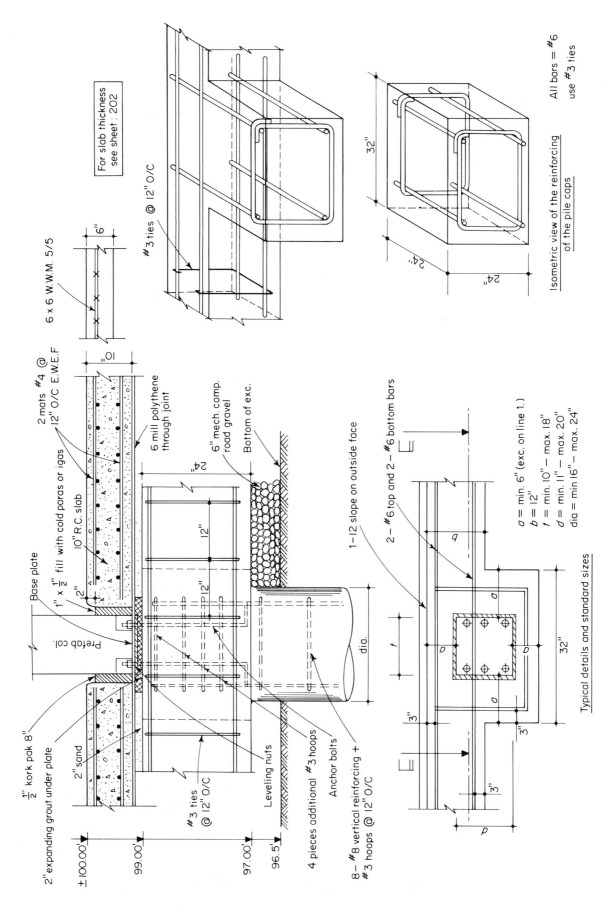

For slab thickness see sheet : 202

6" × 6" W.W.M. 5/5

#3 ties @ 12" O/C

All bars = #6
use #3 ties

32"

24"

Isometric view of the reinforcing of the pile caps

2 mats #4 @ 12" O/C E.W.E.F

1" × ½" fill with cold paras or igas

10" R.C. slab

6 mill polythene through joint

6" mech. comp. road gravel

Bottom of exc.

Base plate

Pretab col.

½" kork pak 8"

2" expanding grout under plate

2" sand

#3 ties @ 12" O/C

Leveling nuts

4 pieces additional #3 hoops

Anchor bolts

8 − #8 vertical reinforcing + #3 hoops @ 12" O/C

+100.00'

99.00'

97.00'

96.5'

2"

10"

24"

12"

P12"

dia.

1-12 slope on outside face

2 − #6 top and 2 − #6 bottom bars

32"

3"

3"

3"

t

a

a

a

D

D

q

b

p

E   E

a = min. 6" (exc. on line 1.)
b = 12"
t = min. 10" − max. 18"
d = min. 11" − max. 20"
dia = min 16" − max. 24"

Typical details and standard sizes

Fig. 13-15. Typical details and standard sizes in plan and section E-E.

278

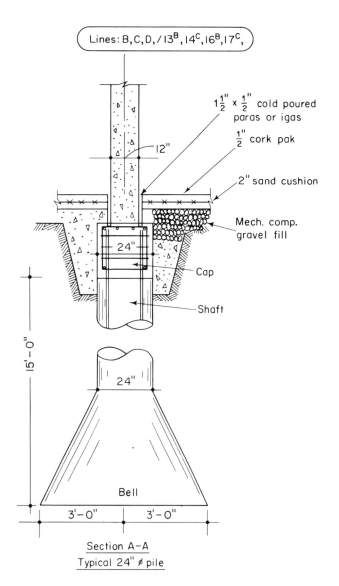

Lines: B, C, D, /13^B, 14^C, 16^B, 17^C,

$1\frac{1}{2}$″ × $\frac{1}{2}$″ cold poured paras or igas

$\frac{1}{2}$″ cork pak

2″ sand cushion

Mech. comp. gravel fill

Cap

Shaft

12″

24″

15′-0″

24″

Bell

3′-0″   3′-0″

Section A–A
Typical 24″ ∅ pile

Fig. 13-16.

Drawing No. 203—details

Fig. 13.15 shows typical details and standard sizes in plan and sect E-E. Along with this dwg are also shown two isometric views of the reinforcing for pile caps. This is a most important detail; the original is drawn to the scale of 1″ to 1′-0″.

PILE DATA					
Dia. inches	Bell dia.	Length of pile	Length of vertical bars	Size of vertical bars	Ties
24″	6′-0″	20′-0″	12′-0″	8-#8	#3 @ 12″
18″	5′-0″	20′-0″	12′-0″	8-#8	#3 @ 12″
16″	4′-8″	20′-0″	12′-0″	8-#8	#3 @ 16″

At Fig. 13.16 is show Section A-A of a 24″ ∅ pile and at Fig. 13.17 is shown a 24″ deep ∅ grade beam.

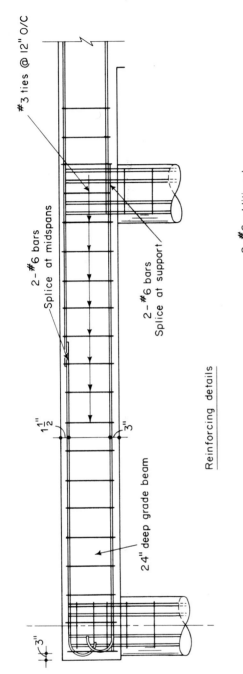

#3 ties @ 12" O/C

2-#6 bars
Splice at midspans

2-#6 bars
Splice at support

$1\frac{1}{2}$"

3"

3"

24" deep grade beam

Reinforcing details

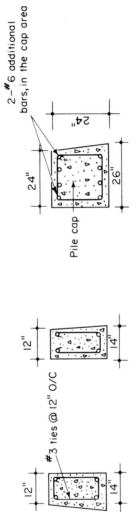

2-#6 additional
bars, in the cap area

24"

24"

26"

Pile cap

12"

14"

12"

14"

#3 ties @ 12" O/C

Typical cross sections of the grade beam

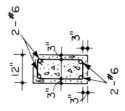

2-#6

12"

3"

3"

3"

3"

2-#6

Fig. 13-17.

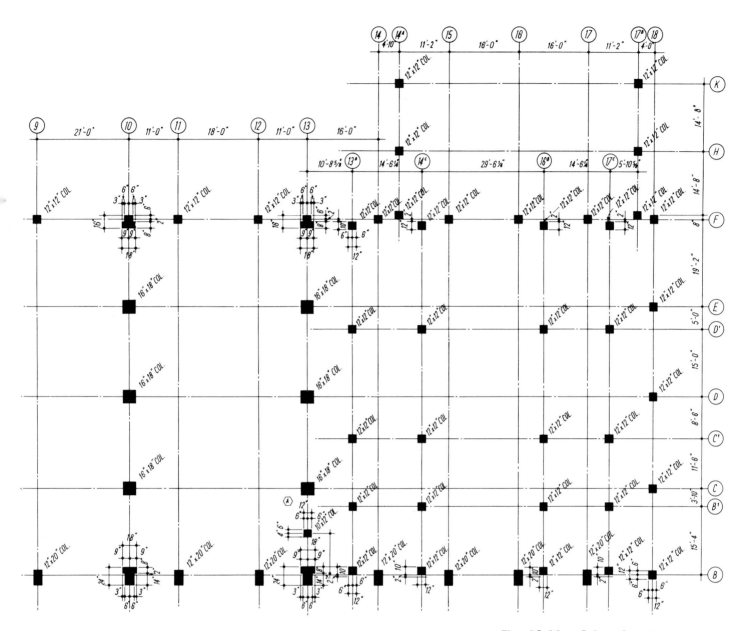

Fig. 13-18. Column layout.

Drawing No. 204—column layout (precast)

At Fig. 13.18 one can see the care with which the column layout must be drawn; every column drawn in its appointed place and the contractor to place every column as appointed. A great deal of very careful work went into this dwg.

At this time we have a real concept of the architectural and structural dwgs for the framing of this workshop building. After the piles had been completed and the ground beam cast in place, the framing, including the roof beams, was completed in fourteen working days.

With this type of construction, as soon as the roof beams are in place, work can proceed irrespective of weather conditions. This is a very important consideration when the local temperatures may be below zero in the winter and 112° or more in the summer.

14 A COUNTY OFFICE BUILDING

In this chapter we are going to examine some of the dwgs for a County Office Building. The following material is by courtesy of Maxwell and Campbell Consulting Engineers, Calgary, Alberta. The structure is built with prestressed concrete framing, main floor, and folded plate roof. The roof has a clean span of 67'-0", and the curtain walls are masonry units.

Again you are reminded to keep always in mind that your dwgs are for others to interpret and use during noisy building operations. Make them vivid and free from ambiguities. Discuss your dwgs with others in your office. It is easy to become casual with those things with which we are most familiar. Many offices have one or more architect's inspectors on their staff, whose duty is to ensure that work is carried out to the full *meaning and intent* of the dwgs and specs. These men are often recruited from the field and have had many years of experience as building superintendents. If they cannot readily understand your dwgs, it is fair to suppose that estimators, building superintendents, technicians, and foremen are going to have difficulty too.

PRESTRESSED CONCRETE

The following information is published by courtesy of Titan Prestressing Corporation, Ltd., Calgary, Alberta.

The term "prestressed concrete" refers to the principle of inducing internal forces in a member to offset the external applied forces. In ordinary reinforced concrete, loads are applied and internal forces result. In pre-stressed concrete, internal forces are induced prior to loading, which in turn counteract the forces induced when loading does occur.

Basically, internal forces are created by placing the concrete in compression so that under actual loading all of the internal compression stresses must be counteracted before any tensile stresses can occur.

In reinforced concrete, the designer has to be content with the internal forces that occur as a result of externally applied loads. In prestressed concrete we have greater control over stresses, cracking, and deflection, because the designer can create the forces that he requires, with the result that the concrete very seldom goes out of compression.

Prestressing can be accomplished by one of two methods, pre-tensioning or post-tensioning. Unfortunately pre-tensioning lends itself only to members that can be pre-cast and readily transported, and precludes the advantages of monolithic cast-in-place construction. Post-tensioning on the other hand lends itself very well to monolithic cast-in-place construction. *This special application of prestressing consists of imbedding high tensile wire strands (eight times as strong as mild steel) protected by greased plastic hoses, in the concrete.*

These strands are placed so as to follow the lines of maximum stress, and create internal upward forces which counteract the external downward forces caused by loading the structure.

After the concrete is cast and has reached sufficient strength, the strands are stressed by light-weight hydraulic jacks and then anchored with non-slip anchorages.

With post-tensioning the advantages of prestressing can now be applied to long monolithic continuous beams, flat plate monolithic slabs, pan joist structures, thin shells, folded plates, and many other shapes in which pre-stressing could not be practically applied before. For the designer, Titan can provide assistance as to the feasibility of post-tensioning on specific projects, as well as sharing its experience in structural design and layouts, and is available to discuss details such as strang placement, stressing methods, and the economic advantages of post-tensioning.

Post-tensioning and, in particular, post-tensioning by Titan Prestressing Corporation offers the economic and functional advantages of the advanced techniques of prestressing, using the traditional continuous monolithic cast-in-place construction. These features, coupled with the inherent economies of the Titan method, offer the architect and engineer a new medium in design freedom.

Let us examine a few of the dwgs for this building.

ARCHITECTURAL DRAWINGS

Sheet 2—Basement plan

Sheet 3—Main floor plan

Sheet 4—North and west elevations

Sheet 5—South & east elevations

Sheet 6—Wall section details

Sheet 7—Wall sections

STRUCTURAL DRAWINGS

Sheet 4—Main floor slab   Sheet 5—Roof plan

   Before making a close study of these details, let us first riffle through the dwgs to get the feel of the building.

Drawing No. 2

   This is a good one with which to start. It is a plan. See Fig. 14.1. Let us first find the compass point so that we will know and remember the way the building fronts. Note the grid lettering for the columns across the top of the dwg and that figures are used on the left side. Some of these indicate internal columns. Imagine yourself walking through the corridors of the basement and into every vestibule and room. Read the dwg and find out why some areas are shaded, but remember that at this stage we are only making a cursory inspection of the dwgs.

Drawing No. 3

   This is a plan of the main floor. See Fig. 14.2. Note the general layout of this floor with its general office in the center and other offices and main rooms on the outside walls. Here we are at once struck by the freedom for the arranging of rooms by size and shape that modern architects now enjoy. This building has a 67'-0" span, and rooms can be arranged or rearranged to suit the owner or future owners without having to consider any supporting walls below. Not too many years ago it was necessary to arrange for the walls of the upper floors to be supported by bearing walls directly underneath them. An exception to this general arrangement on these and most plans is to have all the plumbing units placed directly over each other, floor by floor, to facilitate and economize on piping and drainage.

Drawing No. 4

   A quick look at this dwg, which is for the north and west elevations, shows the main entrance steps and doors, masonry unit walls, symmetrical glass arrangement, and the folded plate concrete roof. See Fig. 14.3. On the right-hand side of the dwg are given the heights, with a datum of 100'-0" for the main floor. This datum is used only for this building and has no relationship to height above sea level. It is usual for a datum of 100'-0" to be set for a building and then all measurements are so much above or below this assumed level. *Note the 0'-4" slope shown above the roof line on the west side elevation. This is a very important detail; such items must be remembered.*

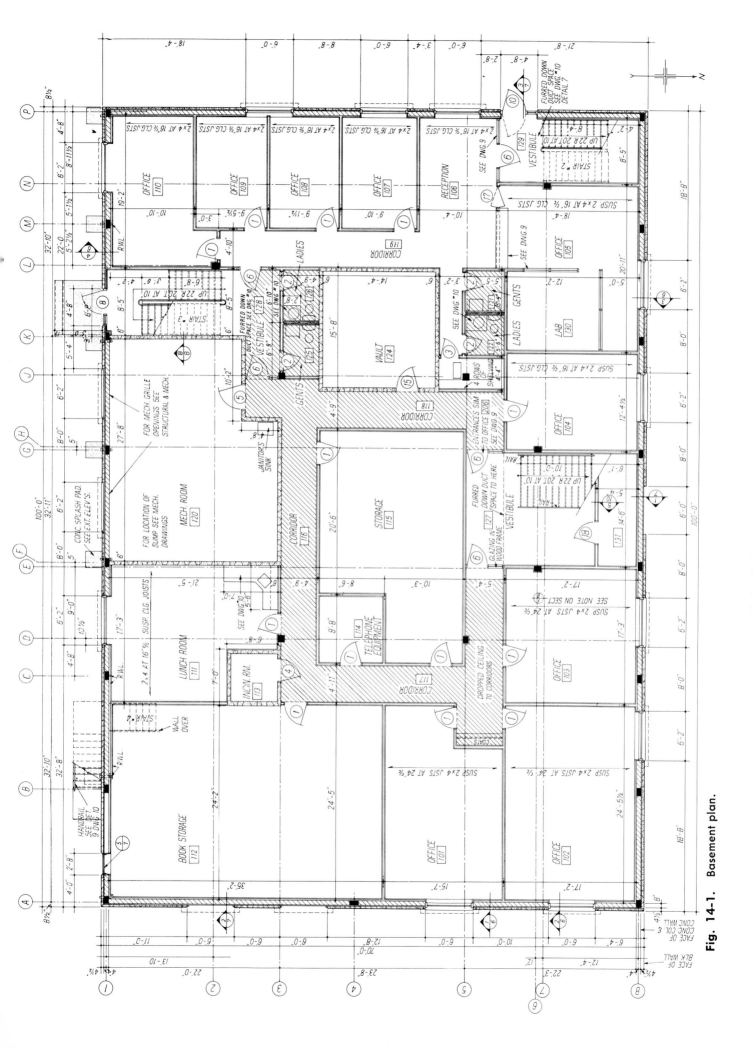

Fig. 14-1. Basement plan.

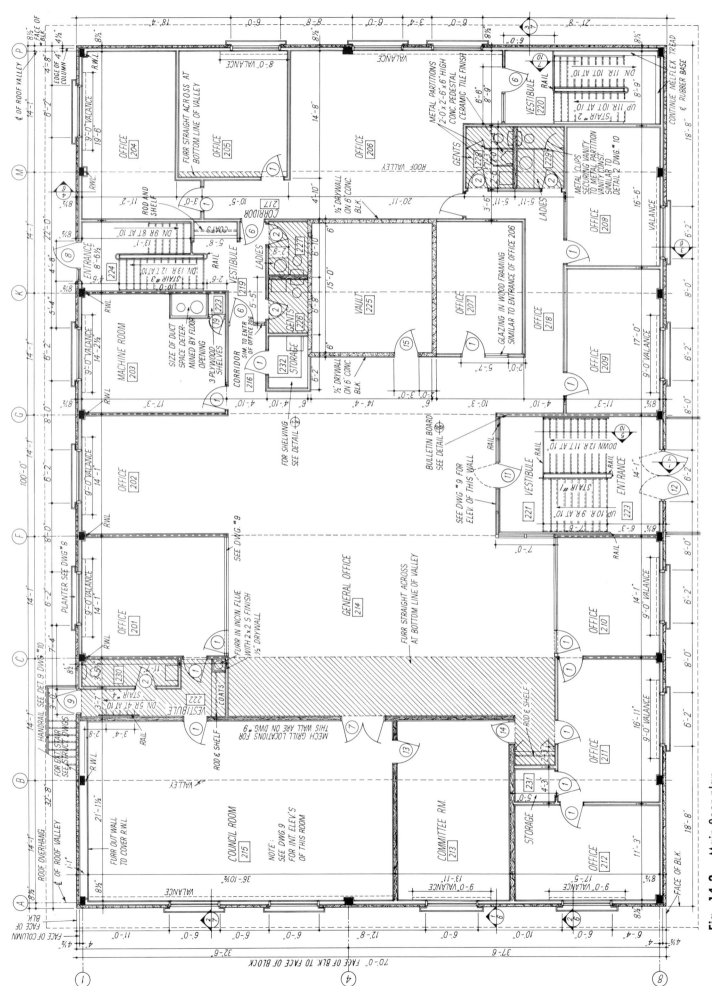

Fig. 14-2. Main floor plan.

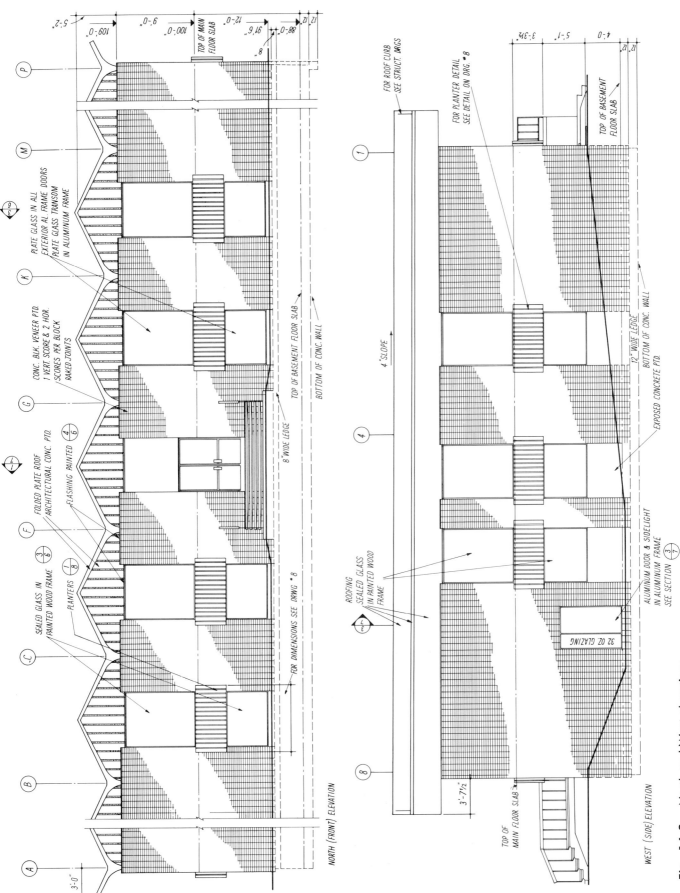

Fig. 14-3. North and West elevations.

Drawing No. 5

This drawing gives the other two elevations (south and east). We now have a complete picture of the building in our minds. See Fig. 14.4.

Drawing No. 6

On this dwg are shown four separate typical wall sections. See Fig. 14.5. Each section has its own section mark (sometimes called a flag) shown at the bottom thus: 1/6 thru 4/6. The bottom number in this particular system indicates the sheet number on which the section appears (in this case it is Sheet No. 6). The top number in each instance indicates the sequentially numbered arrangement of the sectional dwgs on the sheet.

Drawing No. 7

This completes all the architectural dwgs that we are studying for this building. See Fig. 14.6. On the title at the bottom right corner, this sheet is shown as 7 of 11, there being eleven architectural dwgs of which this is the seventh.

ASSIGNMENT:

1. Turn to Fig. 14.1 and count the number of concrete columns in this bldg.
2. Relate all the section marks on Figs. 14.1 and 14.2 to Figs. 14.3, 14.4, and 14.5.
3. Make a southwest and then a southeast freehand perspective dwg of the building.
4. Make a close study of Section 1/7 Fig. 14.6 and make a freehand perspective view of it.

EXAMINATION OF ARCHITECTURAL DRAWINGS

Now that we have made a complete overall appreciation of these dwgs, let us examine them in greater detail.

Step 1

Locate section marks 1/6 and 2/6 on Fig. 14.1 and follow them through to Figs. 14.2 and 14.4. It is on Fig. 14.4 and 14.5 that we begin to understand that Fig. 1/6 shows a section through the wall and that 2/6 shows a section through the basement and main floor windows. For the detail of the planters we would have to examine Sheet 8, which is not included here.

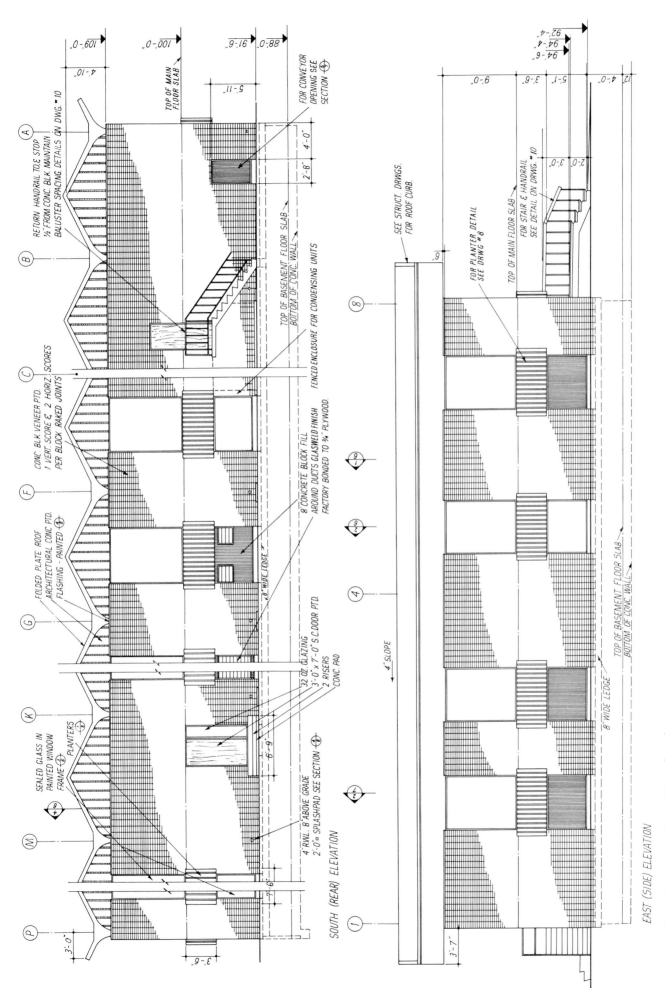

Fig. 14-4. South and East elevations.

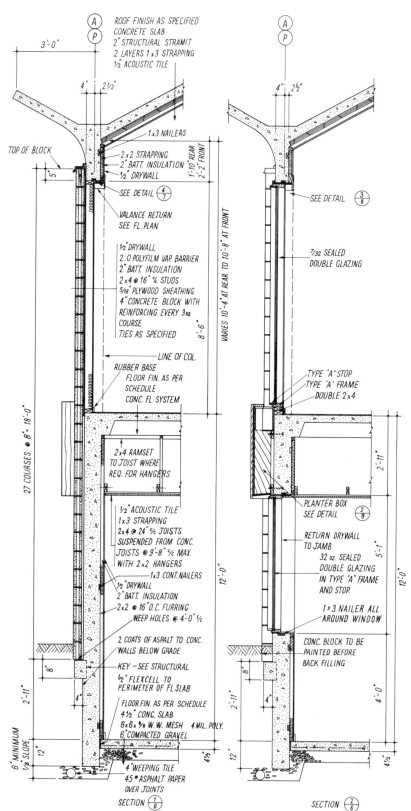

Ⓐ
Ⓟ
ROOF FINISH AS SPECIFIED
CONCRETE SLAB
2" STRUCTURAL STRAMIT
2 LAYERS 1 x 3 STRAPPING
½" ACOUSTIC TILE

3'-0"

4"   2½"

TOP OF BLOCK

5"

1 x 3 NAILERS

2 x 2 STRAPPING
2" BATT. INSULATION
½" DRYWALL

SEE DETAIL (4/7)

VALANCE RETURN
SEE FL. PLAN

1-10" REAR
2'-2" FRONT

½" DRYWALL
2.0 POLYFILM VAP. BARRIER
2" BATT. INSULATION
2 x 4 @ 16" ⁿ/c STUDS
⁵/₁₆" PLYWOOD SHEATHING
4" CONCRETE BLOCK WITH
REINFORCING EVERY 3ᴿᴰ
COURSE
TIES AS SPECIFIED

8'-6"

VARIES 10'-4" AT REAR TO 10'-8" AT FRONT

LINE OF COL.
RUBBER BASE
FLOOR FIN. AS PER
SCHEDULE
CONC. FL. SYSTEM

27 COURSES @ 8" - 18'-0"

2 x 4 RAMSET
TO JOIST WHERE
REQ. FOR HANGERS

½" ACOUSTIC TILE
1 x 3 STRAPPING
2 x 4 @ 24" ⁿ/c JOISTS
SUSPENDED FROM CONC.
JOISTS @ 9'-8" ⁿ/c MAX.
WITH 2 x 2 HANGERS
1 x 3 CONT. NAILERS
½" DRYWALL
2" BATT. INSULATION
2 x 2 @ 16" O.C. FURRING
WEEP HOLES @ 4'-0" ⁿ/c

12'-0"

2 COATS OF ASPALT TO CONC.
WALLS BELOW GRADE

8"

KEY – SEE STRUCTURAL

½" FLEXCELL TO
PERIMETER OF FL SLAB

FLOOR FIN. AS PER SCHEDULE
4½" CONC. SLAB
6 x 6 x ⁵/₈ W.W. MESH   4 MIL. POLY.
6" COMPACTED GRAVEL

2'-11"

6" MINIMUM
⅛ SLOPE

12"

4"

4½"

4" WEEPING TILE
45 # ASPHALT PAPER
OVER JOINTS

SECTION (1/6)

Ⓐ
Ⓟ

4"   2½"

SEE DETAIL (3/8)

⁷/₃₂ SEALED
DOUBLE GLAZING

TYPE 'A' STOP
TYPE 'A' FRAME
DOUBLE 2 x 4

2'-11"

PLANTER BOX
SEE DETAIL (2/8)

RETURN DRYWALL
TO JAMB
32 oz. SEALED
DOUBLE GLAZING
IN TYPE 'A' FRAME
AND STOP.

1 x 3 NAILER ALL
AROUND WINDOW

CONC. BLOCK TO BE
PAINTED BEFORE
BACK FILLING

5'-1"

12'-0"

4'-0"

8"

2'-11"

12"

4"

4½"

SECTION (2/6)

Fig. 14-5.   Wall sections.

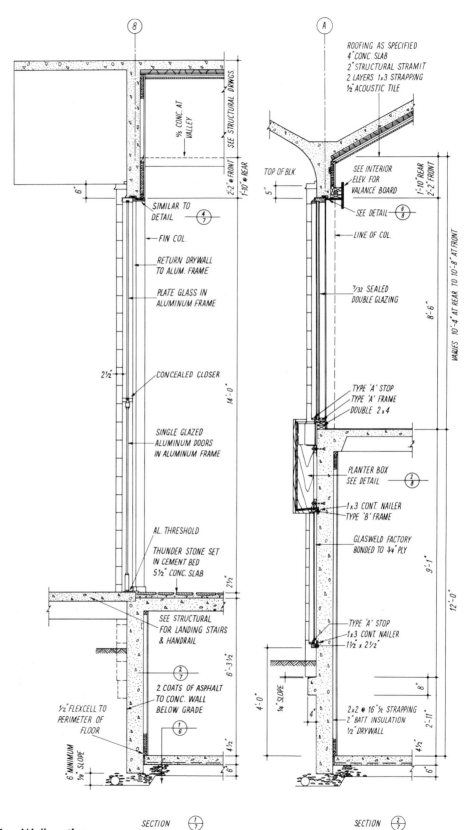

Fig. 14-6. Wall sections.

Step 2

Turn to Fig. 14.5 and find sections 1/6 and 2/6 where we get a better understanding of the column, the wall section, and the folded plate roof with its overhang at the west and east walls. Note the line of the columns on both these dwgs and see the grid letters A/P above each of these sections.

Step 3

Locate on Fig. 14.7 and Fig. 14.8 "A" and "P" and closely study all the section markings on all the dwgs.

ASSIGNMENT:

1. How is this folded plate roof for this building supported?
2. Make a freehand sketch of the framing for the south and west elevations showing the columns, the main floor slab, and the 67'-0" clear span folded plate roof. Remember to include the internal columns!

STRUCTURAL DRAWINGS

Drawing No. S4

Structural dwgs are prefaced with the letter "S" before the sheet number. On the original sheet, S4, is shown the structural framing plan and all the sectional details required for the main floor slab. At Fig. 14.7 is shown a portion of the plan only; the sectional details are shown at Fig. 14.8. They must be read together. It must be remembered that the whole of the framing and floor slab is placed as one integral monolithic unit of reinforced concrete. Locate 1/S4 thru 5/S4. The bottom letter and numeral mean: *Structural Drawing number four.* The top number indicates the sequential number of the dwg on the sheet.

The sections for 1/S4 thru 5/S4 are shown at Fig. 14.8. *Section 1/S4* shows the detail Line A on the plan and it is also the opposite hand of Line "P" on the plan. The latter is located at the top right of Fig. 14.1.

Section 2/S4 is shown on plan at the north wall.

Section 3/S4 depicts the largest beam and shows twelve strands both on plan and section. *See Line "J" Fig. 14.1.*

Section 4/S4 shows a typical rib section framing into the beam 3/S4.

Section 5/S4 shows a typical rib section framing into joists 4/S4.

Drawing No. S5

Part of the Roof Plan is shown at Fig. 14.9 with the positioning of the ½" ø strands for the post-tensioning of the folded plate roof. Study this very carefully.

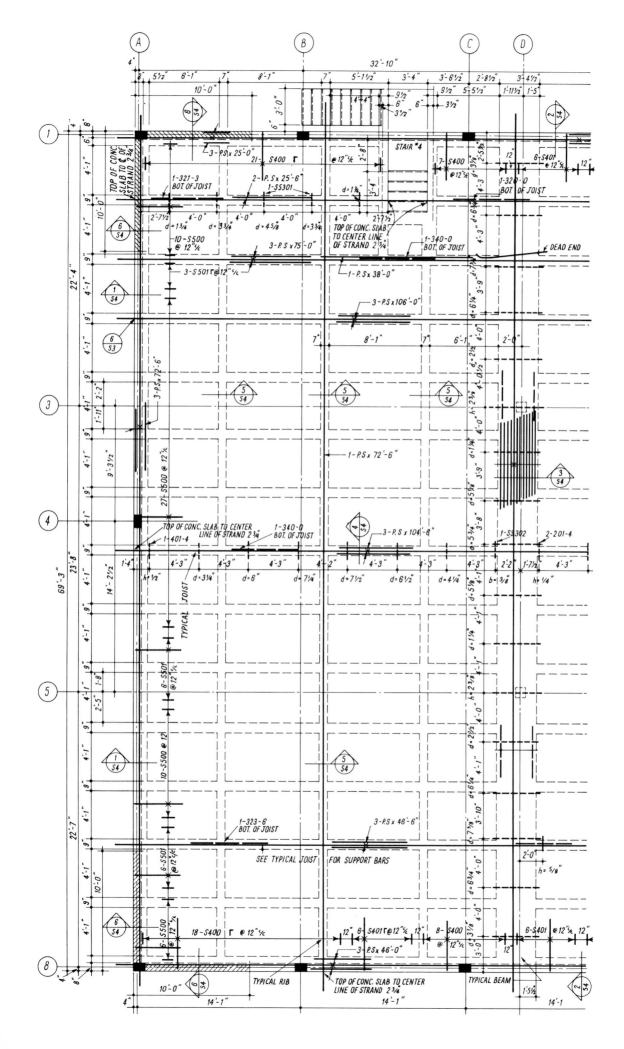

Fig. 14-7. Main floor slab.

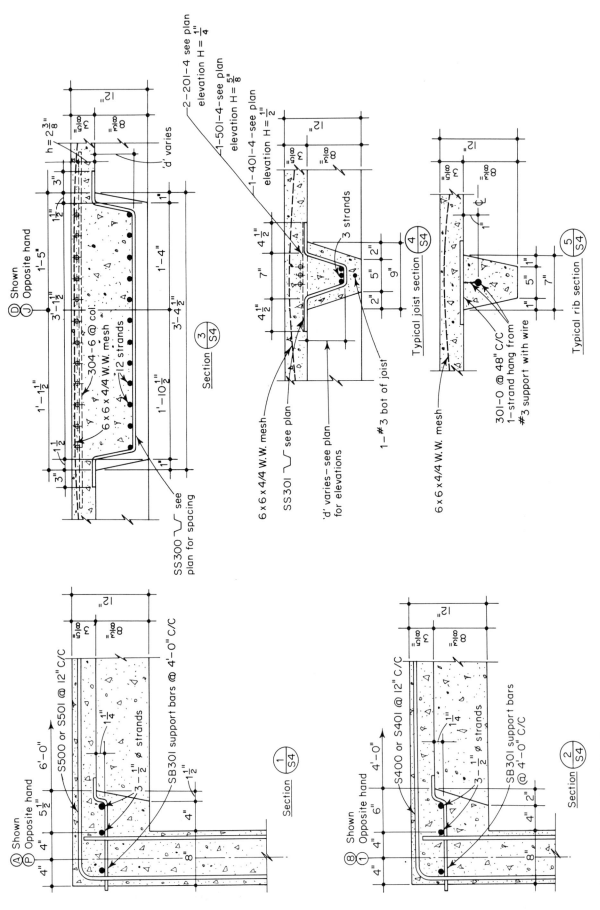

Fig. 14-8. Sectional details.

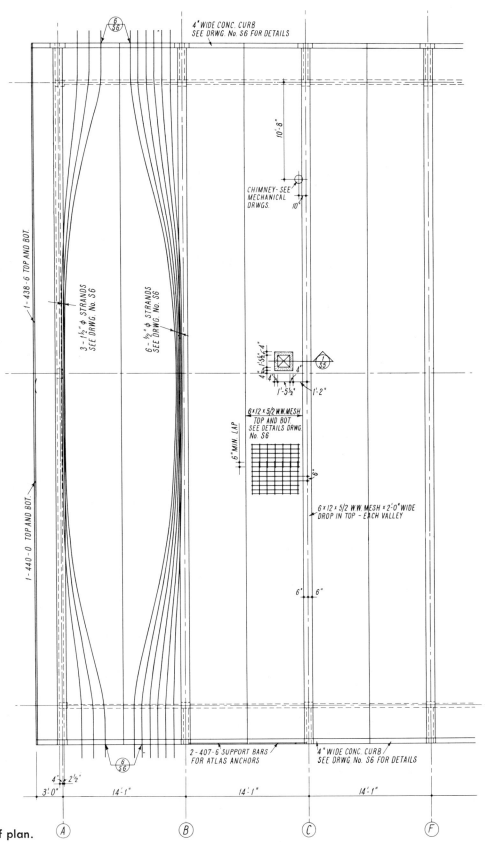

Fig. 14-9. Roof plan.

⊳ATLAS SERVICE CORPORATION

14809 CALVERT STREET △ VAN NUYS, CALIFORNIA 91401   TELEPHONE △ STate 2-4291

ATLAS HIGH-STRENGTH CAST-IRON ANCHORAGES FOR SINGLE-STRAND POST-TENSIONING

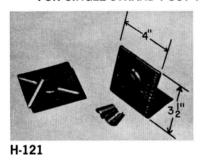

H-121   **H-122**

Grippers are included with the anchorage, and are available for all standard sizes of 7-wire strand from ⅜" thru ½", as well as specific types of rod and wire.

RUBBER GROMMETS G-2 (patented)

Re-usable void-formers which keep wet concrete out of the conical hole in the bearing plate, and serve as spacers to recess the anchorage inside the concrete.

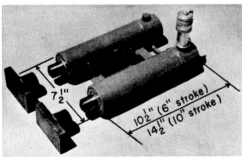

ATLAS TWIN-RAM OPEN-THROAT JACKS J-206 & J-210

J-206 has 6" stroke & weighs 30 pounds
J-210 has 10" stroke & weighs 40 pounds
Total piston area = 6.28 square inches.
Twin "feet" as shown bear directly upon concrete member being stressed.

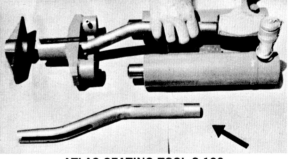

ATLAS SEATING TOOL S-100

For use with MSA-120 shown below.

HYDRAULIC SEATING ATTACHMENT HSA-120

Seats strand grippers by means of hydraulic power.

STRESSING ATTACHMENT MSA-120

Stressing jack bears upon anchorage rather than concrete. Grippers are seated manually with tool S-100 as shown above.

JACK GRIPPERS JG-2

Extra grippers are available for all standard sizes of seven-wire strand.

Fig. 14-10.   Post-tensioning equipment.

ASSIGNMENT:

Make a model (as large as facilities will permit) of two adjoining folds for this roof and place the strands and chairs supporting them.

POST-TENSIONING EQUIPMENT AND MATERIALS

The following five pictures show post-tensioning equipment, the post-tensioning equipment in use, the placing of strands and concrete, and a completed post-tensioned building ready for other trades.

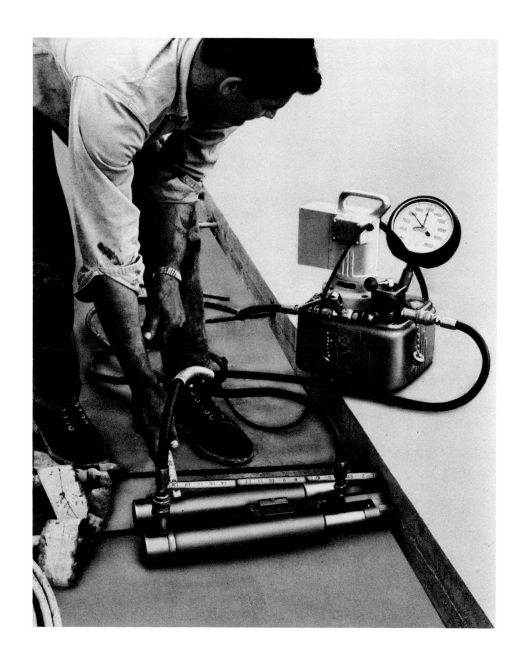

Fig. 14-12.   Placing of strands.

Fig. 14-13.   Placing of concrete.

Fig. 14-14. Completed post-tensioned building.

15 A NURSING HOME

In this chapter we are going to study an unusually interesting plan of a 44-bed Nursing Home. The dwgs are published by courtesy and permission of the architect, Mr. G. A. Blum, B.A., R.A.I.C., of Calgary, Alberta.

FRONT ELEVATION

Fig. 15.1 shows the front elev of the Nursing Home and should be read with Fig. 15.2, which is a plot plan supplied by the city. Notice the irregular shape of the bldg lot, which challenged the architect to draw a plan on the tangent lines; the angle of 35°.21′, enabling him to get the maximum number of sq ft of flr area and off-street parking to comply with city ordinances for bldg lines and parking.

MAIN FLOOR PLAN

Fig. 15.3 shows a central portion of the main floor plan bounded by column lines "L" and "P". Read the dwg from the bottom up and locate the tangent lines; the angle of 35° .21′, and the points on the property line. Now locate the ₵ of column "M" on the front wall. See how the ₵ was located 6′-3½″ at right angles from 12′-6″ of the tangent line to the ₵ of the column.

Locate column "M" on the back wall and observe how the ₵ was de-

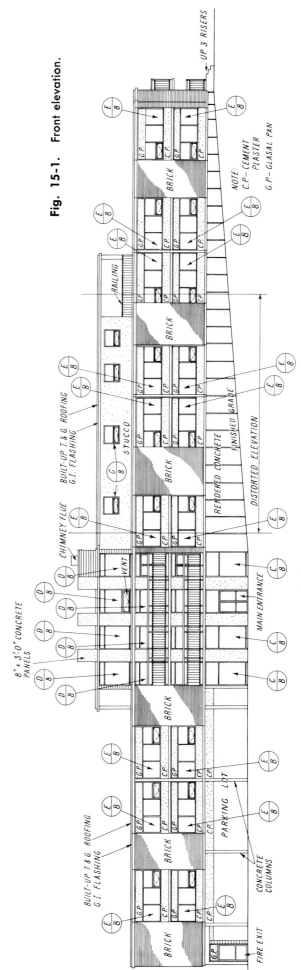

Fig. 15-1. Front elevation.

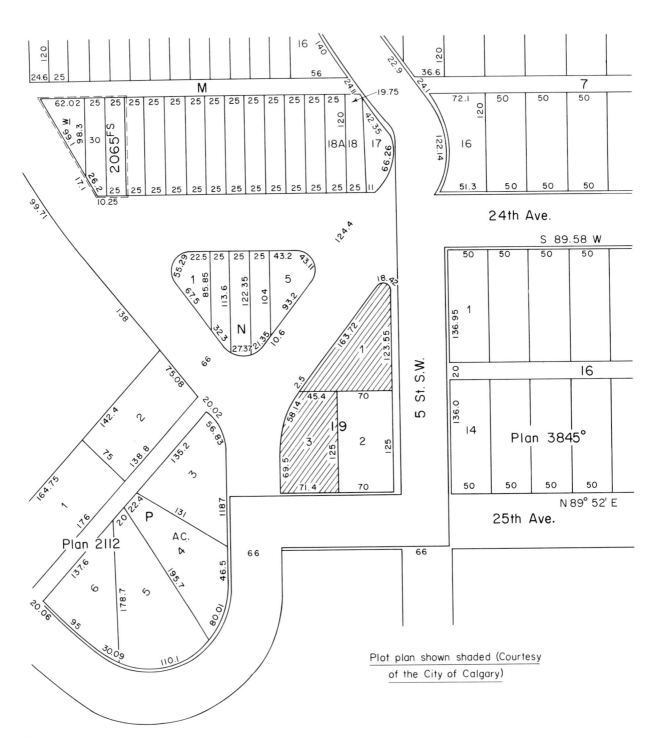

Fig. 15-2. Plot plan.

rived at 3'-2" at right angles from the tangent offset. Study the locations of columns "N" and "P" front and back.

All the dwgs and field work in connection with the column layout for this bldg demanded skill and precision. Challenging work is interesting. The columns in the corridor walls had to be exactly in radial alignment and positioned for the corridor walls to be built tight to the columns. One can see from the dwgs and the plot plan that the pivotal point for the whole concept of the bldg was the 35°.21' angle of the tangent. It is from points such as these that architectural concepts originate. Note the elevator shaft (Room 004) located about the center of the bldg and in the main lobby.

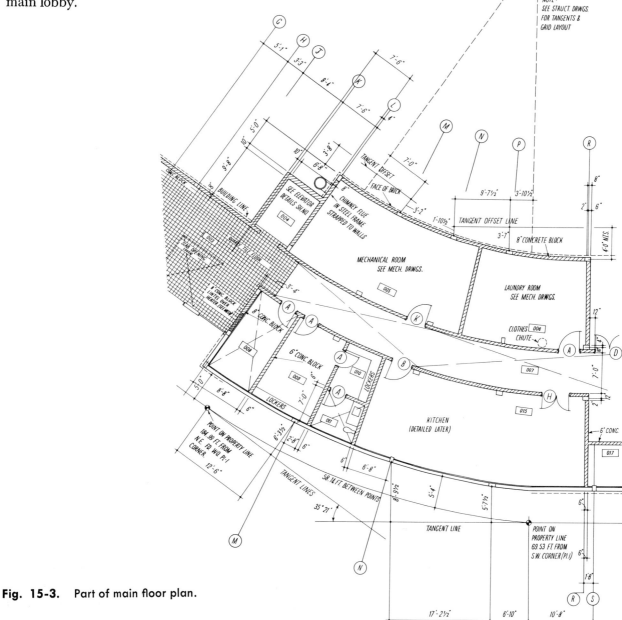

Fig. 15-3. Part of main floor plan.

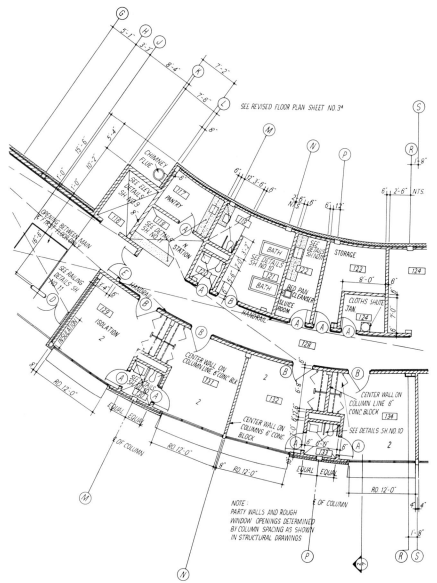

Fig. 15-4. Part of first-floor plan.

ASSIGNMENT:

Reproduce to the scale of ½″ to 1′-0″ that part of Fig. 15.3 bounded by column lines "L" thru "P".

FIRST FLOOR PLAN

Fig. 15.4 shows that part of the first-floor plan located immediately over the floor shown on the preceding dwg. The bldg is of post-tensioned concrete design. A picture taken during bldg operations showing the strands and chairs in place and ready for the placing of concrete is shown at Fig. 15.5, and a fuller treatment of post-tensioned concrete construction is given in Chapter 14. With a close inspection of these two floors it may be seen with what freedom the architect can arrange any of the internal rooms without regard to the shape or size of the rooms below. An exception occurs in the planning of plumbing units, which are usually placed over each other floor by floor. The second-floor plan is similar to the first, except for minor differences as noted on the original dwgs.

TYPICAL WALL SECTION

Locate section mark 2/7 on Fig. 15.4. This refers to the second wall section dwg on the original dwg sheet and is shown at Fig. 15.6. This wall is self-explanatory; it is well presented with a sufficiency of notation for all estimating and building purposes. See the notation at the top of the dwg referring to roof flashing details shown at Fig. 15.7.

Fig. 15-5.   Strands and chairs in place.

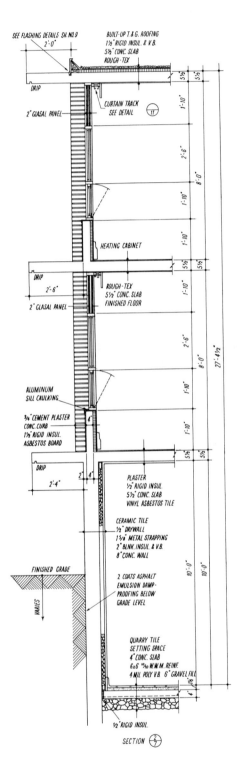

SEE FLASHING DETAILS SH.NO.9
2'-0"
BUILT-UP T.& G. ROOFING
1½" RIGID INSUL. & V.B.
5½" CONC. SLAB
ROUGH-TEX

DRIP

2" GLASAL PANEL

CURTAIN TRACK
SEE DETAIL

HEATING CABINET

DRIP
2'-6"

2" GLASAL PANEL

ROUGH-TEX
5½" CONC. SLAB
FINISHED FLOOR

ALUMINUM
SILL CAULKING

¾" CEMENT PLASTER
CONC. CURB
1½" RIGID INSUL.
ASBESTOS BOARD

DRIP
2'-4"

PLASTER
½" RIGID INSUL.
5½" CONC. SLAB
VINYL ASBESTOS TILE

CERAMIC TILE
½" DRYWALL
1⅝" METAL STRAPPING
2" BLNK. INSUL. & V.B.
8" CONC. WALL

FINISHED GRADE

2 COATS ASPHALT
EMULSION DAMP-
PROOFING BELOW
GRADE LEVEL

VARIES

QUARRY TILE
SETTING SPACE
4" CONC. SLAB
6x6 ¹⁰⁄₁₀ W.W.M. REINF.
4 MIL POLY V.B. 6" GRAVEL FILL

½" RIGID INSUL.

SECTION

Fig. 15-6. Wall section.

ROOF FLASHING DETAILS

Fig. 15.7 shows detail A/9 of the flashing. On the original dwg sheet several flashing details and wall sects are shown to the scale of 3″ to 1′0″. Time is well spent on presenting details to as large a scale as possible (sometimes to full scale). They encourage fair bids and lower bldg costs.

WEST ELEVATION

Fig. 15.8 shows a distorted elevation (because the plan is an arc of a circle) of part of the front of the Nursing Home with its penthouse on the fourth floor. Notice the roof of the hoistway in front of the chimney flue and also the railing to the roof Terrace.

ASSIGNMENT:

Draw to the scale of ½″ to 1′-0″ a distorted elevation of similar construction to Fig. 15.8 from your dwg assignment of Fig. 15.3.

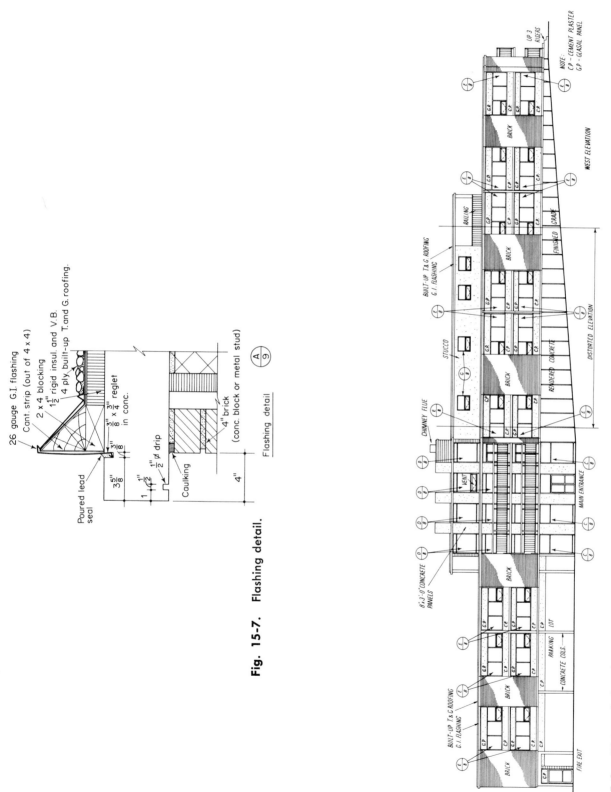

26 gauge G.I. flashing

Cant. strip (out of 4 x 4)

2 x 4 blocking

1½" rigid insul. and V.B.

4 ply, built-up T.and G. roofing.

Poured lead seal

$3\frac{5}{8}"$

$1\frac{1}{2}"$

$3\frac{3}{8}"$

$\frac{3}{8}" \times \frac{3}{4}"$ reglet in conc.

$\frac{1}{2}"$ ∅ drip

Caulking

4" brick (conc. block or metal stud)

4"

A / 9

Flashing detail

Fig. 15-7. Flashing detail.

UP 3 RISERS

NOTE: CP – CEMENT PLASTER GP – GLASAL PANEL

BRICK

WEST ELEVATION

FINISHED GRADE

DISTORTED ELEVATION

RENDERED CONCRETE

RAILING

BUILT-UP T.&G. ROOFING

G.I. FLASHING

STUCCO

CHIMNEY FLUE

VENT

MAIN ENTRANCE

8'-3'-0 CONCRETE PANELS

PARKING LOT

CONCRETE COLS.

BUILT-UP T.&G. ROOFING

G.I. FLASHING

BRICK

FIRE EXIT

Fig. 15-8. Distorted elevation.

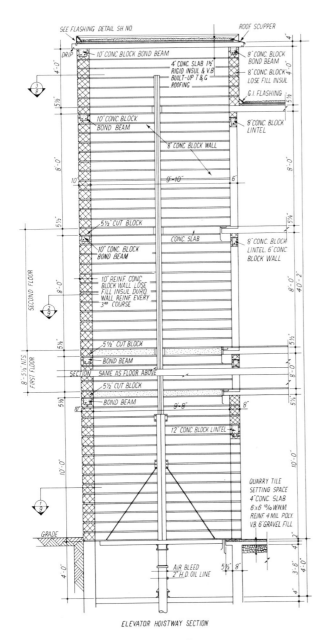

Fig. 15-9 (a). Hoistway section.

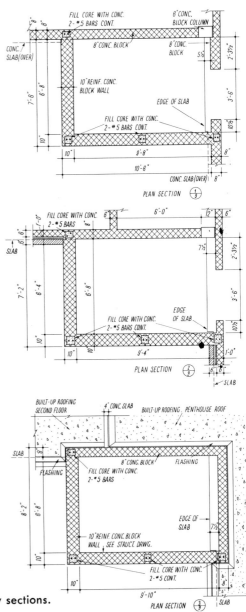

Fig. 15-9 (b). Hoistway sections.

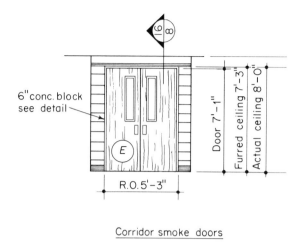

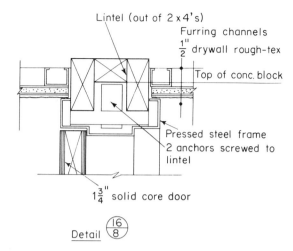

Corridor smoke doors

Detail $\frac{16}{8}$

Fig. 15-10. Typical door detail.

ELEVATOR HOISTWAY

Figs. 15.9(a) and 15.9(b) show the elevator hoistway sects which originate on the main floor (Room 004) and conveniently adjoin the mechanical room.

Reading up on the hoistway section, the quarry tile is to the main floor lobby. Section mark 1/9 refers to the top left-hand plan section showing two 5 ø bars in four cores running from ground floor to roof with a concrete block column at the other corner. Two walls are 10″ and the others are 8″, all reinforced concrete block walls. Notice the bond beam on the hoistway section with a 5½″ cut block at all the floor levels to bond to floor lines. This is important detailing. Section mark 2/9 shows the detail for two floors which are similar, and 3/9 shows the above penthouse including the roof. Elevators and escalators come under the general heading of vertical transportation. There is an excellent field of study in this subject and great rewards for experts; we live in an ever increasingly urbanized and vertically-transported society.

CORRIDOR SMOKE DOORS

At Fig. 15.10 is shown a typical method of presenting a door detail. It is type "E". See Fig. 15.4. All the door letter numbers are shown at their openings on the plans, and their dwgs (in this case) are shown on the original dwg sheet "Room Finish & Door Schedules." They would also be described in the specs.

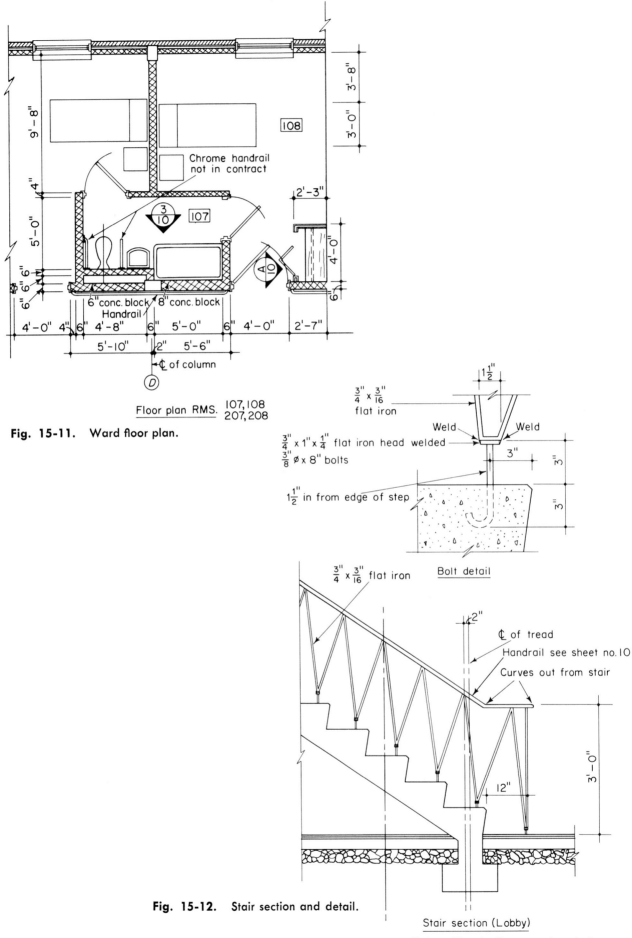

Fig. 15-11. Ward floor plan.

Floor plan RMS. 107,108
207,208

108

Chrome handrail
not in contract

3
10

107

A
10

6" conc. block   8" conc. block
Handrail

3-8"

3'-0"

2'-3"

4'-0"

6"

9'-8"

4"

5'-0"

6"
6"
6"

4'-0" 4" 6" 4'-8" 6" 5'-0" 6" 4'-0" 2'-7"

5'-10" 2" 5'-6"

℄ of column

D

3/4" x 3/16"
flat iron

1 1/2"

Weld   Weld

3/4" x 1" x 1/4" flat iron head welded
3/8" Ø x 8" bolts

3"

3"

3"

1 1/2" in from edge of step

Bolt detail

3/4" x 3/16" flat iron

2"

℄ of tread

Handrail see sheet no. 10

Curves out from stair

3'-0"

12"

Fig. 15-12. Stair section and detail.

Stair section (Lobby)

Note: railing in floor opening similar

PLAN OF SINGLE-BED WARDS

Fig. 15.11 shows the floor plan for two adjoining single-bed wards, both served by one bathroom. The rooms are on two floors. Note column "D" and all the very clearly dimensioned sizes.

STAIR SECTION

Fig. 15.12 shows a stair section and the bolt detail securing the $\frac{3}{4}'' \times \frac{3}{16}''$ flat iron balustrades to the concrete steps. It is most important that handrails be well detailed both for the stairs and in the halls for such places as Senior Citizen's Homes, Hospitals, and Nursing Homes, where they are subject to daily heavy stresses. It is very important to remember that the contractor may build to no better standards than you detail.

These clearly defined dwgs are excellently conceived and planned, utilizing the land to its full potential to meet the clients' requirements with quiet aesthetic charm at a minimum cost.

16 STEEL FRAMING AND STEEL DECKS

STEEL FRAMING

The following dwgs are taken from a hospital bldg and are published with the permission of Mr. H. F. Malkin, Principal Architect, and Mr. J. Griffiths, Assistant Director, Administration and Finance, Public Buildings Department, Adelaide, South Australia.

Apart from structural details accompanying arch. dwgs, engineers call for shop dwgs (very large-scale detail dwgs prepared by the contractor) to be presented before fabrication of the steel framing begins.

Some welding is often done in the shop under controlled conditions, which is of great advantage where extremes of climate prevail. Welding in the field should be regulated to afford a minimum of distortion of the total framing. All steel framing details on any one project are interrelated and peculiar to that structure.

STEEL FRAMING DETAILS

Fig. 16.1 shows a plan and two vert sect of steel framing details for a 5th flr col. *Note:*
(a) *plan* of framing at col.
(b) beam $18'' \times 6'' \times 55$ # terminates with a gap at the col.

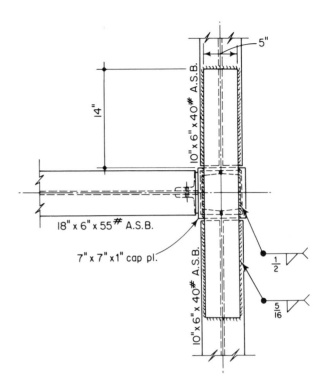

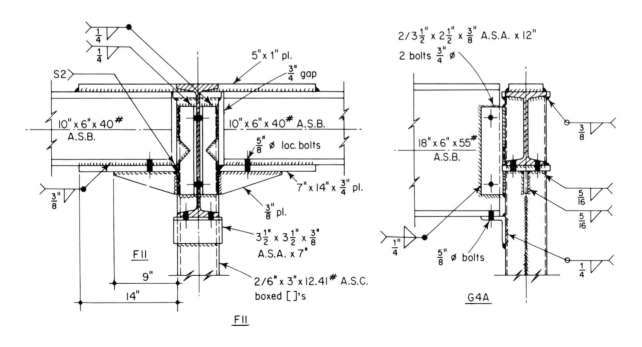

Detail 6
(Cols. 24A, 25A 5th Floor)

Fig. 16-1.

(c) beams 10″ × 6″ × 40 # are secured to boxed [ ] shown by hidden lines and having 7″ × 7″ × 1″ cap plate.

(d) 5″ × 14″ plate welded to 10″ × 6″ × 40 # beams.

(e) the welds by sizes at all details.

(f) *sect G4A* shows 18″ × 6″ × 55 # beam with 3½″ × 2½″ × ⅜″ × 12″ angle welded to each side of the beam and to the face of the col. Such angles are shown on some dwgs as LLO (long leg outstanding from the beam to which it is secured) and SLV (short leg vertical to the col to which it is outstanding).

(g) *sect F-11* shows a cross section of the large beam and two 10″ × 6″ × 40 # beams secured to it with ⅝″ location bolts and welded through the flanges and plates of the beams to the seat angle below.

(h) under the large beam see the 3½″ × 3½″ × ⅜″ × 7″ seat angle, location bolted and welded to the flange of the beam. Locate these bolts on sect G4A.

It is most important that you understand these details before proceeding any further.

ASSIGNMENT:

Using a scale of 1½″ to 1′-0″ make a stiff board model of all the members described in these details.

Fig. 16.2 shows four details, all for the same ground flr col. Very carefully study all these details in relation to one another. *Note:*

(a) the top left plan is a horiz sect of the detail immediately below.

(b) the top right *Plan Section V-V* is a plan thru the *V-V Section* of the detail immediately below. Locate the "V" at each side of the lower detail.

(c) The three beams framing into the col at the top left plan are all different sizes. Notice the 1″ plates, location bolts, and welding.

(d) the btm left sect shows the large beam framing into the col. Notice the gap between the col and beam also shown on the plan above.

(e) the top right horiz sect shows the lower webs of all beams with plates, location bolts, seat angles, and welds.

(f) the btm right detail shows two different sized beams framing to the col. Relate top left detail to btm right, and the top right to btm left.

ASSIGNMENT:

Make an isometric drawing showing the largest beam to the left of the dwg framing into the column with the other two beams in relative positions. Your drawing should show as many fastening devices as would be visible in a photograph taken from the same viewpoint.

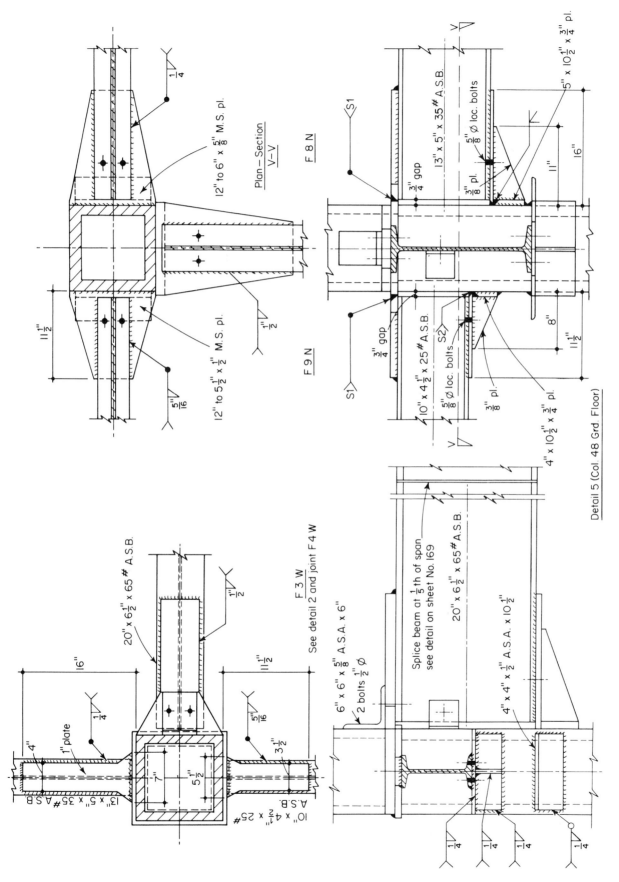

Plan – Section V–V

$12'$ to $6'' \times \frac{5}{8}''$ M.S. pl.

F 8 N

$12'$ to $5\frac{1}{2}'' \times 1\frac{1}{2}''$ M.S. pl.

F 9 N

$13'' \times 5'' \times 35\#$ A.S.B.

$5'' \times 10\frac{1}{2}'' \times \frac{3}{4}''$ pl.

$\frac{5}{8}'' \varnothing$ loc. bolts

$\frac{3}{4}''$ gap

$\frac{3}{8}''$ pl.

$16''$

$11''$

S1

$\frac{3}{4}''$ gap

S2

$10'' \times 4\frac{1}{2}'' \times 25\#$ A.S.B.

$\frac{5}{8}'' \varnothing$ loc. bolts

$\frac{3}{8}''$ pl.

$4'' \times 10\frac{1}{2}'' \times \frac{3}{4}''$ pl.

$8''$

$11\frac{1}{2}''$

Detail 5 (Col. 48 Grd. Floor)

$20'' \times 6\frac{1}{2}'' \times 65\#$ A.S.B.

F 3 W
See detail 2 and joint F 4 W

$16''$

$11\frac{1}{2}''$

$1''$ plate

$4''$

$7''$

$5\frac{1}{2}''$

$3\frac{1}{2}''$

$13'' \times 5'' \times 35\#$ A.S.B.

$10'' \times 4\frac{1}{2}'' \times 25\#$

Splice beam at $\frac{1}{5}$th of span
see detail on sheet No. 169

$20'' \times 6\frac{1}{2}'' \times 65\#$ A.S.B.

$6'' \times 6'' \times \frac{5}{8}''$ A.S.A. $\times 6''$

2 bolts $\frac{1}{2}'' \varnothing$

$4'' \times 4'' \times \frac{1}{2}''$ A.S.A. $\times 10\frac{1}{2}''$

Fig. 16-2.

315

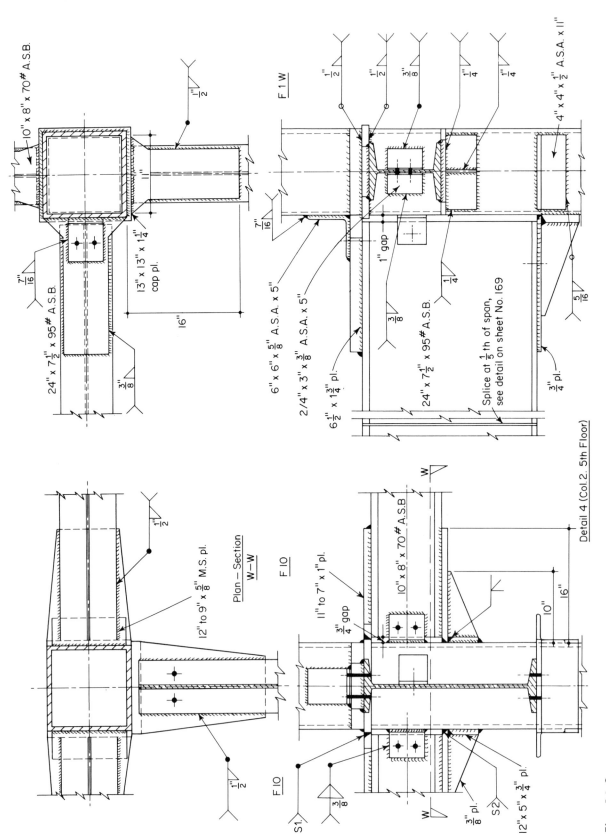

Fig. 16-3.

Fig. 16.3 shows four details for the same fifth-flr col. Study these details in relation to each other. *Note:*

(a) the top right plan of the col and three beams show a horiz sect of the detail immediately below. *Note the cap plate.*

(b) the btm right sect shows the large beam framing into the col and is presented in great detail. Study the seat angles, plate sizes, welds, and heavy cap plate to receive the cont col above.

(c) the top left *Plan Section W-W* is a plan thru the *W-W Section* of the detail immediately below. Locate the "W" at each side of the lower detail. Notice the shapes of the plates on plan.

(d) the btm left sect shows the two smaller beams framing into the col. Note the cap plate to receive the weld for the cont col above. Relate the btm details to each other and the top details to their diagonals.

ASSIGNMENT:

1. Using the scale of 1½ " to 1'-0", make a wood scale model of this framing assembly. Use sheet metal for seat angles and fastening devices.

2. Make a field trip and take a photograph of four different steel framing assemblies (from simple to complex); return to your desk and prepare working dwgs modeled from them.

ALUMINUM SHEATHING AND ROOF DECK STEEL

The following self-explanatory material on aluminum sheathing and roof deck steel has been selected from a wide source of technical data published by Rosco Metal Products Limited and reproduced with permission. Note the A.I.A. File Nos. on these papers. Build up your own files by writing to manufacturers for technical data!

SPECIFICATIONS
FOR T-175 ALUMINUM ROOFING AND SIDING

General:

The general conditions of the contract form an integral part of the specification. Roofing and siding shall be of T-175 profile as fabricated and erected by Rosco Metal Products Ltd.

Material:

All T-175 roofing and/or siding sheets shall be fabricated from sheets of Industrial (or Utility Grade) Aluminum Alloy. The sheets shall be (specify thickness of metal, pitch and depth of configuration) and shall be supplied in the correct lengths and widths as shown on the drawings. Indicate here if sheet is to be plain, stucco finish or with baked enamel finish.

Design:

T-175 sheets shall be of adequate gauge and shape as to support a live load of.................lbs. per square foot plus dead load and a deflection not to exceed ....th of the span.

Erection:

All sheeting units shall be laid in accordance with erection drawings. Sheets shall be fastened at a maximum of 12″ o.c. to intermediate girts (6″ o.c. at end laps). Side laps shall be fastened at 24″ o.c. (18″ o.c. for roofing) by means of (indicate type of fastener). All fasteners shall be designed to prevent water leakage through fastener holes. Separate dissimilar metal and masonry surfaces from aluminum siding and/or roofing sheets and flashings. Siding sheets shall have an end lap of 4″. Roofing sheets on slopes of 3″ in 12″ shall have an end lap of 6″. Closures and flashings shall be erected by this contractor when specified. Closures and flashings shall be fastened on 12″ o.c. The erector shall cut and flash all openings located and dimensioned at time of erecting sheeting.

Work Not Included:

The structural frame members, including girts, purlins, anchor bolts, filler pieces necessary for the support of the cladding are to be furnished and erected by others. All gutters, down spouts and ventilators shall be supplied and installed by others unless specifically noted as being supplied by this contractor.

Fig. 16-4.

ALUMINUM T-175 SHEETING

Available in Industrial Grade Aluminum in .025; .032; .040 and .051 thickness in plain or stucco finish. Available in painted Utility sheet in .025; .032; and .040 thickness in White; Grey; Green; Blue; Red; Coral; Brown; Cream.
In lengths to 36 feet.

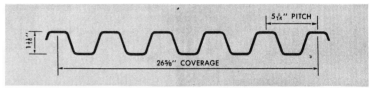

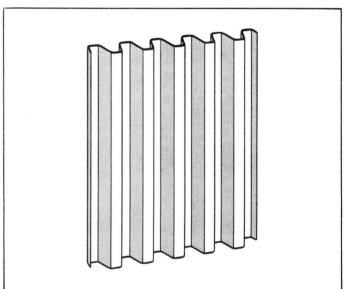

ROSCO
METAL PRODUCTS LTD.

A Division of WESTEEL PRODUCTS LTD.
HALIFAX - SAINT JOHN - QUEBEC - MONTREAL - OTTAWA - TORONTO - LONDON
WINNIPEG - REGINA - SASKATOON - CALGARY - EDMONTON - VANCOUVER

A.I.A. FILE No. 17-A

SPECIFICATIONS

General:

Roof Deck shall be fabricated and erected by Rosco Metal Products Ltd.

Material:

Roof Deck shall be formed from Zinc Coated Steel conforming to A.S.T.M. Specification A446-60T Grade A with a coating class of .... oz. per sq. ft.

Design:

The A.I.S.I. specification for Light Gauge Cold Formed Steel shall govern the design of Roof Deck Units. Deck shall be of such a gauge and profile as to support a live load of .... lbs. per sq. foot plus dead load, at a unit stress not to exceed 20,000 p.s.i. and a deflection not to exceed .... th of the span. Wherever possible deck units shall span over three or more supports. All units are to be a standard width and supplied to proper length.

Erection:

All Roof Deck Units shall be laid in accordance with erection drawings prepared by Rosco Metal Products Ltd. The deck shall be welded through the low corrugations to all supporting steel by means of ¾" diameter fusion welds at 12" maximum centers. Side joints shall be fastened on not over 36" centers. All welds shall be touched up with paint by the deck erector. The Roof Deck erector shall cut all openings which are located and dimensioned at the time of erecting the deck. Openings 6" diameter or larger shall be reinforced. Openings 24" or greater shall be structurally framed by structural contractor. When specified, flashings, cants, closures etc. shall be furnished and installed by the Roof Deck manufacturer.

Materials Not Included:

The following materials shall be furnished by other trades: (a) Wood nailers; (b) Structural steel supports including bearing plates, anchors, etc.; (c) Insulation and built up roofing; (d) Architectural trim around eaves.

T-30 ROOF DECK

Available in Galvanized or Light Zinc Coated Steel in 22 ga., 20 ga., 18 ga., 16 ga., 14 ga., 12 ga., and "Colorite" protected steel in 22 ga., 20 ga.

Each sheet provides a coverage of 18 or 24 inches with interlocking side lips.

Formerly Rosco Type "E" and Col/Rol Type CR-30

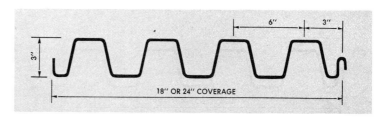

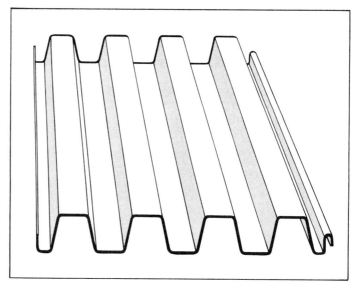

ROSCO
METAL PRODUCTS LTD.

A Division of WESTEEL PRODUCTS LTD.
HALIFAX - SAINT JOHN - QUEBEC - MONTREAL - OTTAWA - TORONTO - LONDON
WINNIPEG - REGINA - SASKATOON - CALGARY - EDMONTON - VANCOUVER

A.I.A. FILE No. 12-C, 13-H

Fig. 16-5.

SPECIFICATIONS

General:

Roof Deck shall be fabricated and erected by Rosco Metal Products Ltd.

Material:

Roof Deck shall be formed from Zinc Coated Steel conforming to A.S.T.M. Specification A446-60T Grade 'A' with a coating class of................oz. per sq. ft.

Design:

The A.I.S.I. specification for Light Gauge Cold Formed Steel (or C.S.A. Specification S-136) shall govern the design of Roof Deck Units. Deck shall be of such a gauge and profile as to support a live load of................ lbs. per sq. ft. plus dead load, at a unit stress not to exceed 20,000 p.s.i. and a deflection not to exceed ....th of the span. Wherever possible deck units shall span over three or more supports. All units are to be a standard width and supplied to proper length.

Erection:

All Roof Deck Units shall be laid in accordance with erection drawings prepared by Rosco Metal Products Ltd. The deck shall be welded through the low corrugations to all supporting steel by means of ¾" diameter fusion welds at 6" maximum centers. Side joints shall be fastened on not over 36" centers. All welds shall be touched up with paint by the deck erector.

The Roof Deck erector shall cut all openings which are located and dimensioned at the time of erecting the deck. Opening 24" or greater shall be structurally framed by structural contractor.

When specified, flashings, cants, closures, etc. shall be furnished and installed by the Roof Deck Manufacturer.

Materials Not Included:

The following material shall be furnished by other trades: (a) Wood nailers; (b) Structural steel supports including bearing plates, anchors, etc.; (c) Insulation and built up roofing; (d) Architectural trim around eaves.

Fig. 16-6.

T-45 ROOF DECK

Available in Galvanized or Light Zinc Coated Steel in 20 ga., 18 ga., 16 ga., 14 ga., and "Colorite" coated steel in 20 ga.
In Lengths to 36 feet.
Each sheet provides a coverage of 12 inches with interlocking side lips.

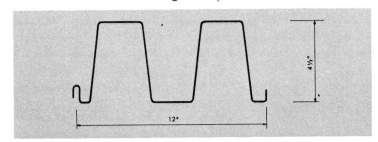

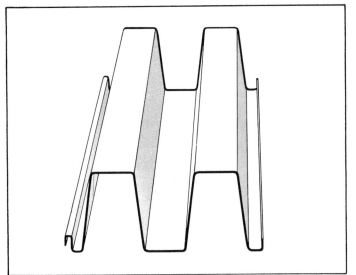

MEMBER **Canadian**
Sheet Steel Building Institute

ROSCO
METAL PRODUCTS LTD.

A Division of WESTEEL PRODUCTS LTD.
HALIFAX - SAINT JOHN - QUEBEC - MONTREAL - OTTAWA - TORONTO - LONDON
WINNIPEG - REGINA - SASKATOON - CALGARY - EDMONTON - VANCOUVER

A.I.A. FILE No. 12-C; 13-H

CONSTRUCTION DETAILS FOR TYPES B, N AND H ROOF DECKS AND ACOUSTIDECK

SCALE 1″ = 1′-0″

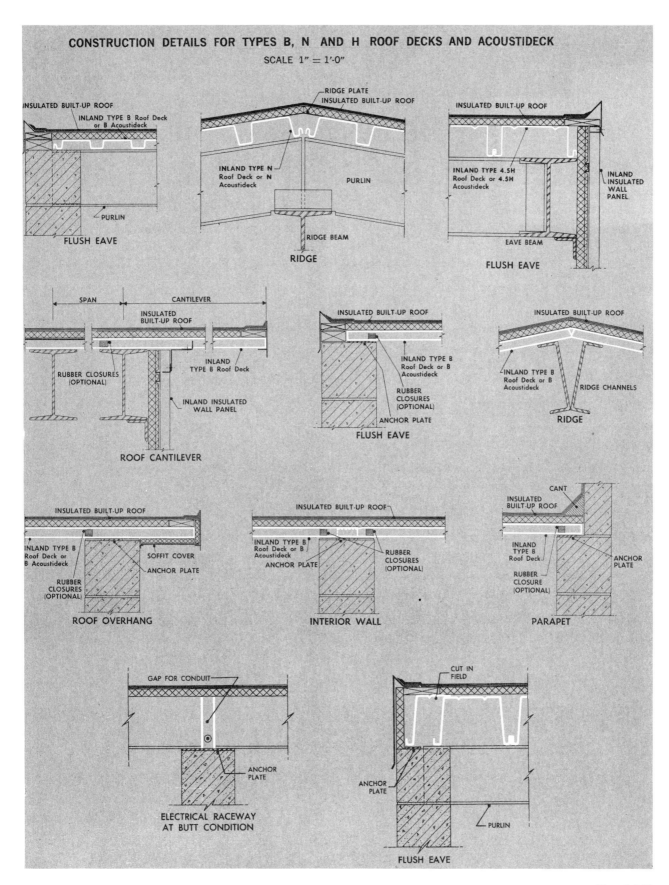

Fig. 16-7

321

CONSTRUCTION DETAILS FOR STEEL ROOF SYSTEMS

The set of dwgs on p. 321 has been selected from a catalogue published by the Inland Steel Company and appears here through their courtesy. All of the information in this chapter must be supplemented by your own research if it is to lead to a better understanding of the material which follows.

VIERENDEEL 17
TRUSSES

The following material on Vierendeel trusses (VT) was supplied and is published through the courtesy of Smith Carter Searle Milley Associates, Architects and Consulting Engineers. The welded trusses were fabricated by Dominion Bridge Co. Ltd.

These trusses were used in an addition to a high school and are located between the second-floor corridor and classrooms; they span over multipurpose rooms below. Conventional trusses with diagonals would have prevented making door openings between the classrooms and corridor. Photographs showing the assembling of the trusses are in Figs. 17.1 and 17.2.

One can see the advantages of using such trusses for some schools and industrial bldgs. Technological changes require frequent redesigning of large internal areas of existing bldgs to house new instruments and for work and demonstration areas. Using perimeter wall columns, curtain walls, and VT, all lower inside walls may be removed, total areas redesigned at minimum cost, and alterations may proceed irrespective of weather conditions. These are important considerations.

GROUND FLOOR FRAMING PLAN

Fig. 17.3 shows a portion of the east end plan. The following extracted notes are taken from the same dwg.

(a) All dimensions shown in the structural dwgs must be checked with

Fig. 17-1.

Fig. 17-2.

the architectural dwgs and any inconsistencies reported to the engineer before proceeding with the work.

(b) All caissons shall be founded on hardpan capable of sustaining 15,000 lbs per sq ft.

(c) Concrete or steel beams resting on masonry walls shall have a minimum bearing of 8″ unless otherwise noted. Bearing shall be solid block laid in cement mortar for a depth equal to the width of the bearing.

(d) Beams and slabs shall be poured monolithically with supporting or grade beams. Where this is not feasible, slabs are to be pocketed 4″ and dowelled to suit top slab steel. Beams are to be pocketed 8″ and dowels supplied for beam reinforcing.

(e) Top of concrete slab is to be 1½″ below finish floor level in areas crossed and noted thus: ////////////

Reading from the btm of Fig. 17.3, note the ground beam sizes at the perimeter, GB 14 × 36 and interior beam sizes and numbers. Locate the steel columns centered on two of the (third line) piles which support the VT and relate these to the architectural dwg at Fig. 17.4. All the trusses are supported on six steel columns. Relate the symbol //////// of note (e) to the dwg.

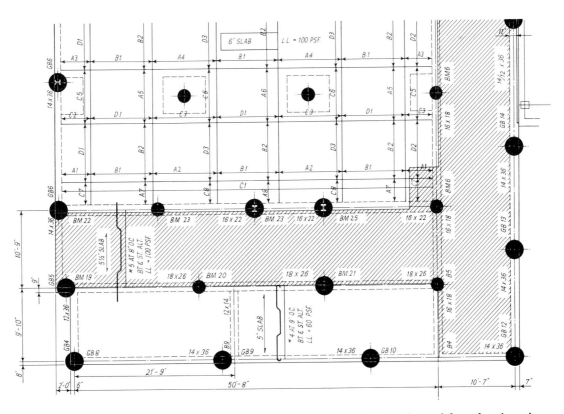

Fig. 17-3. Ground floor framing plan.

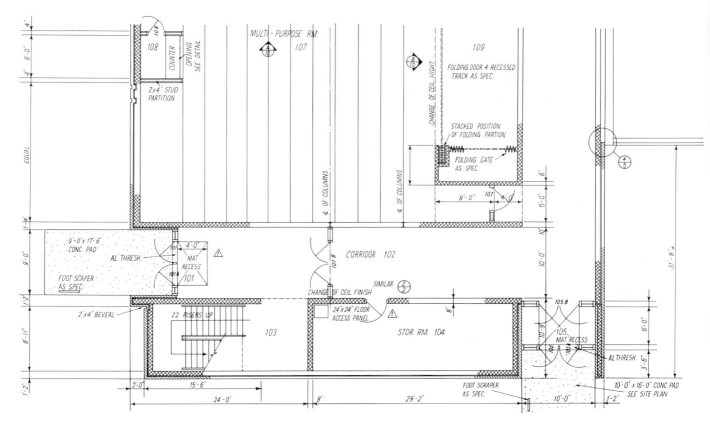

Fig. 17-4. Ground floor plan.

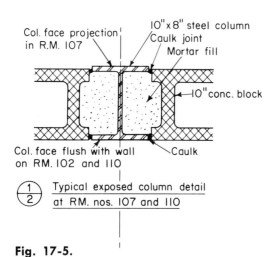

Fig. 17-5.

GROUND FLOOR PLAN

Fig. 17.4 shows that part of the ground floor plan immediately over the Fig. 17.3 plan. Relate the walls of Room 103 to the piles and beams GB 8, GB 9 and BM 22 to the partition walls of Fig. 17.3.

Locate ℄ of columns on the corridor wall and the walls of Rooms 102 and 107. Fig. 17.5 shows the detail of a typical exposed column.

VIERENDEEL TRUSSES LONGITUDINAL SECTIONS

Fig. 17.6 shows a section of the VT which is 89′-0″ long, 9′-4″ wide and 14′-0″ deep. Read the dwg from the bottom up and note:

(a) base plate sizes
(b) elevation of top of base plates
(c) ground floor elevation
(d) steel column sizes
(e) btm and top chord sizes
(f) cap plate over center column
(g) section mark 2/S5 (See Fig. 17.7.)
(h) camber allowance
(i) sizes of upright truss members
(j) relate details of photographs

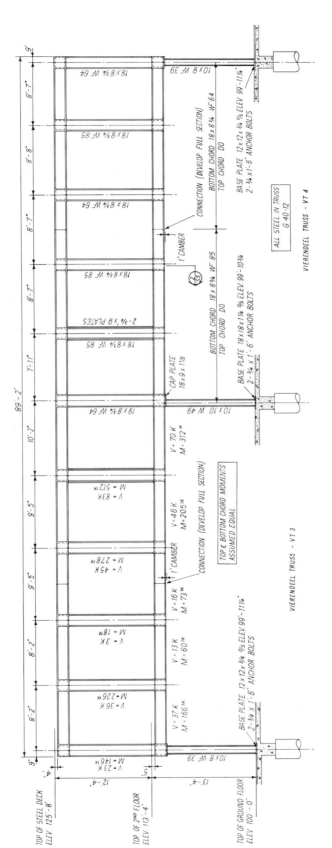

Fig. 17-6. Longitudinal section.

VIERENDEEL TRUSS JOINT DETAIL

Fig. 17.7 shows a typical joint detail, reference 2/S5 which is taken from the btm chord at Fig. 17.6. Relate the detail to the photographs, Figs. 17.1 and 17.2.

TRUSS LOADING DIAGRAM

Fig. 17.8 shows the truss loading diagram. *A kip is a unit of force equal to 1,000 lbs.*

CROSS SECTION OF VIERENDEEL TRUSS

Fig. 17.9 shows a cross section of the trusses from which an appreciation of the size of the corridor may be seen. The corridor will be subject to sudden live loads as students change classrooms many times during the school term.

Fig. 17-7. Typical joint detail.

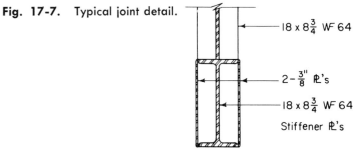

18 x 8¾ WF 64

2 - ⅜" ₺'s

18 x 8¾ WF 64

Stiffener ₺'s

Fig. 17-8. Truss loading diagram (all loads in kips).

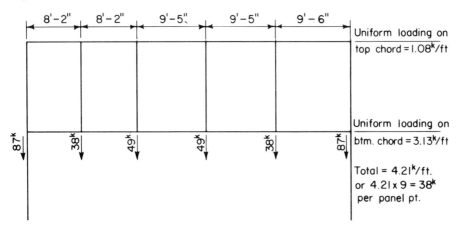

8'-2"   8'-2"   9'-5"   9'-5"   9'-6"

Uniform loading on
top chord = 1.08ᵏ/ft

Uniform loading on
btm. chord = 3.13ᵏ/ft

Total = 4.21ᵏ/ft.
or 4.21 x 9 = 38ᵏ
per panel pt.

87ᵏ   38ᵏ   49ᵏ   49ᵏ   38ᵏ   87ᵏ

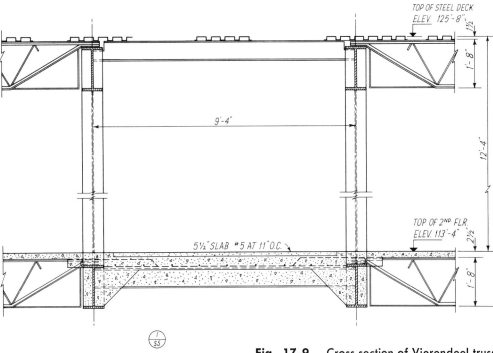

Fig. 17-9.   Cross section of Vierendeel truss.

ARCHITECTURAL WALL SECTION THRU TRUSS

Fig. 17.10 shows an architectural wall section of a truss between the corridor and the classroom. Study Figs. 17.6 thru 17.10 together with the photographs. All these dwgs are vivid with no wasted words nor lines and ready for the technicians to interpret into physical being.

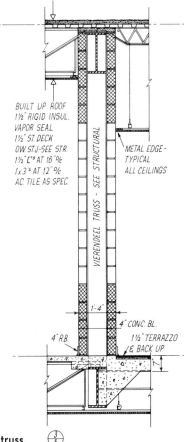

Fig. 17-10.   Wall section thru truss.

TYPICAL PERIMETER WALL SECTION

Fig. 17.11 shows a wall section (reference 2/5) taken from perimeter wall shown at Fig. 17.4. Read the dwg upwards:

(a) rigid insulation
(b) crawl space vents
(c) flashing
(d) offset brick
(e) weep holes
(f) wood framing for classroom risers. See Fig. 17.11
(g) wall construction

(h) first floor construction, hollow of concrete block reinforced. Note the angle iron
(i) window. Details would appear on another dwg
(j) window canopy with flashing and weep hole
(k) note the different inside finish above the window
(l) canopy.

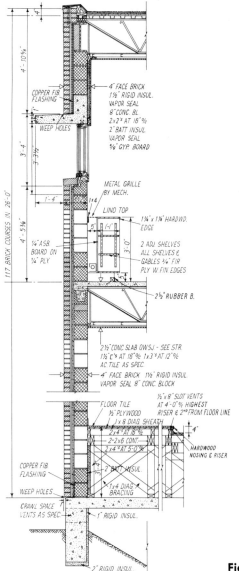

Fig. 17-11. Typical perimeter wall section.

HOME FOR THE AGED WITH FALLOUT SHELTER 18

The material for the Somerset County Home for the Aged is published with permission of the architects, J. Richard Ross, A.I.A., and Edwin O. Crammer, A.I.A. Mr. Ross is also fallout analyst. The design and engineering details of the fallout shelter conform to the specifications of the Technical Support Branch, Architectural and Engineering Services Division, Department of the Army, Washington, D.C.

At Fig. 18.1 is shown an exterior perspective of the whole complex.

The entire superstructure of the bldg is of steel tube columns, both round and rectangular, steel beams, and galvanized steel roof deck. All foundation and basement areas are constructed of reinforced concrete. All masonry walls are faced with blue glazed brick. Three sections of the building, including the Infirmary Wing, Men's Dormitory, and Service Wing are one story, while the Women's Dormitory has a complete basement and two-story section. The area of the bldg itself covers approximately 50,000 square feet. The service area is located centrally to facilitate service to the three main wings. Provision has been made for future extension to the Infirmary Wing and the dormitory units without the addition of any future service facilities.

The basement is located under the entire Women's Dormitory Wing on the west side of the bldg. The whole of the basement area has been constructed of 12″ thick reinforced walls and floor slab and will provide maximum protection as a fallout shelter. *One large room under the two-story unit has been designed as the patients' fallout shelter* and will shelter the entire

Fig. 18-1. Exterior perspective.

population of the home. Complete emergency facilities for food, water, toilet, heat, light, and ventilation are provided. The balance of the basement area has been divided into storage rooms. A central corridor connects these rooms with the maintenance shop and garage. The rest of this area could provide fallout protection to many other families in case of emergency. Storage rooms under the single-story section are part of the fallout area and are used to store clothing, food, maintenance equipment, and so on. Two stairways and the passenger elevator connect the basement, first, and second floors.

All the following dwgs have been extracted from the originals and have been assembled to present a progressive, coherent unfolding of the architectural and engineering design for this complex. This chapter is deserving of close study, and all cross references to other dwgs should be followed up immediately.

FIRST FLOOR PLAN

Fig. 18.2 shows the complete first floor plan. Imagine yourself walking into this bldg at the front lobby (east side). On the right are the administration offices, infirmary, centrally located doctors' office, and private visiting, solarium, and isolation areas.

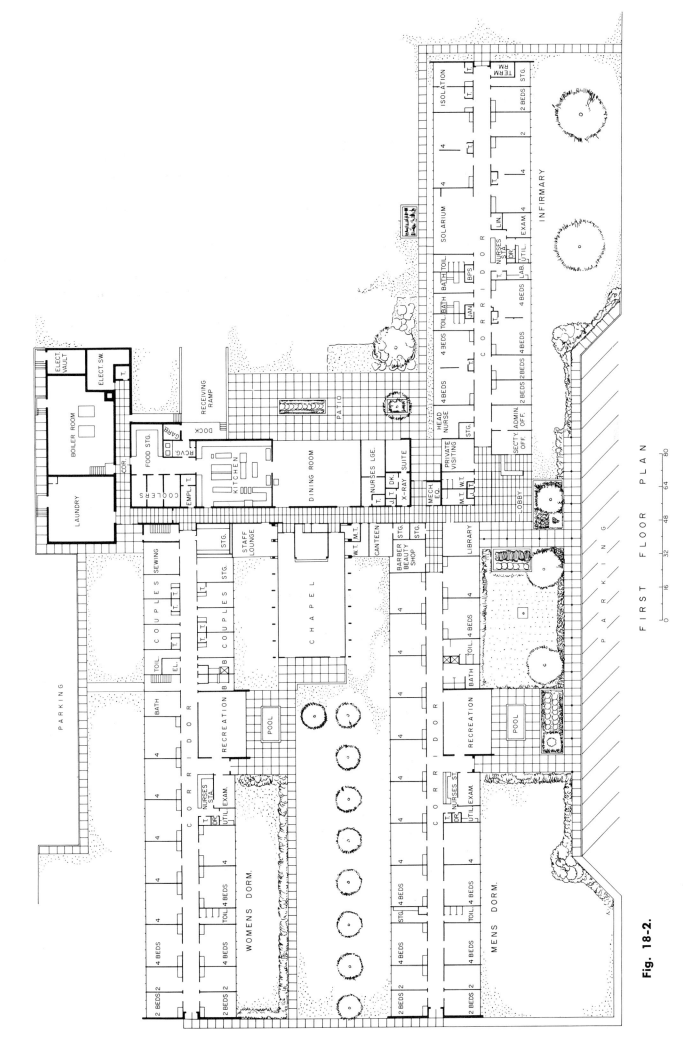

Fig. 18-2.

FIRST FLOOR PLAN

0   16   32   48   64   80

On the left are the library, barber and beauty shop, recreation room facing a pool, doctors' office, and men's dormitory. *For a complete understanding of this bldg you must have the smell of antiseptic in your nostrils as you examine it.*

Ahead, notice the X-ray suite, canteen, chapel, dining room, patio, staff lounge, kitchen area, receiving ramp, food storage, and further ahead, the laundry and boiler room. Examine Fig. 18.1 again and locate the "A"-Framed Chapel.

Turning left from the kitchen, notice the quarters for couples with sewing and recreation rooms, pool, doctors' office, and women's dormitory. The two-story section of this wing is immediately over the fallout shelter, and the remaining single-story portion is over the fallout shelter storage and maintenance rooms. This is "D" Wing.

FALLOUT SHELTER

Fig. 18.3 shows the basement fallout area located beneath the two-story "D" Wing on the west side. *Locate the two separate stairways at Fig. 18.2 leading from the main floor to the patients' fallout shelter.* It is very important to locate this section since our study will be directed to this wing of the bldg and especially to the two-story section. Remember that not all fallout shelters are located in basements.

FALLOUT SHELTER FOUNDATION PLAN

Fig. 18.4 shows the foundation plan of "D" Wing. Let us closely examine this dwg. Start at the ramp to the garage (top left) which has 12" ø (conc) walls with supporting counterparts or buttresses, as shown on plan. The outsides of the walls are filled with stone, straw, and earth and are provided with weep holes @ 4'-0" oc.

There are eighteen spaces named in the basement from the garage B-1 to B-18. *Locate all these rooms and spaces and note:*

(a) in room B-1 the 5'-0" × 5'-0" × 20" ø col ftg supporting a 12" × 12" ø conc col with 14" wide "T" beam over. In all, there are 8 col ftgs; locate them.

(b) the 8" masonry storeroom walls and the cavity walls for plumbing fixtures in the toilet wall.

(c) the watertight expansion joint in the outside wall at the intersection of B-10 and 13 and at B-11 and 12. *These joints are very important and will be referred to later.*

(d) the section marks B-1 through room B-14 and section marks B-2 through storage room B-8 and B-9. See Fig. 18.5.

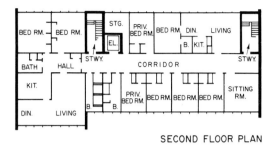

SECOND FLOOR PLAN

BASEMENT PLAN

0   20   40

SECTION—TWO STORY WING

TYPICAL CROSS SECTION

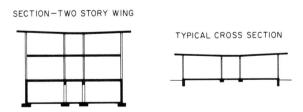

Fig. 18-3. Basement fallout area.

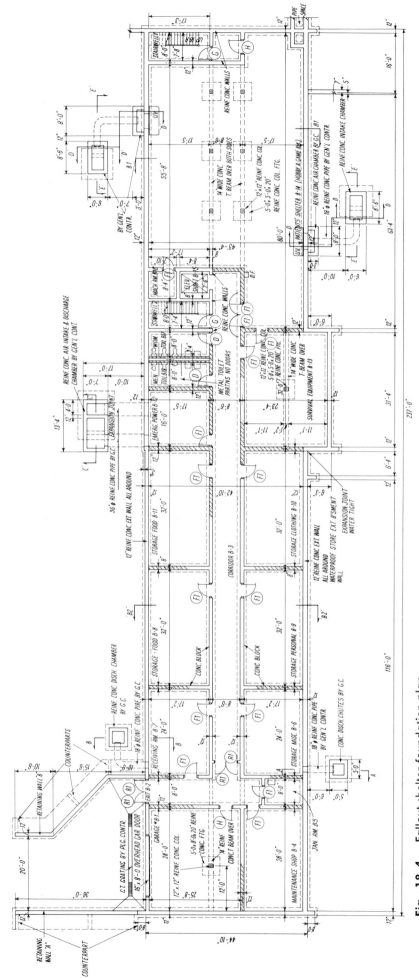

Fig. 18-4. Fallout shelter foundation plan.

FALLOUT SHELTER CROSS SECTION

Fig. 18.5 shows a cross section of B-1 and B-2. *Note:*
(a) all ftgs except for cols are 2'-6" × 12" with four cont ¾" ø rods.
(b) the outside perimeter ftgs are provided with weeping tiles.
(c) the col ftgs are provided with twelve ¾ ø EW (each way) and four ¾" dowels to each col.
(d) the outside of the basement walls is waterproofed.
(e) the internal walls to corridor are shown at sect B-2 and are 12" conc block Duro-Wal.
(f) the 4" conc floor has 6" × 6"—10 × 10 w.w. mesh imbedded with vapor barrier and stone fill under.

Fig. 18-5.

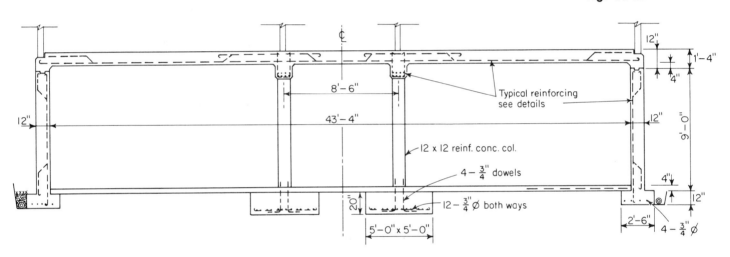

Cross Section B—1

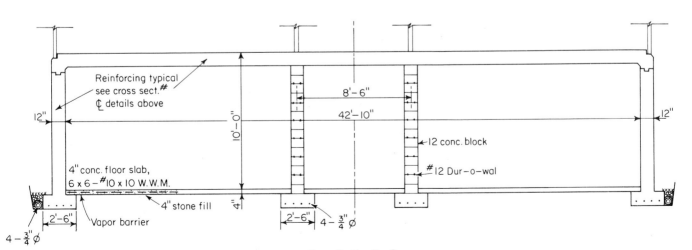

Cross Section B—2

MESH: STEEL WELDED REINFORCING

Fabricated reinforcing mesh is used largely in concrete floors, driveways, and roads. It is also used in other areas of building construction as temperature reinforcing. Some of the main things that an estimator should know about this type of reinforcing are as follows:
(a) it is fabricated in both square and rectangular mesh.
(b) the longitudinal gage of the wire may be of a heavier gage than the transverse wire.
(c) when there is any difference in the gages of the wire for any one type of mesh, the longitudinal wire is the heavier gage.
(d) the style of the mesh may be described as 4″ × 4″—9 × 12 (or 44-912) which means that the area of each mesh is 4″ × 4″ and that the transverse wire is No. 12 (for a 4″ × 8″—9 × 12 or 48-912 welded steel mesh, each mesh is 4″ × 8″ and the gages of the wire are No. 9 and 12 respectively).
(e) the smaller the number of the gage, the thicker the wire.

FALLOUT SHELTER WALL AND FIRST FLOOR SLAB

Fig. 18.6 shows details of the basement wall and first floor slab. *Note:*
(a) wall thickness 12″
(b) typical waterproofing
(c) horizontal ½″ temp rods @ 12″ oc
(d) upright ⅝″ ø 24″ oc with center of bend 1'-9″ from top of wall. See Fig. 18-5 (wall) for the bend at the top and btm.
(e) key joint at wall and slab with ¾″ dowels @ 24″ oc
(f) anchor ø bolt @ 4'-0″ oc securing 7″ × 4″ × ⅜″ angle iron
(g) rect (rectangular) tube col 6 × 8 × ⅛″ for superstructure

BASEMENT SHELTER REINFORCED CONCRETE "T" BEAM SECTION

Fig. 18.7 shows a sect of the "T" beam. *Note:*
(a) 12″ floor slab, total depth of "T" is 24″, and btm is 14″ wide.
(b) it is 4″ from the btm of "T" to center of conc between two separate, four row rods of ¾″ reinforcing, the next Fig. 18-8 shows how the top row rods are bent up.
(c) stirrups are ½″ ø.
(d) the beam has ⅝″ ø placed at 4″ oc. Alternate rods are bent at the south side (left) at 3'-4″ to the center of the bend from the edge of "T" and there are ⅜″ temp ø rods at 12″ oc.

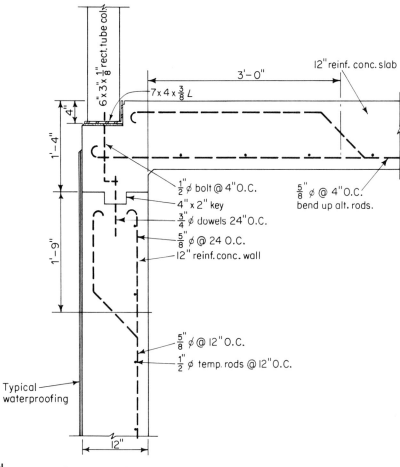

6" x 3" x 1/8" rect. tube col.

7 x 4 x 3/8 L

4"

12" reinf. conc. slab

3'-0"

1'-4"

1/2" ∅ bolt @ 4" O.C.

4" x 2" key

3/4" ∅ dowels 24" O.C.

5/8" ∅ @ 24 O.C.

12" reinf. conc. wall

5/8" ∅ @ 4" O.C. bend up alt. rods.

1'-9"

5/8" ∅ @ 12" O.C.

1/2" ∅ temp. rods @ 12" O.C.

Typical waterproofing

12"

Basement wall (D wing)

Fig. 18-6. Basement wall and first-floor slab.

Fig. 18-7. Reinforced concrete T-beam section.

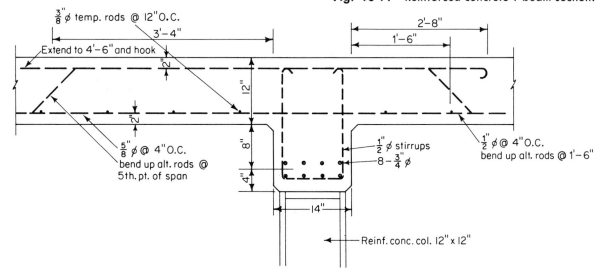

3/8" ∅ temp. rods @ 12" O.C.

3'-4"

Extend to 4'-6" and hook

2'-8"

1'-6"

2"

12"

2"

5/8" ∅ @ 4" O.C. bend up alt. rods @ 5th. pt. of span

8"

4"

1/2" ∅ stirrups

8 - 3/4" ∅

1/2" ∅ @ 4" O.C. bend up alt. rods @ 1'-6"

14"

Reinf. conc. col. 12" x 12"

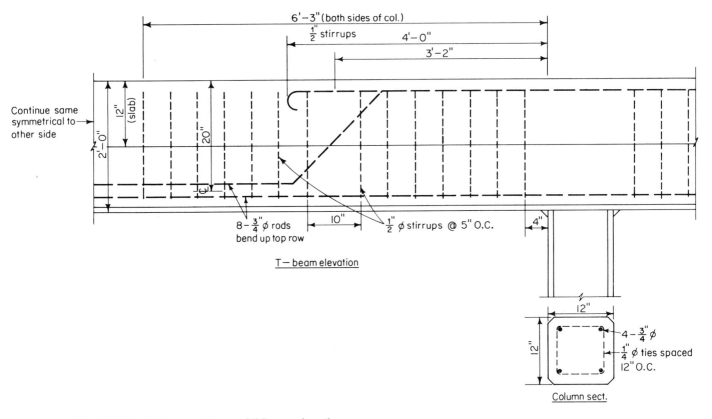

Fig. 18-8. Column section and T-beam elevation.

BASEMENT SHELTER COLUMN SECTION AND "T" BEAM ELEVATION

Fig. 18.8 shows a detail of the col and longitudinal sect of a "T" beam.
Note:
(a) the overall depth of the beam including the stem is 2'-0"; the center line depicts the 12" floor depth.
(b) the beam has ½" ø stirrups @ 5" oc and eight ¾" ø rods.
(c) the top row of ¾" longitudinal ø is bent up and tied to the ø over the cols at the critical point.
(d) dimensions shown above the dwg must be carefully studied.

FALLOUT PROTECTION

The fallout protection in the basement area was provided by use of 12" thick reinforced conc walls and floor slab. Usually such a floor would be 8". Architects and engineers knowledgeable in shielding techniques can incorporate the additional fallout protection for little cost increase whether the bldg be a school, bank, library, church, office bldg, or home for the aged.

FIRST AND SECOND FLOOR PLAN

Figs. 18.9(a) and 18.9(b) show that part of the first and second floor plan that is opposite the pool and over the fallout shelter. Carefully read the sect marks indicating structural details. *Note:*

(a) pool dimensions

(b) recreation room dimensions

(c) sect marks A—A (above, right, and left of pool). See Fig. 18.10.

(d) sect marks ① ② ③ ④ ⑧ and ⑨. See Fig. 18.9(a).

(e) dining room, living room, and kitchen of second floor at Fig. 18.9(b).

(f) 3 large and 4 small decorative rect cols (front wall) first floor to roof members. See Fig. 18.10.

Fig. 18-9 (a).   First floor plan.

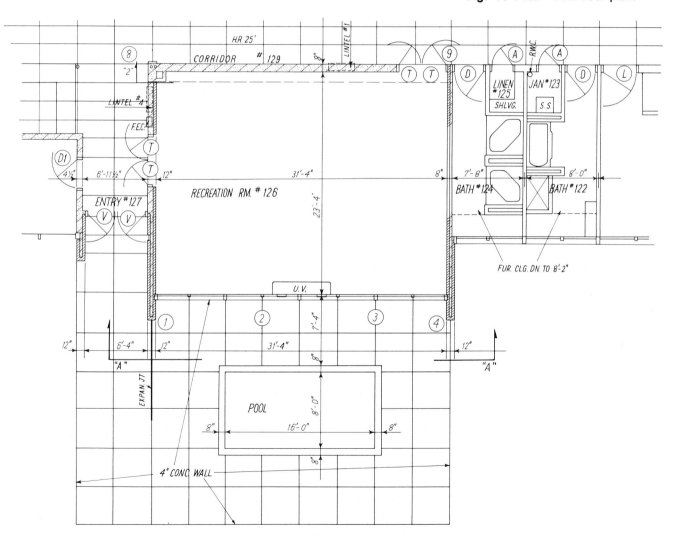

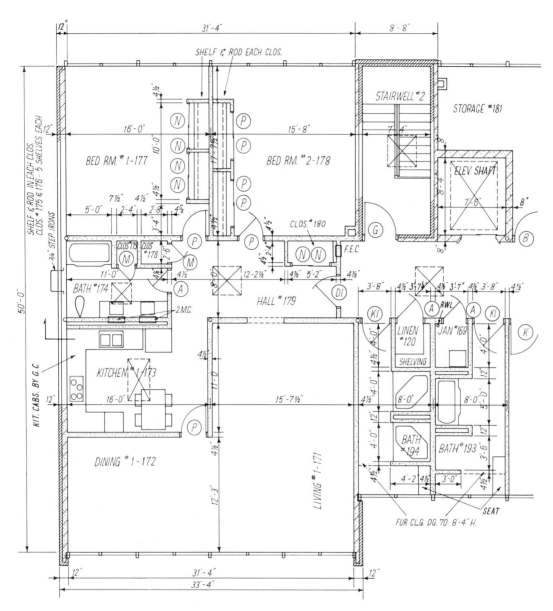

Fig. 18-9 (b). Second floor plan.

OUTSIDE WALL DETAILS, TWO-STORY UNIT

Fig. 18.10 shows a horizontal detail of the walls of the recreation room from Fig. 18.9. *Note:*

(a) finished brickwork with masonry core and built in rect tube col (at left) for door support of single story adjoining.

(b) plan of decorative rect tube cols at the curtain wall.

(c) two circular tube cols at ⑧ where provision is made for an expansion joint. *This is important; see conc wall at Fig.18.9(a).*

(d) circular col ⑨ is an inside wall at corridor; see Fig. 18.4.

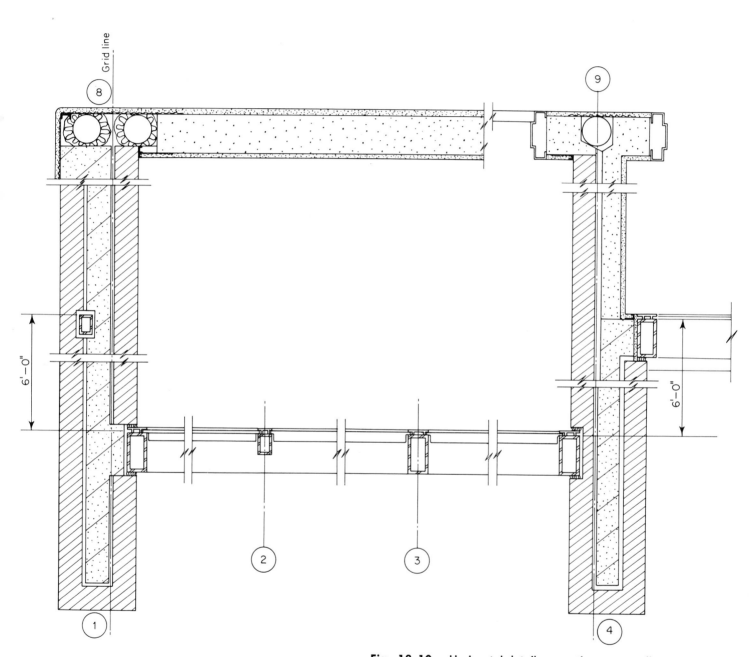

Fig. 18-10.   Horizontal detail, recreation room walls.

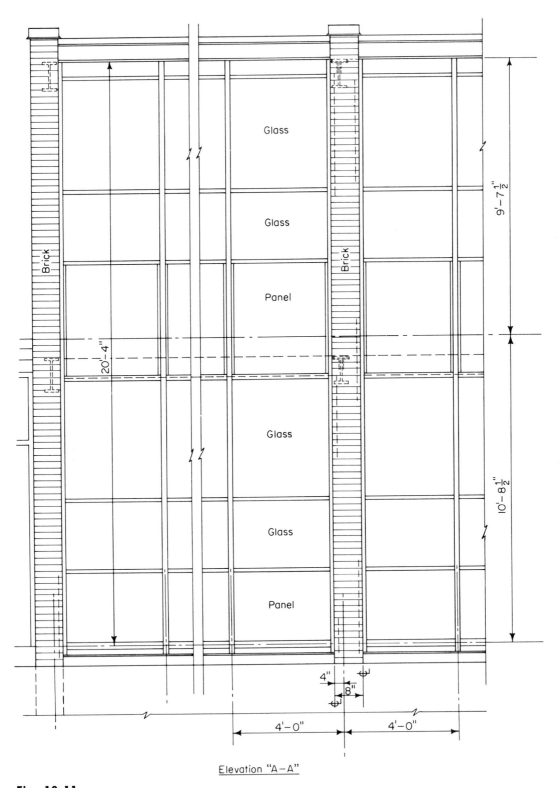

Elevation "A—A"

Fig. 18-11.

ELEVATION A—A TWO-STORY WING

Fig. 18.11 shows an elevation of part of the two-story wing immediately opposite the pool and depicting the curtain wall with brick facing, steel framing members, panels, glass, and rect decorative rect tube cols.

WALL SECTIONS OF ONE- AND TWO-STORY UNITS

Fig. 18.12 shows sects 1 and 2 respectively of walls of "D" Wing. Sect 1 depicts the left wall of the single-story unit. *Note:*
(a) *section 1* shows typical slab over fallout area.
(b) blue glazed face brick bonded to Duro-Wal conc blocks.
(c) ½″ × 12″ bolts @ 6'-0″ oc securing the coping of the parapet.
(d) sections of #12-16 GA (galvanized) steel roof deck with ø in every second trough which is supported on cont 6 [8.2 (sizes have been taken from other dwgs).
(e) *sect 2 shows* the wall between the two-story and the adjoining single story of "D" Wing.
(f) conc joint. *This is the expansion joint shown at Figs. 18.2 and 18.10.*
(g) C of cols. *See Fig. 18.10 for double circ cols for expansion joint.*
(h) brickwork to first floor.
(i) steel beam supporting steel deck and lightweight conc floor.
(j) flashing .032 alum (aluminum) flashing.
(k) face brick and Duro-Wal.
(l) steel beam supported on circ col and with circ col over.
(m) coping.

SECTION THRU RECREATION ROOM

Fig. 18.13 shows a section thru the recreation room. *Note:*
(a) 12″ ø conc slab over fallout shelter
(b) 7″ × 4″ × ⅜″ ∟ (btm left)
(c) 6 × 3 × ⅜″ rect col of curtain wall
(d) steel 8 [11.5 secured to rect col
(e) clg (ceiling) line
(f) steel deck supporting lightweight conc for second floor
(g) roof assembly at top of decorative rect col
(h) 4-½″ ø bolts (btm right col)
(i) ₵ of circ col
(j) thickness of wall is 6″
(k) 4″ circ 10.79 col
(l) difference in clg lines
(m) steel beam 12 WF 27 supporting second floor
(n) steel beam supporting steel roof deck

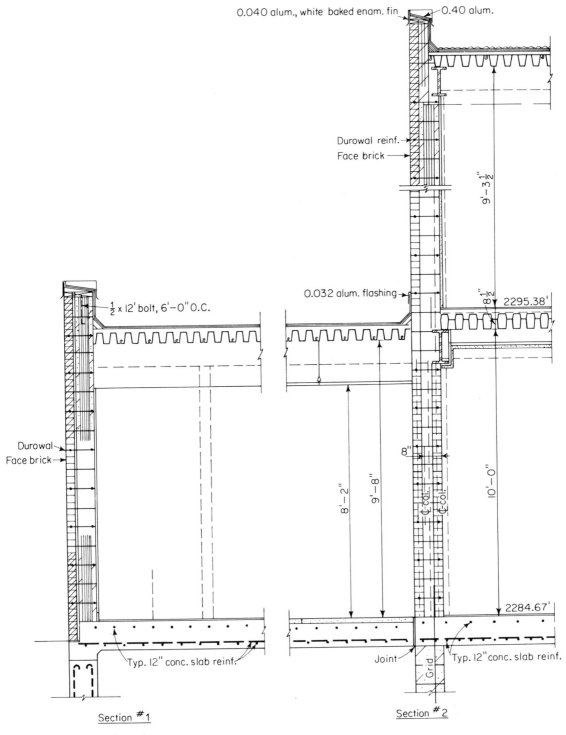

Fig. 18-12.   Wall sections.

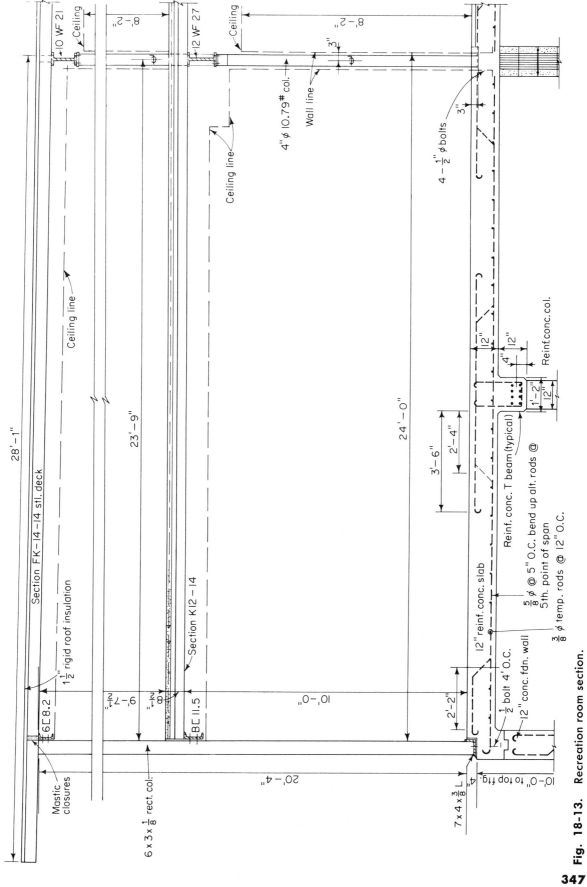

Fig. 18-13. Recreation room section.

347

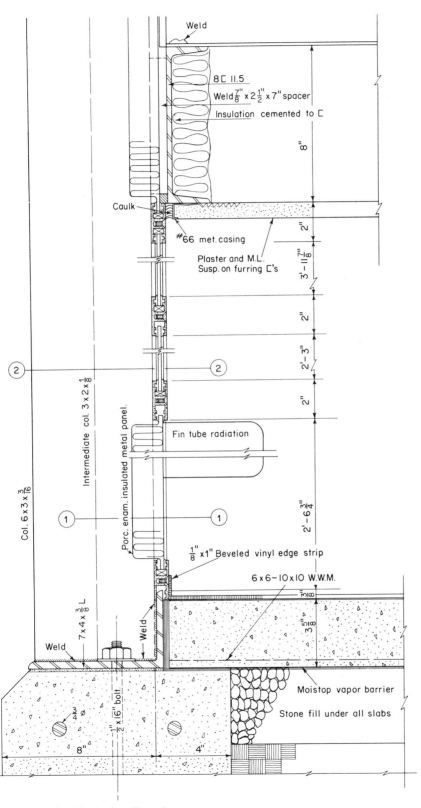

Fig. 18-14. Typical wall section.

TYPICAL WALL SECTION, TWO-STORY UNIT

Fig. 18.14 shows some of the details of a typical wall section. Remember that the entire structure is of steel tube cols, both round and rect and with steel beams, steel decking to the first floor, and GA steel roof deck. The building's exterior is composed of three basic materials in varying quantities: blue glazed brick, vari-colored porcelain steel insulated panels, exposed white vertical steel cols, and glass. The exterior is maintenance-free. *Note:*

(a) the original wall section is drawn to ½ full size.
(b) ½" × 16" anchor bolt securing ∟ to the conc wall.
(c) the weld of the rectangular 6 × 3 × ³⁄₁₆" tube col.
(d) 6" × 6"—10 × 10 w.w.m in lt wt (light weight) conc supported on steel decking to the first floor.
(e) curtain wall, insulated metal pan covering top face of first floor and btm face of second floor.
(f) section marks 1-1, 2-2 and 3-3. See Fig. 18.15.

RECTANGULAR CURTAIN WALL TUBE COLUMNS

Fig. 18.15 shows sections of rectangular metal tube cols. *Note:*

(a) sect ① for the fastening device of the intermediate col supporting the porcelain enamel insulated metal pan.
(b) sect ② and the fastening device for the large col supporting glass.
(c) sect ③ shows large col supporting porcelain metal pan. Notice how this col is furred out with wood to bring it in line with sect ② above. This panel forms the top face of the first floor and the btm face of the second floor.

Fig. 18-15.   Rectangular column sections.

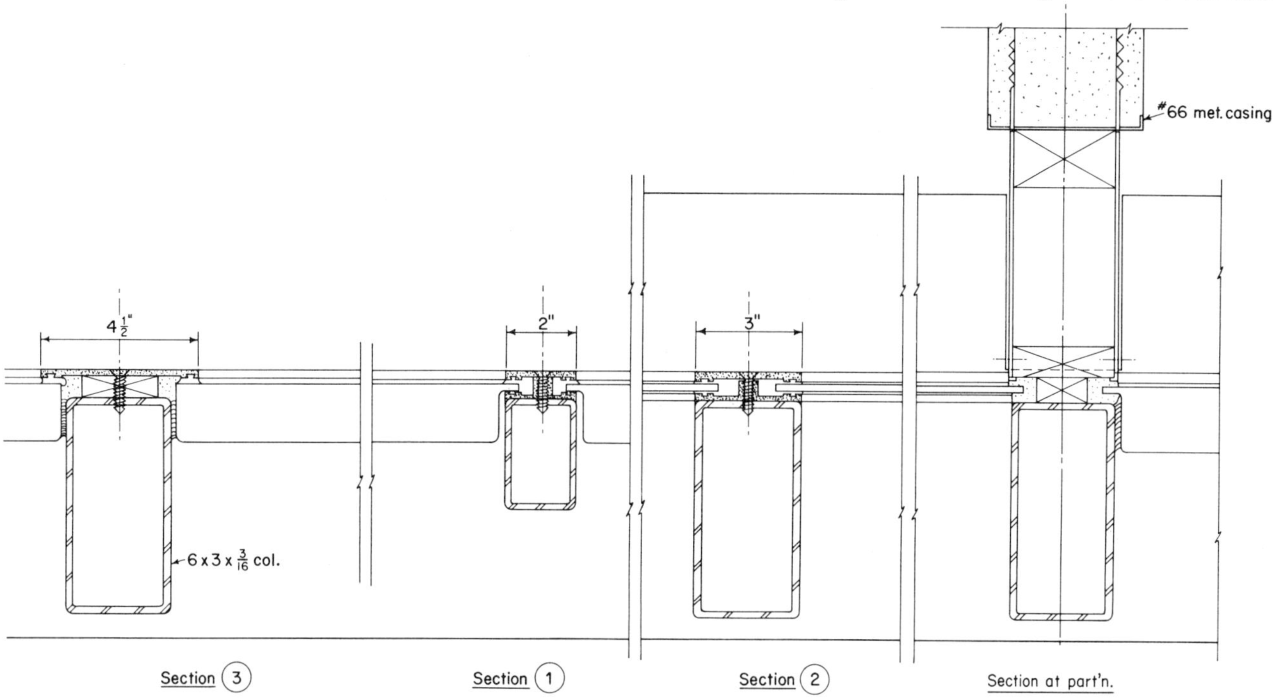

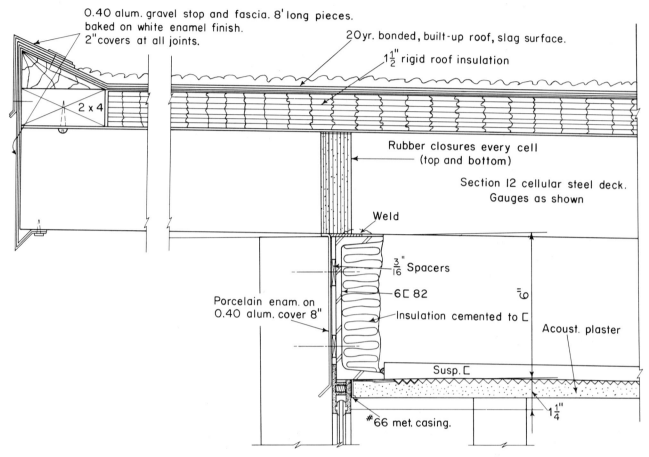

0.40 alum. gravel stop and fascia. 8' long pieces.
baked on white enamel finish.
2" covers at all joints.

2 x 4

20 yr. bonded, built-up roof, slag surface.

1½" rigid roof insulation

Rubber closures every cell
(top and bottom)

Section 12 cellular steel deck.
Gauges as shown

Weld

3/16" Spacers

6 ⊏ 82

Porcelain enam. on
0.40 alum. cover 8"

Insulation cemented to ⊏

6"

Acoust. plaster

Susp. ⊏

1¼"

#66 met. casing.

Fig. 18-16. Wall-to-roof assembly.

TYPICAL WALL-TO-ROOF ASSEMBLY

Fig. 18.16 shows a typical section of wall-to-roof assembly. *Note:*
(a) acoustic plaster on suspended clg
(b) insulation cemented to 6 [8.2
(c) ³⁄₁₆″ wood spacers
(d) porcelain enamel on .040 aluminum cover
(e) weld of 6 [8.2 to section of cellular steel deck
(f) rubber closure on every cell of steel deck
(g) 20 year bonded built-up roof, slag surface and 1½″ rigid insulation
(h) fascia and gravel stop at eaves.

ROOF AND ADJOINING FIRST-FLOOR DETAIL

Fig. 18.17 shows sect 4 structural detail of the single-story roof adjoining the second-story floor. The reference is shown at Fig. 18.9 (corridor). Locate it, please! *Note:*

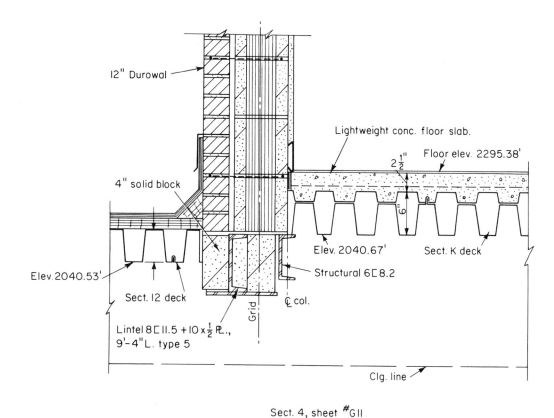

Sect. 4, sheet #G11

Fig. 18-17.   Roof detail.

(a) lintel 8 [11.5 and 10 × 1½″ ℞ (plate) with solid conc block over and supported by circ cols.

(b) structural 6 [8.2 supporting floor deck. See Fig. 18.18. Steel framing plan for double cols (*expansion joint*) supporting 6 [8.2 over corridor.

(c) the difference between the steel decking for roof and floor.

(d) metal baseboard to finished plaster.

STEEL FRAMING PLAN

Fig. 18.18 shows the steel framing plan for that portion of the plan of "D" Wing shown on the plans of Fig. 18.9. *Read from the front and left of dwg and note:*

(a) 32′-0″ sect K 12—14 steel deck

(b) 4 cols of 3 × 2 × ⅛″ and 5 cols of 6 × 3 × 3⁄₁₆″

(c) cont 8 [11.5

(d) beam 14 ᵂᶠ 30

(e) connection slotted with adjoining member for *expansion joint*. See Figs. 18.4, 18.10, 18.19. *This is very important.*

(f) double circ cols at corridor and through to expansion joint formed between two *rect cols* on the opposite outside wall. See Fig. 18.19.

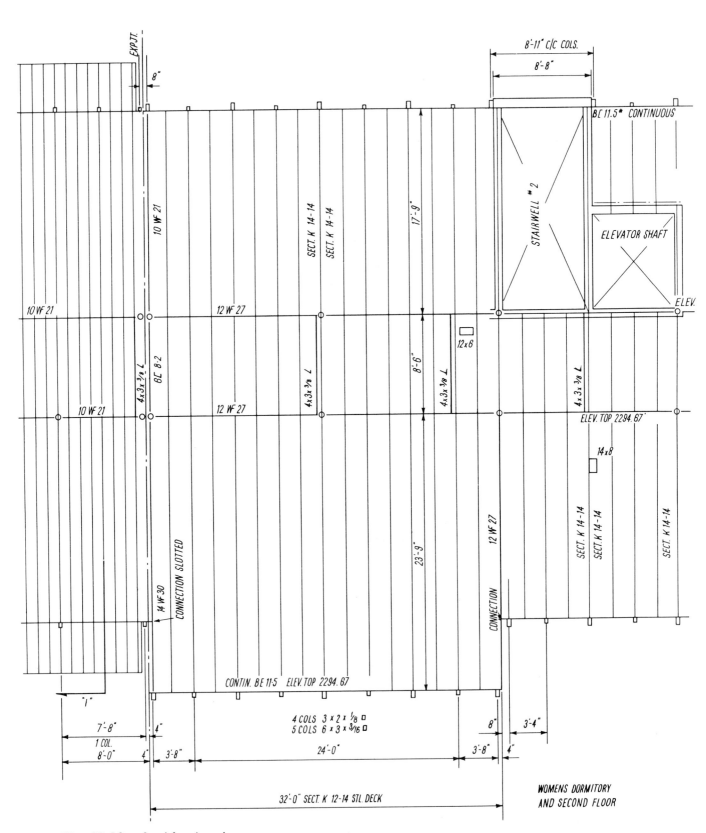

Fig. 18-18.   Steel framing plan.

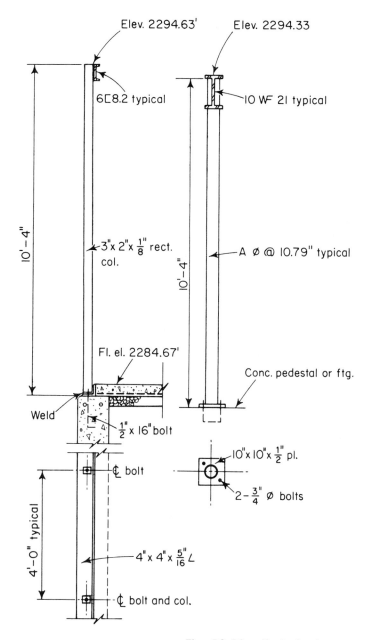

Fig. 18-19. Typical columns.

TYPICAL COLUMNS

Fig. 18.19 shows typical rect and circ cols. *Note:*
(a) rect steel column for curtain walls (left)
(b) ½″ × 16″ anchor bolts to ₵ of col
(c) weld to angle iron at foot
(d) 6 [8.2 to support roof deck
(e) 10 × 10 × ½″ ₧ and 2-¾″ ø bolts
(f) A ø @ 10.79. (Pipe cols have the same strength in all directions.)
(g) typical beam 10 WF 21

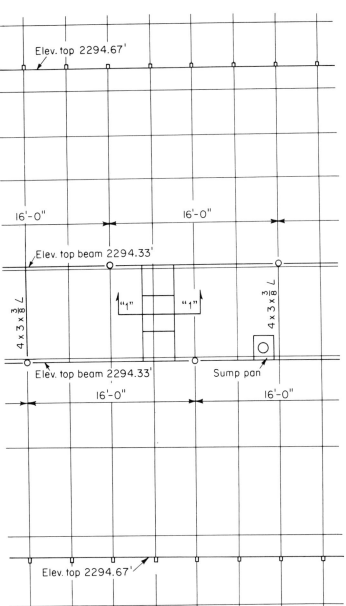

Fig. 18-20 (a). Skydome framing.

Elev. top 2294.67'

16'-0"   16'-0"

Elev. top beam 2294.33'

$4 \times 3 \times \frac{3}{8}$ ∠

"1"   "1"

$4 \times 3 \times \frac{3}{8}$ ∠

Elev. top beam 2294.33'   Sump pan

16'-0"   16'-0"

Elev. top 2294.67'

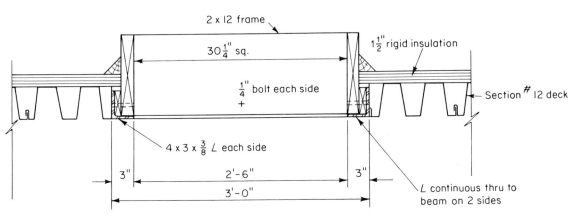

2 x 12 frame

$30\frac{1}{4}"$ sq. $1\frac{1}{2}"$ rigid insulation

$\frac{1}{4}"$ bolt each side

Section # 12 deck

$4 \times 3 \times \frac{3}{8}$ ∠ each side

∠ continuous thru to beam on 2 sides

3"   2'-6"   3"

3'-0"

Fig. 18-20 (b). Skydome framing section.

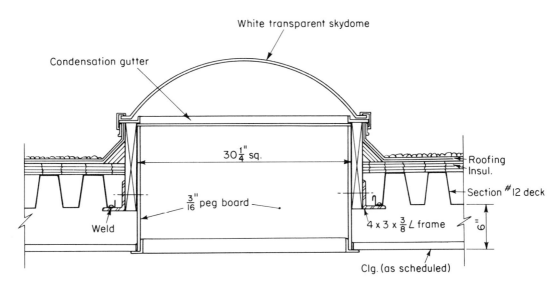

White transparent skydome

Condensation gutter

$30\frac{1}{4}"$ sq.

$\frac{3}{16}"$ peg board

Weld

Roofing Insul.

Section #12 deck

$4 \times 3 \times \frac{3}{8}$ ∠ frame

6"

Clg. (as scheduled)

Fig. 18-20 (c).   Skydome section.

SKYDOME, FRAMING, AND SECTION

Fig. 18.20(a) shows the skydome steel framing plan. *Note:*
(a) the longitudinal beams between 10 ᵂᶠ 21 supporting the steel deck.
(b) the $4 \times 3 \times \frac{3}{16}"$ ∠ corridor and skydome framing.

Fig. 18.20(b) shows sect 1-1 of the skydome framing. *Note:*
(a) inside and outside dimension of ∠ is 2'-6" and 3'-0" respectively.
(b) sect 12 roof deck.
(c) 2×12 wood framing 30¼" square (inside).

Fig. 18.20(c) shows the skydome section. *Note:*
(a) suspended clg as scheduled.
(b) $4 \times 3 \times \frac{3}{8}"$ ∠ frame welded to roof deck.
(c) $\frac{3}{16}"$ peg board lining.
(d) condensation gutter of white translucent skydome.

EXPANSION JOINTS

Fig. 18.21(a) shows an expansion joint at a double rect col which is broken with an insulated 12-gage aluminum shield. This type is used in the curtain wall over the 12" concrete basement wall between rooms B-11 and 12 at Fig. 18.4.

Fig. 18.21(b) shows an expansion joint at an internal col. *Note:*
(a) ½" × 12" × 8" ℔ let into col.
(b) 1½" slotted holes in ℔.
(c) two 1½" slotted holes in beam web for bolt connection.

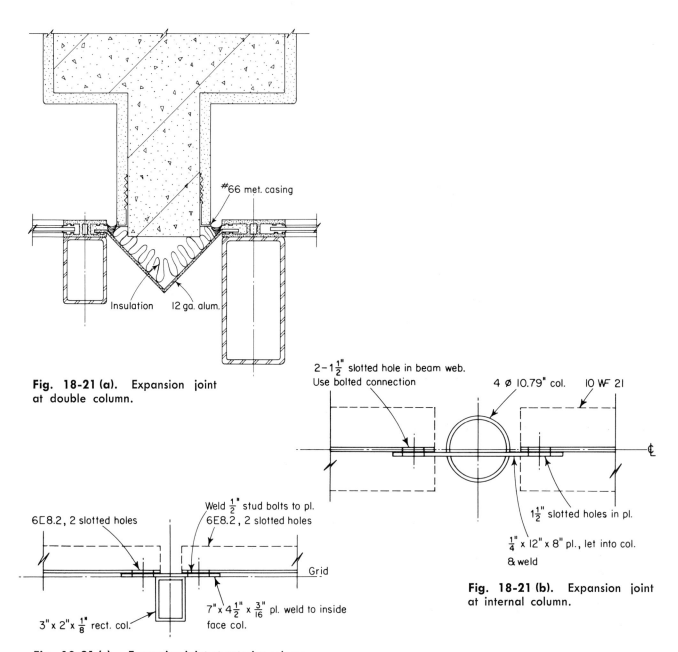

Fig. 18-21 (a). Expansion joint at double column.

#66 met. casing

Insulation   12 ga. alum.

2-1½" slotted hole in beam web. Use bolted connection

4 Ø 10.79" col.   10 WF 21

1½" slotted holes in pl.

¼" x 12" x 8" pl., let into col. & weld

Fig. 18-21 (b). Expansion joint at internal column.

6[8.2, 2 slotted holes

Weld ½" stud bolts to pl. 6[8.2, 2 slotted holes

Grid

3" x 2" x ⅛" rect. col.

7" x 4½" x 3/16" pl. weld to inside face col.

Fig. 18-21 (c). Expansion joint at exterior column.

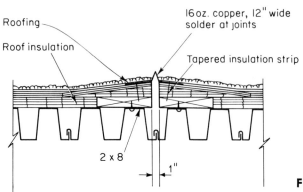

Roofing

Roof insulation

16 oz. copper, 12" wide solder at joints

Tapered insulation strip

2 x 8

1"

Fig. 18-21 (d). Roof expansion joint detail.

356

(d) 10 ʷF 21 beam and 4 ⌀ 10.79 cols.

Fig. 18.21(c) shows an expansion joint at a single $3 \times 2 \times \frac{1}{8}''$ rect col.

Note:

(a) $7 \times 4\frac{1}{2}'' \times \frac{3}{16}''$ welded to inside face of col.

(b) welded $\frac{1}{2}''$ stud bolt to ℞.

(c) 6 [8.2 has slotted holes.

Fig. 18.21(d) shows an expansion joint detail for the roof. *Note:*

(a) the provision made in the steel decking for expansion.

(b) tapered insulation strip on either side of joint.

(c) roof insulation over steel decking.

(d) roofing.

(e) 16-oz. copper 12″ wide and soldered joints.

19 A STEEL BRIDGE

BRIDGE OVER THE SASKATCHEWAN RIVER

In this chapter we are going to study as many dwgs of a steel framed bridge as can reasonably be included in one chapter. The source of the material is the Government of Saskatchewan, Canada, and it is published through the courtesy of Mr. L. O. Thomson, Chief Bridge Engineer. The steel was fabricated by Dominion Bridge Company.

The bridge is 1411.0 ft long with an electric lighted 28'-0" carriageway, a 5'-0" sidewalk on one side, and a concrete curb on the other. The river flows approx west-east with a HWL elev 1536.0' (high water level) and a LWL elev 1518.0'. The height of the bridge from LWL is 40 ft, and the deepest pier is 32 ft below river bed.

Three of the five piers are supported on piles, and some of the foundations are anchored to them. The two parallel continuous steel girders 20 ft cc are fixed over the center pier No. 3. Rocker bearings are provided at piers 2, 4, and 5 to allow for expansion. Each girder has a web of 10'-10" and a 2'-6" flange. The dwgs in this chapter have no scale but are proportionate to the originals.

All the structural details are models of excellence and should be emulated on all such work coming under your jurisdiction.

PLAN AND ELEVATION

Let us examine the plan and elevation at Fig. 19.1 and note:
(a) the scale of the original elevation is 1" to 50'-0".

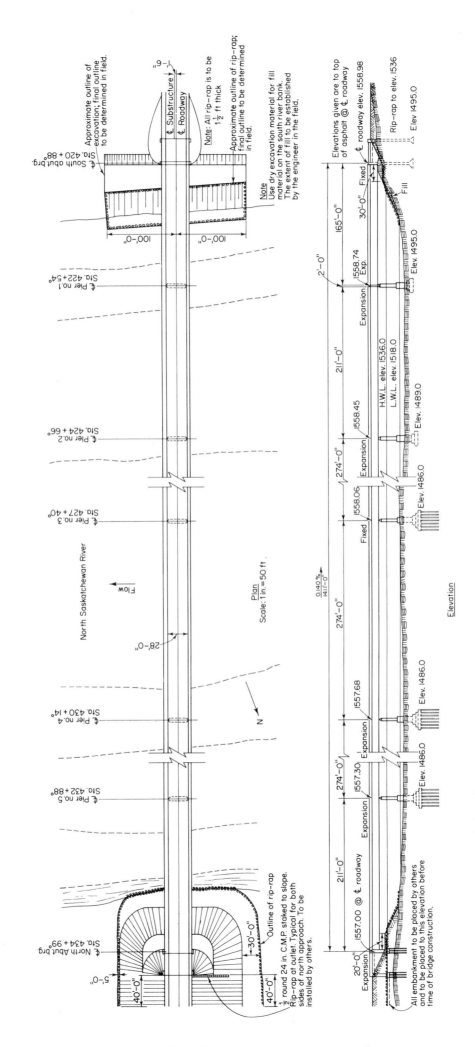

Fig. 19-1. Plan and elevation.

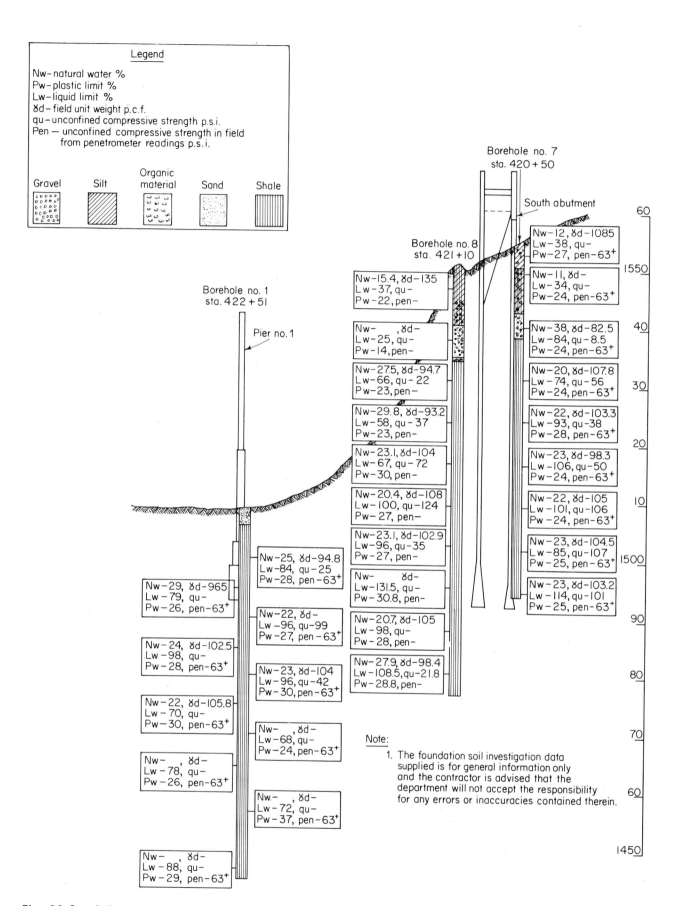

Fig. 19-2. Soil analysis report.

(b) at either end of the bridge an approx outline of the excavation is given, but the final boundary is to be determined in the field.

(c) total quantities of excavations as shown on the dwgs: 7,741 wet and 470 cu yd dry.

(d) there are 3,680 cu yds of rip-rap (wall or foundation of broken stones thrown together irregularly), and the final boundary is to be established in the field.

(e) the bridge grade is 0.140%. *Check this mathematically now, please!*

(f) *not* all pier foundation elev are the same.

(g) the superstructure is fixed over the central pier, and rocker bearings are provided at piers 2, 4, and 5 to allow for expansion.

(h) the flow of the river is approx west-east.

SOIL ANALYSIS

A soil analysis and legend is shown for the south abutment and pier #1 at Fig. 19.2. The scale showing the elevations is on the right of the dwg. Read and remember the note shown under the dwg and study the legend.

TYPICAL PIER SECTION

A typical pier section is shown at Fig. 19.3. Think about these dimensions and compare them with the size of the room you are now in. Note the flow of the river (this is very important); it is deeply frozen every winter.

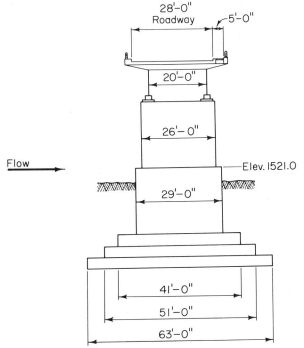
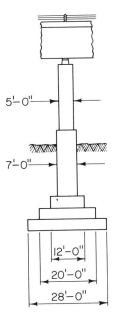

Fig. 19-3. Typical pier section.

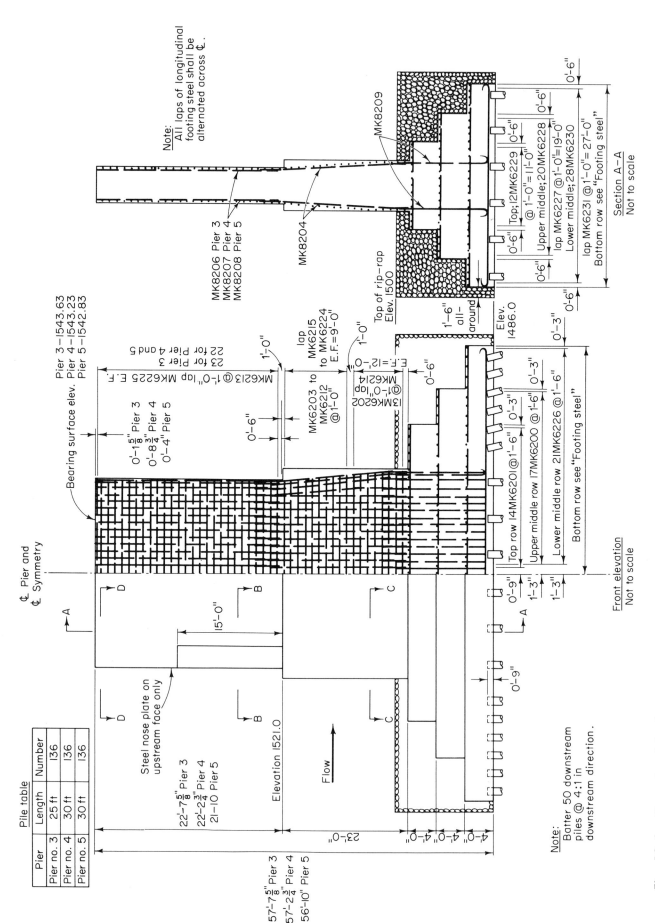

Fig. 19-4. Concrete reinforcing.

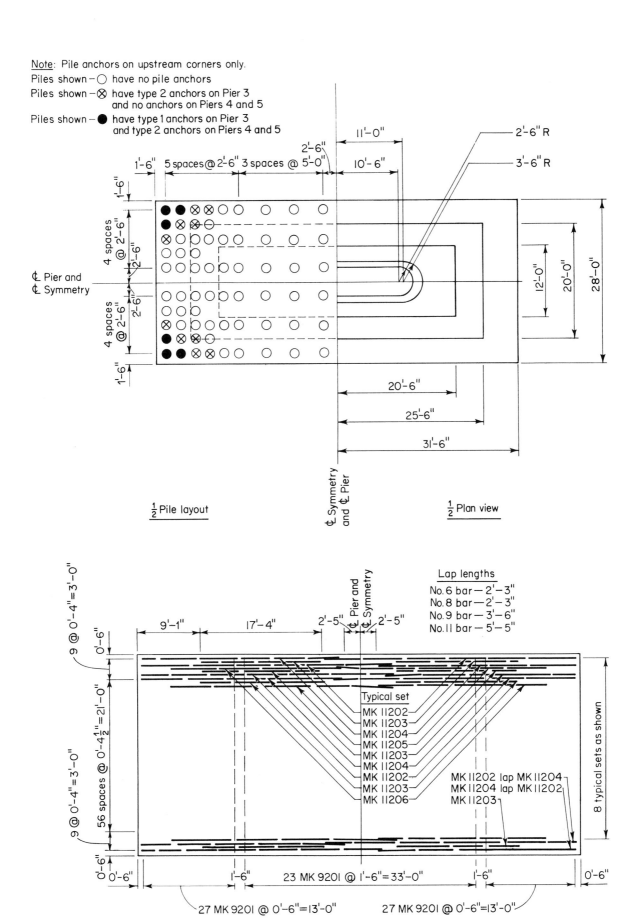

Note: Pile anchors on upstream corners only.
Piles shown – ○ have no pile anchors
Piles shown – ⊗ have type 2 anchors on Pier 3
     and no anchors on Piers 4 and 5
Piles shown – ● have type 1 anchors on Pier 3
     and type 2 anchors on Piers 4 and 5

2'-6" R
3'-6" R

1'-6"   5 spaces @ 2'-6"   3 spaces @ 5'-0"
11'-0"
2'-6"
10'-6"

1'-6"

4 spaces @ 2'-6"
2'-6"

℄ Pier and
℄ Symmetry

4 spaces @ 2'-6"
2'-6"

1'-6"

28'-0"
20'-0"
12'-0"

½ Pile layout

℄ Symmetry
and ℄ Pier

20'-6"
25'-6"
31'-6"

½ Plan view

Lap lengths
No. 6 bar — 2'-3"
No. 8 bar — 2'-3"
No. 9 bar — 3'-6"
No. 11 bar — 5'-5"

9 @ 0'-4"=3'-0"
0'-6"

9'-1"   17'-4"   2'-5"   2'-5"

℄ Pier and
℄ Symmetry

9 @ 0'-4½"=21'-0"

56 spaces @ 0'-4½"=21'-0"

9 @ 0'-4"=3'-0"

Typical set
MK 11202
MK 11203
MK 11204
MK 11205
MK 11203
MK 11204
MK 11202
MK 11203
MK 11206

MK 11202 lap MK 11204
MK 11204 lap MK 11202
MK 11203

8 typical sets as shown

0'-6"
0'-6"   1'-6"   23 MK 9201 @ 1'-6"=33'-0"   1'-6"   0'-6"

27 MK 9201 @ 0'-6"=13'-0"   27 MK 9201 @ 0'-6"=13'-0"

Note:
Contact splices of main footing steel
are to be made by tying one bar on top
of the other i.e. vertical splices.

Footing steel
Not to scale

Figs. 19-5 (a) and (b).

PIER REINFORCING, ELEVATION, AND SECTION A-A

The concrete reinforcing for piers 3, 4, and 5 is shown at Fig. 19.4. Read the front elevation upwards and note:
(a) the length of the btm row of footing steel. (See detail at Fig. 19.5).
(b) the difference in types of steel used laterally and transversely.
(c) *50 piles on the downstream side are battered.*
(d) the flow shown at left.
(e) for sect marked details see Figs. 19.6 and 19.7.

HALF PILE LAYOUT AND PLAN VIEW: FOOTING STEEL

A half plan layout, half pier plan, and ftg steel details are shown at Figs. 19.5(a) and 19.5(b). This dwg should be read with Fig. 19.4. For such an important engr detail, note the simplicity of dwg lines and few words used; but sufficient information together with the specifications is given for contractors to estimate and build. Study the pile legend and note the two types of pile anchors shown at Fig. 19.6.

PILE ANCHORS: PIER SECTIONS

Study the two types of pile anchors and all the sect dwgs at Figs. 19.6(a) and 19.6(b) and note:
(a) turn to Fig. 19.1 and clearly understand the pier numbers in relation to the flow of the river.
(b) this dwg to be read with Fig. 19.5 for batter on downstream piles. Note the pier cap legend.
(c) some piles have #1 pile anchors, some have #2, others are not anchored.
(d) the top of pier detail shows $\math€$ of bearing and girders. The $\math€$ of the roadway is 1'-6" out of center between girders. *This is important!*
(e) Sect D-D shows $\math€$ of pier, bearing, girder, anchor bolts, and rein steel. See Fig. 19.6(b).
(f) steel shown at B-B is another sect for the same portion of pier as D-D, and shows the ⅜ nose welded to rein steel.
(g) the following quantities are shown on the originals: concrete 2,258 cu yd, rein steel 158,950 lbs, struc steel 6,930 lbs, rip-rap 1,700 cu yds, timber pilings untreated 11,560 lin ft.
(h) think about all these quantities. Compare the cu yd capacity of the room you are now in with the quantities given. *Get the feeling for the things you detail.*

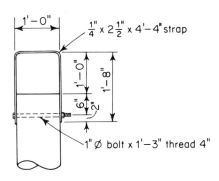

$\frac{1}{4}$ x 2$\frac{1}{2}$" x 4'-4" strap

1" Ø bolt x 1'-3" thread 4"

Type 1 pile anchor

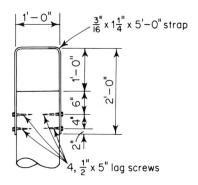

$\frac{3}{16}$" x 1$\frac{1}{4}$" x 5'-0" strap

4, $\frac{1}{2}$" x 5" lag screws

Type 2 pile anchor

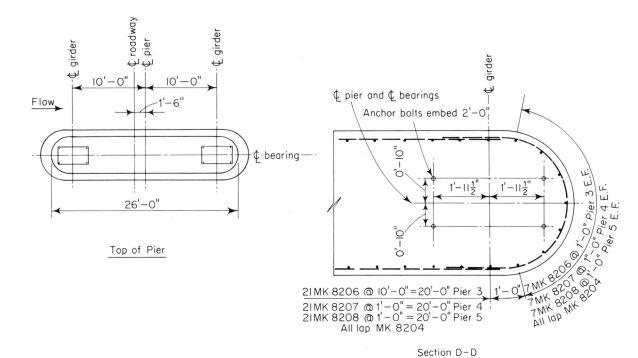

Flow

₵ girder   ₵ roadway ₵ pier   ₵ girder

10'-0"   10'-0"

1'-6"

₵ bearing

26'-0"

Top of Pier

₵ pier and ₵ bearings

Anchor bolts embed 2'-0"

₵ girder

0'-10"   1'-11$\frac{1}{2}$"   1'-11$\frac{1}{2}$"   0'-10"

21MK 8206 @ 10'-0"=20'-0" Pier 3
21MK 8207 @ 1'-0" = 20'-0" Pier 4
21MK 8208 @ 1'-0" = 20'-0" Pier 5
All lap MK 8204

1'-0"   7MK 8206 @ 1'-0" Pier 3 E.F.
7MK 8207 @ 1'-0" Pier 4 E.F.
7MK 8208 @ 1'-0" Pier 5 E.F.
All lap MK 8204

Section D–D
And anchor bolt layout

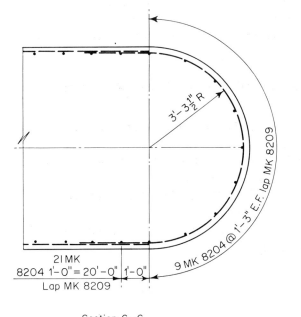

3'-3$\frac{1}{2}$" R

9 MK 8204 @ 1'-3" E.F. lap MK 8209

21MK
8204 1'-0"=20'-0"   1'-0"
Lap MK 8209

Figs. 19-6 (a) and (b).

Section C–C

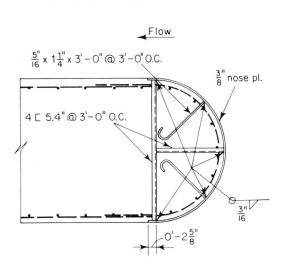

Flow

$\frac{5}{16}$" x 1$\frac{1}{4}$" x 3'-0" @ 3'-0" O.C.

$\frac{3}{8}$" nose pl.

4 ⌷ 5.4" @ 3'-0" O.C.

$\frac{3}{16}$

0'-2$\frac{5}{8}$"

Section B–B

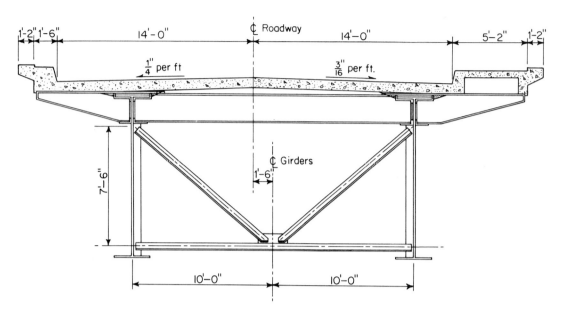

Fig. 19-7. Cross section.

CROSS SECTION OF GIRDERS, ROAD, CURB, AND SIDEWALK

The cross section at Fig. 19.7 shows:
(a) the cont girders with 10'-10" webs and 2'-6" flanges placed at 20'-0" oc. *What is the height of the room you are now in? You must get the feel of this bridge.*
(b) the ₵ of the roadway is 1'-6" nearer the curb than the ₵ between girders.
(c) the total height of the bracing is 7'-6".
(d) the outlines of the floorbeam supporting concrete.
(e) the transverse stiffeners on the interior faces of the girders from lower flange to underside of floorbeam. See Fig. 19.9 for stiffener details.
(f) the difference in the fall of the roadway on either side of ₵.
(g) the concrete road, curb and sidewalk dimensions.

FIELD SPLICE AND LONGITUDINAL STIFFENER

Carefully study the bolted field splice and longitudinal stiffener at Fig. 19.8, noting:
(a) the 2-⅜ × 1-3 × 10-9 web splice plates, one for each side of the girder web with bolt spacings.
(b) the ½ × 7 × 10-9 angle stiffener and see its vertical line between the right side bolts.
(c) the longitudinal stiffeners 2-2 from top and btm of the girder respectively.

(d) the plan at the top showing 2-6 wide flange, 2-5 top plate, and dotted lines for the inside flange plates.

(e) the following original notes should be read with Figs. 19.8, 19.9, and 19.10.

Fig. 19-8.   Field splice and longitudinal stiffener.

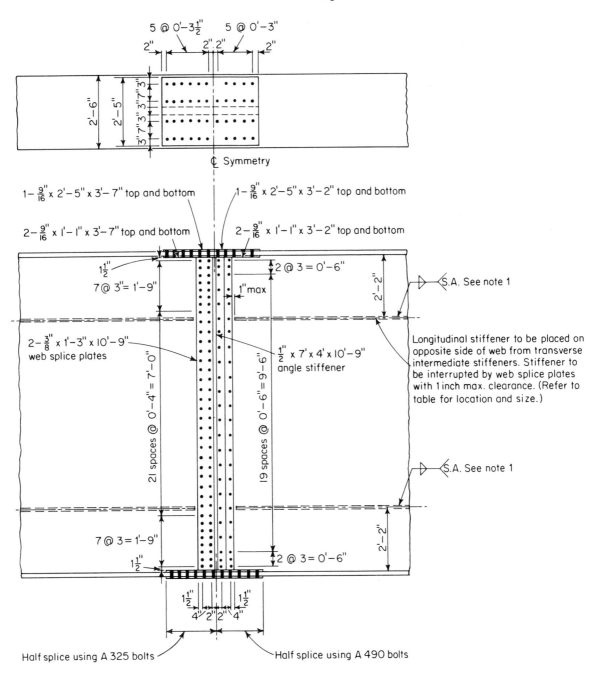

NOTES

1. Web to longitudinal stiffener welds:
   Stiffener thickness ⅝ in. use ¼ in. fillet weld
   All others use ³⁄₁₆ in. fillet weld

2. Flange to stiffener weld:
   Flange thickness 1 to 1½ in. use ⁵⁄₁₆ in. fillet weld
   Flange thickness 1¾ use ⅜ fillet weld

3. All interior corners of stiffeners to be chamfered 1 inch.

4. All intermediate stiffeners to be perpendicular to ₵ of web.

5. All field stiffeners to be parallel to intermediate stiffeners.

6. Bearing stiffeners to be ground to bear on bottom flange, a one in. gap to be maintained at the top flange.

7. The final items to be attached to the girders by welding shall be the bearing stiffeners, these shall be accurately spaced as to span length and shall be plumb in the erect position.

8. Floor beams to be perpendicular to ₵ of web. Fabricate connections to bearing stiffeners @ 0.14% slope.

9. Splice plates shall be cut from parent plates such that the direction of rolling will be lengthwise of the girder.

TRANSVERSE STIFFENER DETAILS

Four different transverse stiffener details are shown at Fig. 19.9, which must be read with Fig. 19.10 and note:

General

(a) excepting bearing stiffeners, all transverse stiffeners are on interior face of the girders.

(b) the tension and compression flanges at the *General, Support, and Floorbeam* details have a gap of 1 in. between the tension flange and the stiffener. *[It is very important to see where the tension is reversed. Author.]*

(c) you must read the previous notes and completely understand them.

At supports

(a) the 1 × 12 stiffeners are welded to the btm flange but there is a gap at the top.

(b) the two different size stiffeners have different size welds.

(c) to the right of the detail is stated the positions for the stiffeners. See Fig. 19.11 at ₵ of piers 2 and 5.

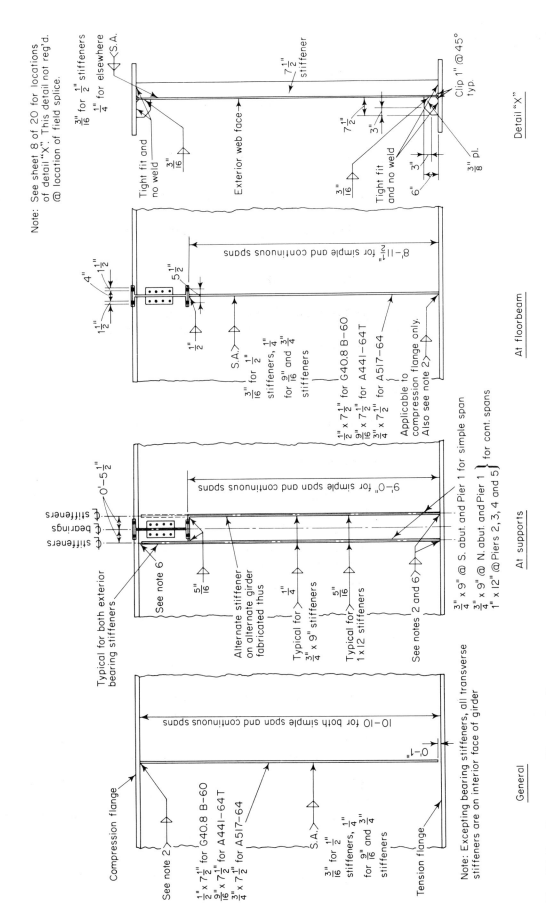

Fig. 19-9. Transverse stiffener details.

369

At floorbeam

(a) the weld at compression flange and the different sizes of stiffeners and welds.

Detail "X"

(a) the top and btm ⅜ in. ℞ and particularly note the edges where there is no weld.
(b) the locations of *Detail "X"* is shown at Fig. 19.11.

CONTINUOUS GIRDER: PART PLAN AND DETAIL

A part plan and detail of a continuous girder together with a deflection curve is shown at Fig. 19.10. There is great detail on this dwg. Study it carefully and note:

Plan

(a) the dimensioned plan showing cont girders, floorbeams, and bracing.

Part girder detail

(a) reading from btm left up—the stiffener spacings and numbers. See Fig. 19.9.
(b) the location of field splices. See Fig. 19.8.
(c) web plates, note the different thicknesses
(d) the dimensioned line for the span
(e) top and btm flange plates, note the differences
(f) detail "X". See Fig. 19.9
(g) the arrowed points of butt welds marked G. Read note 3
(h) the following notes appear on the original dwgs.

NOTES

1. Girder ends to be plumb in erect position.

2. Flange to web welds:
   Flange thickness 1 to 1½ in. use ⁵⁄₁₆ in. fillet weld
   Flange thickness 1¾ use ⅜ in. fillet weld

3. All butt welds marked G must pass radiographic inspection, 10% min of all butt welds not so marked shall be subject to the same test and shall meet same requirements. Grinding of weld surfaces to a smooth finish shall precede all radiographing of welds. All grinding of welds to be done in a direction perpendicular to the ₵ of the weld.

4. All dimensions on this sheet are correct at shop temperatures of 60° Fahrenheit.

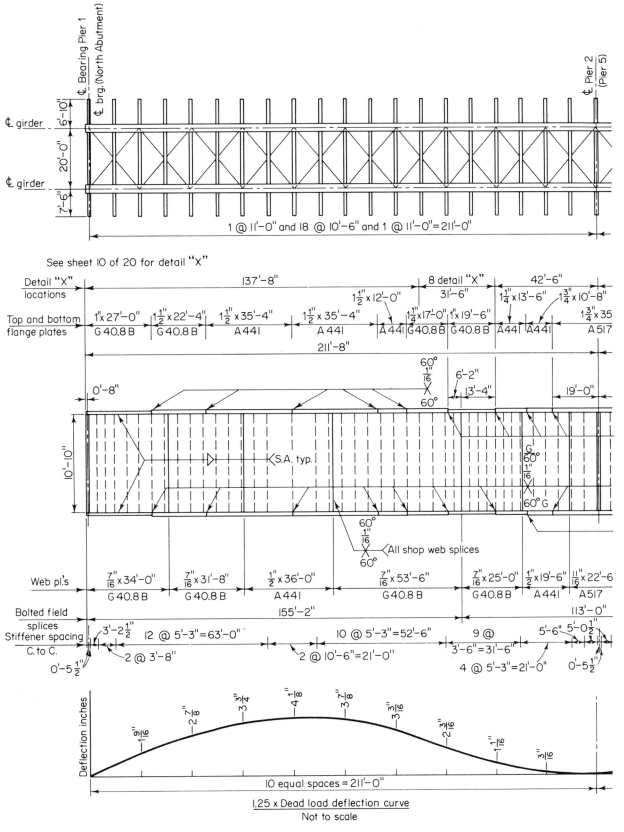

Fig. 19-10. Girder details and D.L. deflection curve.

5. Tolerance for tilt or warpage at btm flanges of girders at all bearings shall be as prescribed for flatness of seats to be set on Steel A.W.S. D2.0-63.

6. Web depth 130 in. and flange width = 30 in. throughout.

7. Fabricator is to supply required number of nuts and bolts plus 5% extra to cover loss and wastage.

8. All stiffeners shall conform to the same specifications to which web is required to conform. All other attachments welded to the web shall conform to C.S.A. Specifications 640- 8B. 60.

9. G.40.8B-60 refers to steel conforming to C.S.A. Specifications G40. 8B.60. A441 and A517 refer to A.S.T.M. Specification A441-64T and A517-64 respectively.

10. Girder sections to be built to fit 1.25 times D.L. deflection curve.

FLOORBEAM DETAILS

The floorbeam details are shown at Fig. 19.11. Read up and note:
(a) the lower dwg shows the type of plate welding and bolt placing for use with cross frame members. *It is important that you read Fig. 19.12 now, please!*
(b) the curb and sidewalk girders are the large cont girders into which the floorbeams are attached; notice on the curb side it is 6'-10" from the ₵ of the girder to the outside, but 7'-6" on the opposite side.
(c) the central floorbeam is 24 W 68 and the outside cantilevered sections have $\frac{7}{16}$ flange ℞ at the curb and $\frac{3}{8} \times 9$ flange ℞ at the opposite side. See details *At Supports* Fig. 19.9.
(d) pay careful attention to bolt spacings, welds, and all dimensions. At the left side is shown a total slope of 1¾ in. from its bend at the intersection with the main girder.
(e) the stiffener to girder flange and under the 24 W 68 floorbeam. *This detail is packed with very pertinent details. Study them with Fig. 19.12.*

BRACING DETAILS

At. Fig. 19.12 are shown four bracing details (there are more on the original dwgs). *These dwgs must be read with Fig. 19.11.* Note the following:

Crossframe details

(a) sect of cont girder.
(b) 7½ vertical stiffener from flange to 24 W 68 above and $\frac{3}{8}$ gusset to which are bolted two horizontal $3 \times 3 \times \frac{5}{16}$ L's.

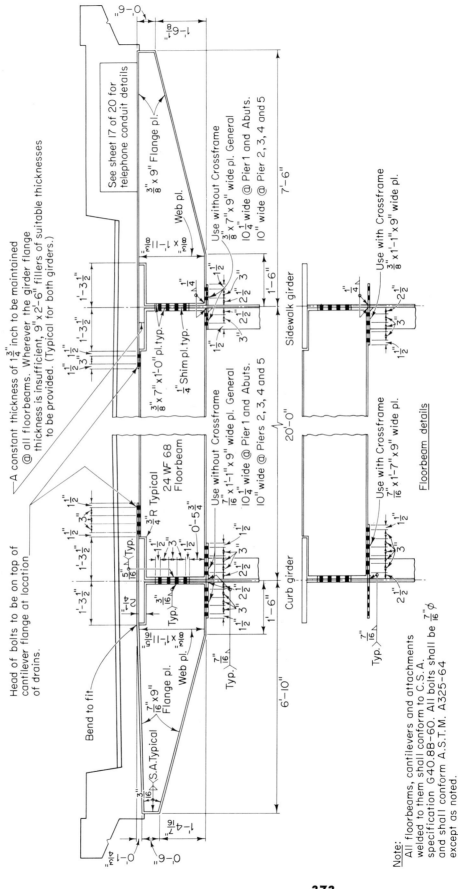

Fig. 19-11. Floorbeam details.

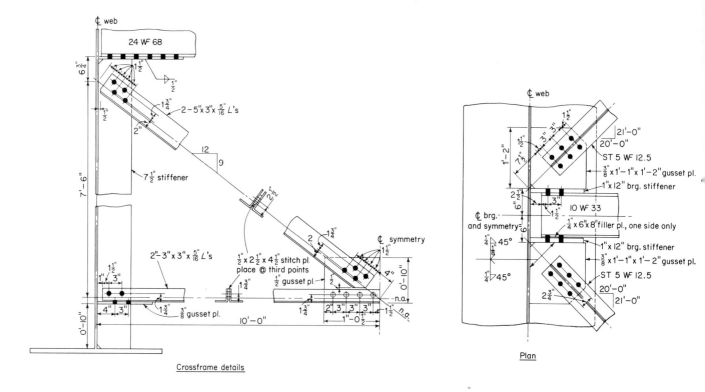

Crossframe details

Plan

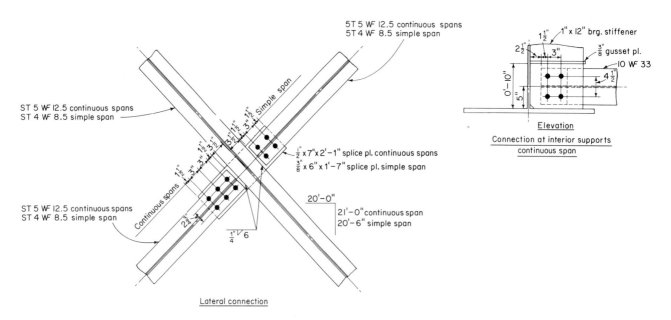

Lateral connection

Elevation
Connection at interior supports
continuous span

Fig. 19-12. Crossframe details and lateral connections.

(c) the diagonal crossframe member consists of two 5 × 3 × ⁵⁄₁₆ L's secured to the top of 7½ stiffener and just below the 24 ᴡ 68 floorbeam shown at Fig. 19.11.
(d) the ½ × 2½ × 4½ stitch ₧ between horizontal and crossframe L's.
(e) the horizontal members are 3 × 3 × ⁵⁄₁₆ L's.

Lateral bracing connections, continuous spans

(a) plan view, see the ⅜ × 1'-0" × 1'-2" gusset ₧.
(b) ST 5 ᴡ 12.5 diagonal braces.
(c) 2-3 × 3 × ⁵⁄₁₆ L's at right angles to girder flange.
(d) bolts, welds, and angles of diagonal member to girder.

Connection at interior support: elevation and plan

(a) elev shows ⅜ gusset ₧ and 1 × 12 bracing stiffener.
(b) 10 ᴡ 33 secured to 1 × 12 bearing stiffener and bolt ₵. See Fig. 19.9
(c) plan shows cont girder with 10 ᴡ 33 at right angles.
(d) gusset ₧ bolt ₵ welds and notice the ¼ × 6× 8 filler ₧ on one side of right angle bracing to girder.

Lateral connections

(a) types of bracing shown for cont and simple spans.
(b) the splice ₧ and notice the different number of bolts on either side of the brace.
(c) the braces are not at right angles to each other.

EXPANSION BEARINGS, ROCKER DETAILS, BASE PLATE AND DETAIL "A"

A bearing plate, rocker details, and base plate are shown at Fig. 19.13. Other bearings and details appear on the original dwgs. Note that the girder is welded to B9 top plate, and see rocker details with *Detail "A"*. Study these dwgs together with the Notes and the Bill of Materials which follow this sect.

The dimensioned plan of base plate B2A is positive. It is 4⅛ thick and 2-8 × 4-4 and weighs 1950 lbs. *This piece of steel, having the surface area of an average table top, weighs nearly a ton and is machined to within a warpage tolerance of ¹⁄₁₀₀th of an inch.*

These excellent dwgs are virtually self-explanatory.

Using a scale of ¾" to 1'-0" make a wooden scale model of these details and assemble them.

GENERAL NOTES

1. All structural steel shall meet A.S.T.M. Specification A441-64-T.

2. All machine finish is required for all rockers, pins, base plates, and other bearing surfaces that are in contact with each other. The surface finish shall comply with AAS.H.O.-61-2.10.25. Machining shall be done after welding wherever practicable.

3. Upon fabrication, all surfaces except machine finish and top of top plate shall be painted with one primer coat of paint. The radii surfaces of pins and standards shall be coated with a hot mixture of white lead and tallow before leaving the shop.

4. The preformed bearing pads shall be supplied by the Department of Highways.

5. Tolerances for warpage and out-of-flatness of all bearing surfaces shall be $\frac{1}{100}$th in. maximum as in AWS. D2.0-63-407.

BILL OF MATERIALS

MK	ITEM	NO.	SIZE	LENGTH	WEIGHT
B1	Bearing pad	6	$\frac{1}{4} \times 2$-4	4-4	
B1A	Bearing pad	2	$\frac{1}{4} \times 2$-8	4-4	
B1B	Bearing pad	8	$\frac{1}{4} \times 1$-10	3-0	
B2	Base plate	4	$3\frac{7}{8} \times 2$-4	4-4	6,390
B2A	Base plate	2	$4\frac{1}{8} \times 2$-8	4-4	3,900
B2B	Base plate	8	$2\frac{1}{2} \times 1$-10	3-0	4,940
B2C	Base plate	2	$4\frac{3}{4} \times 2$-4	4-4	3,920
B3	Anchor bolt	64	$1\frac{1}{2}$-6 UNC	2-7	
B4	Rocker	6	6×1-4	3-8	6,530
B4A	Rocker	6	$2\frac{1}{2} \times 1$-4	2-2	1,380
B5	Standard	18	$2\frac{1}{2} \times 1$-0	1-0$\frac{1}{2}$	1,560
B5A	Standard	18	$1\frac{1}{2} \times 1$-0	1-4	1,210
B5B	Standard	6	$2\frac{1}{2} \times 1$-0	1-6$\frac{1}{8}$	760
B5C	Standard	6	$1\frac{1}{2} \times 1$-0	1-6$\frac{5}{8}$	470
B6	Bolt	8	$1\frac{1}{4}$-7 UNC	1-0	
B6A	Bolt	4	$1\frac{1}{4}$-7 UNC	1-0$\frac{1}{2}$	
B7	Diaphragm	12	1×0-8$\frac{1}{4}$	0-10	280
B7A	Diaphragm	12	1×0-6$\frac{3}{4}$	1-0	270
B7B	Diaphragm	4	1×0-8$\frac{1}{4}$	1-2	130
B7C	Diaphragm	4	1×0-6$\frac{3}{4}$	1-2	110
B8	Connecting plate	16	$\frac{1}{2} \times 0$-6	0-7	90
B8A	Connecting plate	16	$\frac{1}{2} \times 0$-6	0-6$\frac{1}{2}$	80
B9	Top plate	8	$4\frac{1}{8} \times 1$-2	2-0	3,140
B9A	Top plate	8	3×1-2	1-6	1,710
B10	Cap screw	32	$1\frac{1}{4}$-7 UNC	0-2$\frac{1}{2}$	
B11	Pin	8	$3\frac{1}{8}$-R	2-0	810
B11A	Pin	8	$3\frac{1}{8}$-R	1-6	610
B12	Bolt	12	$1\frac{1}{4}$-7 UNC	0-7$\frac{1}{2}$	
	Washers	64	$1\frac{1}{2}$ (heavy)	Strd.	
	Washers	32	$1\frac{1}{4}$ (med.)	Strd.	
	Nuts (hex.)	64	$1\frac{1}{2}$-6 UNC	Strd.	
	Nuts (hex.)	48	$1\frac{1}{4}$-7 UNC	Strd.	
	Lifting hook	32	$\frac{1}{2}$ ⌀ bar	1-1$\frac{7}{16}$	

Total weight of bearings = 38,300 lbs.

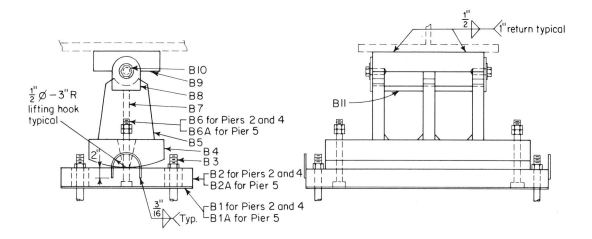

Expansion bearings at Piers 2, 4 and 5

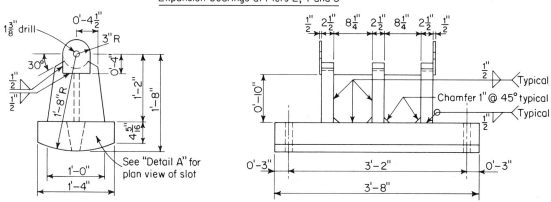

Rocker details

Detail A

Base plate B2A

Fig. 19-13. Bearing plate, rocker details, and base plate.

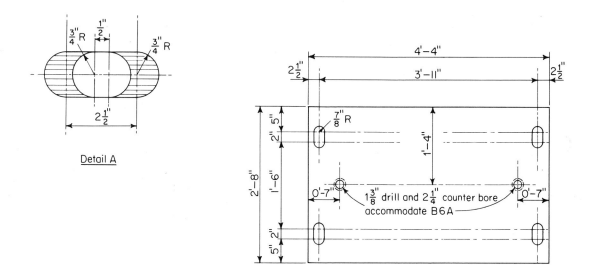

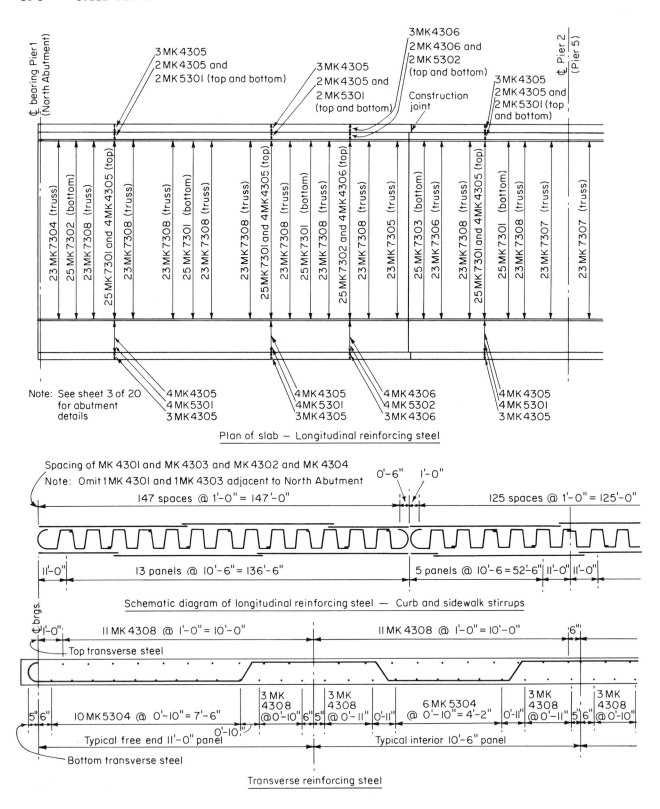

Fig. 19-14. Longitudinal and transverse reinforcing steel.

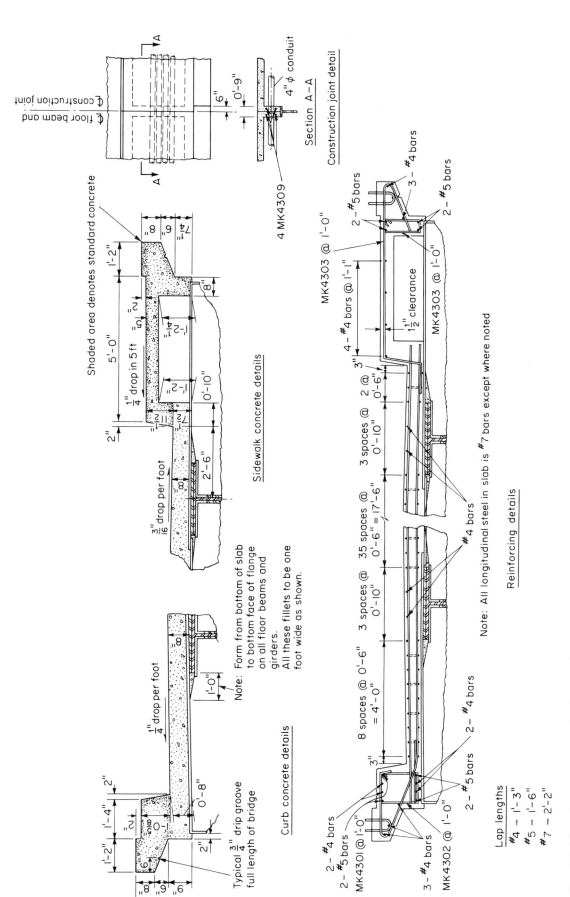

Fig. 19-15. Carriageway and sidewalk details.

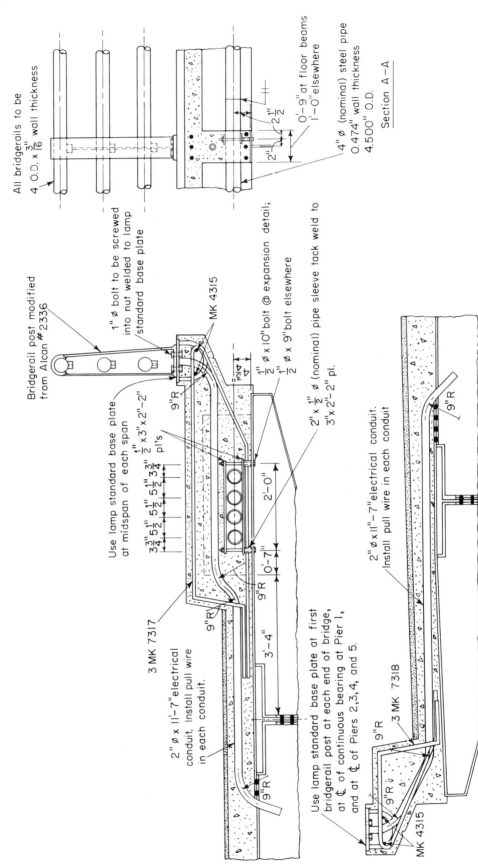

Fig. 19-16. Details at lamp locations.

REINFORCING STEEL

At Fig. 19.14 is shown a plan and schematic diagram of longitudinal steel together with a detail of transverse reinforcing. Note the types of detailed steel, the spacing of panels and L's of Piers 2 and 5. Read these dwgs with Fig. 19.15 and the following original notes:

NOTES

1. The concrete shall contain 5% ± 1% of entrained air and shall attain a minimum 28-day compressive strength of 3,000 p.s.i.

2. Pouring Schedule: slab sections shall be poured in continuous units between transverse construction joints. Before the section over any pier is poured, the section adjacent to it (positive moment section) shall have been poured. Any sequence of pours conforming to these requirements may be adopted.

3. Slab reinforcing steel shall have 1 in. clear cover.

4. Slab to be poured with lightweight concrete. Sidewalk and curb to be standard weight concrete.

5. Maximum size of aggregate for standard weight concrete shall be 1 inch.

CARRIAGEWAY STEEL, CURB, AND SIDEWALK DETAILS

Carriageway rein steel with curb and sidewalk concrete details are shown at Fig. 19.15, which should be read with Fig. 19.14. Note the sizes and spacing of the rein with lap length of #4 1-3, #5 1-6 and #7 2-2. Examine the 1'-0" fillet at girder and floor beam.

A very important concrete detail is the drip groove under the curb and sidewalk running the full length of the bridge.

DETAILS OF STANDARD LAMP LOCATIONS

Standard lamp details are shown at Fig. 19.16. *Note:*
(a) the provision for electric conduit in the concrete.
(b) the detail for securing the bridge rail post to the base plate.
(c) the centering of steel pipes for services shown both in section, and in sect A-A.

INDEX